THE DOG'S BLOGS

To Sue, an amazingly kind lady. Thank you so much for all your support. Get Well Soon! Henry, Axl, Rain & Chi. Always xxx

By Kerry Rhodes

www.Rhodes2Safety.co.uk

THE DOG'S BLOGS

I'd like to pay special acknowledgement
To my Husband, Mam & Dad, for their continual support & belief.

To Sue Whitelock & her beautiful Emma, without whom my wonderful
Chi would be nothing more than a figment of my imagination.

I'd also like to thank the Ridgeback Community and all the people I've
met through Facebook, particularly those who have given me their
advice, knowledge and experience along the way:

Carolyn Savage of the Canine Cavern
Clare Kapma-Saunders of Oostblik Ridgebacks
Claire Staines of Lothlorien DS
Elena Jeffery
Elizabeth Halliday of Kalunda Ridgebacks
My Uncle, Ian McCormack
Jo Field
Joanne Letts & Tor
Jodi Davies of Zenzele Ridgebacks
Lena Piehl of Kiromol Ridgebacks
Petra Dance
Rebecca Kohnke
Sheri Gray
Sue Craigie of Imbali Ridgebacks
Yvonne Bowker of Chomananga Ridgebacks
And of course, to my own pack (present and those at Rainbow Bridge)
for being the best teachers I could ever have had:

Paddy, Maddison, Amber, Axl, Rain & Chi

In Loving Memory of my incredible Axl

17/09/2006 – 27/10/2018

Axl was my one and only, my dog in a million, best friend, confident and all round soulmate. Adored by thousands across the globe, unrivalled and utterly irreplaceable. There are none who can hold a light to his amazing golden heart. During his career he has taught over 16 thousand students alongside me and saved goodness only knows how many furry lives.

With Axl as my wingman, we cemented the very best reputation, a business to be proud of, and blazed the trail for other Ridgebacks to compete when everybody told us that "Ridgebacks can't do agility!" ... Well, Axl would beg to differ as he became only the second ever UK Ridgeback to win an agility warrant title. His lists of achievements are many apart from his title; he qualified for Crufts for life and has his Stud Book Number which means he is recorded in the Ridgeback annals for all time. He was a TV and radio star, won the title of Britain's Best Office Dog, won his Gold Good Citizen's Award, wrote our first book in "Rhodes 2 Recovery ... doggy style!" and gave us the most beautiful litter of 11 puppies, one of which was his legacy, Chi who now also works with me.

Sadly, Axl passed away unexpectedly after a very short illness aged 12 years, 1 month and 10 days, just as this book was finally going to print. No amount of time would ever have been long enough. He loved me just as I loved him – completely and unconditionally and I feel proud and privileged to have been his human.

Run free my special lad, watch over me 'til we meet again xxx

INTRODUCTION:

Welcome to "The Dog's Blogs". This book has been carefully crafted to give every reader, be they professionals or regular dog owners, vital first aid information, when they need it, all in one place. There are so many sources of information these days, spread over many mediums. The Dog's Blogs will save you the time and frustration of searching for the answers to your questions and spoon feed you what you need to know in easily digestible chunks.

The blogs in this book were produced and published over the course of 6 years through the Rhodes 2 Safety website. Each segment was written either in direct response to a specific question from one of our followers, or to "fill in the blanks" that often leave people feeling less than confident. While the pages are not filled with technical jargon, this book is written clearly and concisely in a way only a Yorkshire lass would.

The blogs are grouped into sections so that they form Chapters making it very easy to find your way around the content. A basic index can be found at the front, where you literally look at the picture to pinpoint which part of your dog needs attention. This way, even if you don't know exactly what ailment you are looking for, you will still be able to navigate to the information you need – with or without any knowledge of the appropriate medical terminology.

So sit back, breathe out, and be safe in the knowledge that Rhodes 2 Safety has got you covered.

Kerry x

FOREWORD

It is an absolute delight to be asked to write a foreword for this book.

I have known Kerry for years. Her first aid teaching is both informative and extremely funny, which is exactly what Kerry is; extremely knowledgeable, but doesn't take herself too seriously.

Over the years, I have gone to Kerry for all sorts of advice and sometimes just to chin wag. We both share our love with all things dog, but the Rhodesian Ridgeback sealed our friendship. I would like to think between the two of us we have shown this breed in a different light. Kerry for using (and I mean using as she doesn't pay them nearly enough!!!) her beloved Rain, Axl & Chi in her presentations, showing & agility. Kerry shows the diversity of this amazing breed. I am more a training geek which is where I have been honoured to help Kerry out and I am proud to be mentioned in this incredible book.

What can I say about Kerry ...... she's a Yorkshire lass through and through (it's not her fault she wasn't Scottish), kind, caring & can sink a cocktail or seven and still be up for training in the morning. We have shared ridiculous bar bills, shed tears over problems & also looked to find solutions together that bridge that territory between health and choice for the dogs.

Good luck my friend. The only thing we disagree on is Guns & Roses - The Foo Fighters are still the best band.

Claire Staines PCT-A, PPG, VSPDT
Lothorien Dog Services

Simply locate the area on which you need more information and turn to the relevant page. Alternatively, if your query is about a condition or different topic, check out the contents list at the bottom.

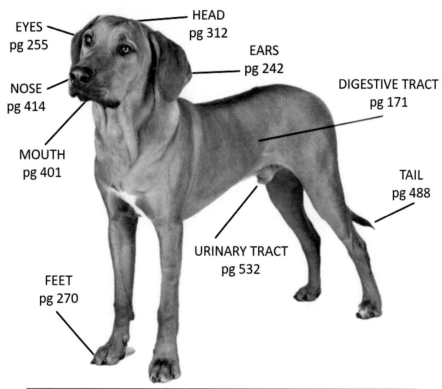

EYES
pg 255

HEAD
pg 312

EARS
pg 242

NOSE
pg 414

DIGESTIVE TRACT
pg 171

MOUTH
pg 401

TAIL
pg 488

URINARY TRACT
pg 532

FEET
pg 270

CONTACTING A VET URGENTLY

Contacting a vet urgently is something we need to be able to do in the blink of an eye. More times than enough, we need urgent assistance at what always appears to be completely the WRONG time – out of office hours, on a bank holiday, at Christmas, you name it. Emergencies just never seem to happen when the vet's office is open and there's a helpful voice at the other end of the 'phone so, what do you need to be READY?

Well, the most important thing to have is your Emergency Vet Number stored in your 'phone and preferably also written down inside your first aid kit, just in case somebody looking after your dog needs the information too. In a serious situation, the number you need to dial is that of the On Call response team, not just your ordinary veterinary reception number. If the only number you have is your usual clinic number, you may well find that when you ring out of office hours all you get is answerphone message telling you to ring elsewhere. When you're panicking, and in the middle of nowhere, it's not always that easy to take down a number and it will certainly mean at the very least that you've wasted valuable time when you could have just got on and rung straight through to the help you need.

When going on holiday, or if you show or compete in hobbies such as agility, flyball or coursing away from home, make sure you have the information for the local vet available just in case your dog becomes ill or has an accident while you are away. Local and on-call vet information can usually be located in the schedules for the shows you are entering. If not, then contact the show secretary who will be glad to help.

There are, however, occasions when you are away from home and walking somewhere unfamiliar that a problem may arise. In these situations, you cannot be expected to know where all the nearest vets are to your current location or even what their 'phone numbers are. If you have a smart 'phone, the best plan is simply to go to Google and put in "vets near me". This will locate your current position via GPS and bring up a map showing the nearest veterinary professionals to you. From this, you will be able to select a vet and 'phone number even though you don't actually know the area personally.

If the emergency arises where you have no signal to speak of, say in a wood or very remote location, you may find the option of Googling is not available. It may also be difficult to call your vet personally if the signal is weak but often in these circumstances you are still able to make Emergency SOS calls. You can call 999 for the UK (112 for Europe, 911 for America, or the emergency number for your country) and explain what has happened. This number is for Emergency Assistance and is not merely for Ambulance, Police and Fire as people often think. It is also for any genuine requests for help from Air/Sea Rescue, Mountain Rescue, Coastguard etc and in this regard, they can contact a vet on your behalf should you be unable to do it for yourself.

If you find an injured dog that is not your own and clearly needs veterinary assistance, you can call the emergency services to explain the situation and they can then organise a vet if required. All vets, though kind and thoughtful people, do have a business to run and have a livelihood to support. As such, if they are called out to an injured animal, then whoever called them out is usually liable for the fee of stabilisation treatment and call out. If you do not feel you would be willing to foot the bill in the absence of an owner being located, then simply passing all information on to the emergency services and allowing them to decide whether or not to send a vet might be your best option.

So, in a nutshell ……

1. Have your EMERGENCY VET NUMBER in your 'phone
2. Find contact information for the vet near wherever you are travelling
3. Use Google to find "vets near me" if you are in an unfamiliar location
4. Use 999/112/911 should your 'phone signal be weak and you need assistance

MUZZLE ACCEPTANCE

How and why to introduce Muzzle Acceptance: The first thing to consider in any first aid situation is your own personal safety, be that from road traffic, fire, electricity, fast flowing water, or particularly when dealing with animals, claws and teeth. If you need to deal with a frightened dog, or one that is disorientated or in pain, then applying a muzzle is the safest way for you and for him. Many dogs would find this a very stressful thing if they'd never worn one before and even the kindest, most well balanced dog could be forgiven for inflicting a nip in such circumstances.

Packed away very small and light in your first aid kit, something like a fabric muzzle is fine for very short periods. Personally, I would rather recommend the use of a Basket "Baskerville" style of muzzle, which is more comfortable allowing the dog safe drinking, panting and much less stress than the tight fitting fabric varieties.

Imagine for a moment that your dog has cut his paw very badly. You've managed to get a dressing on but now he needs to visit the vet to have it properly seen to. Rover is already far from keen on going to the vet and now you are expecting him to sit nicely while somebody he hardly knows starts prodding and poking his very sore paw. Quite a lot for him to take on, and when you know there is good a chance he may try to defend himself and wind up biting the vet, this increases your stress levels still further too.

In such a situation, the simple act of applying a muzzle will take things down a notch or two for all concerned so I'm very grateful to Claire Staines of Lothlorien Dog Services for making a video blog for us to explain HOW to get your dog used to wearing a muzzle using positive reinforcement techniques. This kind of positive introduction means that if you ever need your dog to wear one for real in a situation such as one I've outlined above, they won't freak out. The video blog can be found on our website with the Muzzle Acceptance blog information.

PERMISSION TO ADMINISTER FIRST AID

There is often concern about what you can and cannot do in a first aid capacity. The grey area comes because we have two important pieces of legislation – the Welfare Act and the Law itself – which are a little different.

The Welfare Act says that anybody can carry out first aid in an emergency situation with the express intention of saving or helping the animal and with the intent being to get the dog to professional assistance as soon as possible.

The Law says that only a qualified veterinary professional or the owner of the pet is allowed to diagnose or treat that animal.

This often causes consternation as to whether professionals such as Groomers, Pet Sitters, Walkers etc are legally allowed to do anything to help the animals in their care. So, with that in mind, perhaps the best suggestion would be that you have your client complete a basic form giving permission for emergency first aid to be carried out if required. I attach a document which should cover such situations on which your client can fill in their information and delete any parts with which they are not happy to comply.

Obviously, this is merely a template to point you in the right direction. Feel free to create your own version covering the requirements you feel are appropriate to your line of business and the needs of your clientele.

Hopefully, this will give not just the professional but also their clients the peace of mind to know exactly what can and cannot be expected.

Permission to carry out Emergency First Aid Treatment

Date: .... Dog(s) Name:...

Name: ....

Address: ....

....

Post Code: .... Contact Tel: ....

Email: ....

I (insert client name):... hereby give my permission to allow

(insert Company name): ....

to carry out any emergency first aid procedures as deemed necessary for the safety & welfare of my

dog(s) prior to immediate consultation by a veterinary professional in order that they receive the best

and most appropriate care as soon as possible. I also give permission for my dog(s) to be given any

drug prescribed by my vet as required in my absence, and agree that I have confirmed with him/her

that Piriton antihistamine may be administered safely for the treatment of allergic reactions.

ROAD TRAFFIC ACCIDENTS

Life turns on a sixpence. One minute all is happy and sunny ... the next things can become as black as you could ever imagine. Road Traffic Accidents have to be one of a dog owner's worst nightmares. A lovely walk can quickly spiral into a traumatic experience and if it does, the owner's ability to keep their head and take the right course of action can make all the difference. So, would you know what to do?

Firstly, go through what we call the **DR.ABC** checklist:-

D = Danger – make it safe for you and the dog. Making it safe includes:
* placing the dog on your jacket to carry him carefully from the road
* alerting any oncoming traffic
* securing any other dogs you have with you so that you can help
* muzzling the injured animal to protect yourself if needs be

R = Response – check your dog's level of consciousness by talking to him, letting him smell you and touching the fur just by his eye inner corner. You should see him blink.

A = Airway – tilt the head back, extend the neck and pull the tongue forward as far as you can imagine seeing his tongue out when he is panting on a hot day

B = Breathing – check how many breaths you hear in 10 seconds

C = Circulation – check for a pulse/heartbeat

TELEPHONE YOUR EMERGENCY VET IMMEDIATELY RIGHT AWAY

If circulation is present but **NO BREATHING** – perform artificial respiration
(see our A.R. Blog)

If there is **NO CIRCULATION** – perform CPR
(see our C.P.R. Blog)

If there **IS circulation & breathing**, perform a secondary survey as follows:-

Check for the 4 B's ie **B**leeding, **B**reaks, **B**urns and **B**ruises, starting at the head and checking down the body from chest, spine, ribcage, stomach, thighs and finally legs. As you do this, watch the dog's face with every movement so you notice any tell-tale signs that the bit you are touching is painful. Look at your hand between every part of the body you touch – you don't want to get to the end of your survey, find blood on your hands and not know precisely which part of him it came from.

Treat any bleeding ASAP with pressure.
Support any broken/dislocated limbs in **THE POSTION YOU FIND THEM**

The dog will be going into shock, so ensure you keep him flat and his spine nice and straight, then raise the rear end of the animal to encourage oxygenated blood to travel to the brain (you can kneel next to him and rest his back end on your thighs but try to ensure he remains straight rather than sagging in the middle) and cover him with your jacket to keep him warm.
(see our blog on shock)

If you notice a firmness in the abdomen, this could denote internal bleeding in which case we must elevate the rear end to utilise as much of his oxygenated blood as best we can.
(see blog on internal bleeding)

If you believe that the dog may have had a spinal injury, keep him flat and avoid any movement of his spine.

(see blog on spinal injuries)

Monitor his breathing rate, heart rate and gum colour to determine if he is deteriorating and be ready to step in with artificial respiration (AR) or cardio pulmonary resuscitation (CPR) if his situation changes.

HEART RATE - MONITORING BREATHING & PULSE

Just as a general quick check, knowing how many breaths and the normal heart rate for your dog in 10 seconds will give you a good idea of their level of health (ie, if they are going in to shock or if they are having a crisis with their breathing).

To monitor the breathing/heart rate more exactly, the following instructions from a Canine Cardiac Specialist should help. The example he was referring to was with a Ridgeback so the respiration rates are pertinent to a large breed dog. N.B. Smaller breeds naturally breathe more quickly.

Monitor the breathing rate at rest.

The normal breathing rate (one complete rise and fall of the chest) should be less than 35 – 40 breaths per minute while resting or sleeping.

To count the heart rate more exactly, you can place your hands on each side of the chest just behind the elbows, as you would if you were to lift the front legs off the ground.

Count the beats over one minute

HEART RATE: PULSE

Whenever your dog is sick, we always suggest that you take his pulse to get an idea of how sick he really may be. There are 2 things about this that are worth mentioning:

Firstly, do you know **WHERE** to find your dog's pulse? The easiest place is directly over the heart, but you can also find it in the groove just above the wrist joint in the front leg and in the groin along the femoral artery.

Secondly, do you know what is the **NORMAL** pulse rate for **YOUR** dog? Average doggy pulse rates range from 60-120 beats per minute, usually depending on the size, age, health and breed of the dog (the smaller breeds beating more quickly – my RR's beat at about 65 per minute)

Please don't wait until your dog is ill to a) discover you don't know how/where to locate a pulse and b) don't know what is normal for your dog.

When he's all chilled out watching the TV with you this evening, just have a little go at trying to find it so you will know what is NORMAL for him so that if he ever becomes ill, you are aware of the difference and will know that he is genuinely poorly.

Finding the Heartbeat

When checking the heart, remember that a dog's heart, like ours, is on the left side so lay them on their right side. The heart will be easy to feel beating away. Take your dog's front leg and bend it back so that his elbow touches his ribcage at about the 4th to

6th rib. Just put your hand, lightly over those 3 ribs and you should be able to find it without too much trouble.

People don't often listen to their dog's heart beat and it doesn't necessarily beat like they'd expect. Young, healthy dogs often have an irregular rhythm which speeds up and slows down in time with their breathing. Although it may seem irregular to you, there will be a predictable alteration to the pattern which will repeat itself. Provided the pattern repeats, all is well.

Finding the Femoral Artery

The femoral pulse is the big pounding artery that runs down the inner thigh of humans and dogs and is easiest to track down in the groin area. It pumps a lot of blood through to the legs at very high pressure so every time the heart beats, you can feel a throb as the blood travels through it.

You can find it easily with him standing or lying, and it's detectable on either side. Hold him around his back leg at the knee so that your thumb is on the furry outside of his leg and all 4 of your fingers are on the warm, inside bit of his thigh. Gently slide your fingers along his inner thigh until they reach the crease in his skin where his leg meets his tummy. Now slide the flat of your fingers from side to side, across his inner thigh until you can feel a ridge beneath your fingers. This ridge or chord type structure is the femoral artery. With your fingers over this ridge you should be able to detect the rhythmic beat of the pulse. Don't squeeze too tightly or your big clumsy fingers will prevent the blood from travelling along under your fingertips. Practice makes paw-fect!

Finding the pulse below the Wrist

The third place to look is even trickier, so I'd practice the other two first to get a bit of confidence before you start trying to find this one. With him sitting or lying, run your middle and index finger down inside the groove between the tendons, just above the stopper pad. With a very delicate touch, patience and practice, you should soon be able to strike gold here too. It's the same place that you see nurses checking on patients in hospital when they pick up the patient's wrist. Have a go on yourself in the groove of your wrist just above your hand and you'll know what to look for in Fido. (Remember that you have a pulse in your thumb, so never use your thumb to take you dog's pulse.)

Check for 10 seconds. Count how many beats you feel in that 10 second period and multiply by 6 to get the heart rate / beats per minute

eg: 15   (beats in 10 seconds)

X6

=   90   (beats per minute)

CPR

C = Cardio (heart)
P = Pulmonary (breathing/lungs)
R = Resuscitation (the act of beating the heart and breathing for a third party to revive them)

CPR is ONLY performed when the animal is neither breathing nor has a heartbeat.

If he DOES have a heart beat but is NOT breathing, perform Artificial Respiration instead (see blog on Artificial Respiration for clear instruction on carrying out this procedure)

CPR: Where to place your hands?

Knowing where to place your hands during CPR for a dog is something that worries many people. We generally say aim for between the 4th-6th rib, but an easy way to get the "spot" is by lying the dog on his right side, feet pointing away from you and you kneeling at his back. Bend his front leg back and where the elbow touches the ribcage, this is pretty much where you want to be.

For a deep chested dog such as a Rhodesian Ridgeback, Whippet, Greyhound etc., use this method and then aim about an inch further forwards towards the armpit. This slight modification will make it even more effective for such breeds.

For a barrel chested dog such as a British Bulldog, lay the dog on his back as you would a human and position your hand in the middle of the chest, on the breast bone above the point where the ribs meet.

How many hands should I use?

Medium or Large dog:
Use **TWO** hands, one on top of the other, fingers interlocked

Small dog: Use the heel of **ONE** hand

Tiny dog: Use **ONE** hand around his ribcage applying pressure with the muscle at the base of your **thumb**.

Newborn pups (or even cats): Hold around the ribcage as above, and squeeze pressing with your **thumb pad** only.

ONLY ever perform CPR on an animal (or human) that has no pulse.

*** IMPORTANT ****

Change of information regarding CPR for dogs.

The ratio of chest compressions to breaths in dogs has been revised following a study performed in 2012. The ratios for canine CPR now fall into line with human ratios ie: **30 chest compressions to every 2 breaths.**

The speed of compressions is also now consistent with human CPR in that we aim for a rate of 110-120 beats per minute.

Before you commence the **30:2** compressions to breaths ratio sequence for a dog, remember to quickly check the time and then administer **5 good rescue** breaths to top them up with oxygen before you start. There is no point in commencing compressions if there is no oxygen in the blood stream to transport.

Tilt the dog's head back to straighten the airway and pull the tongue forward, right out of the mouth. Now move the tongue to the side so that it slots out through the gap just behind the large fang tooth. Hold the dog around the muzzle with both hands which will grip the tongue in place with the teeth and prevent it going back into the dog's mouth.

Now breathe down the nostrils (for a very small dog you can put your mouth all the way around the nose and muzzle to ensure you do not breathe too hard).

Once your 5 breaths have gone in and you have seen the ribcage rise with each breath, you can then commence the 30:2 sequence.

Continue for 1 minute then stop to check for a pulse, breathing and signs of life. If no signs are detected, continue for 2 minutes and recheck (repeat this sequence). If there is no change after 20 minutes .... Rainbow Bridge is calling.

While it is always preferable to administer the chest compressions with the dog lying on his right side so that the left side of his chest (and therefore his heart) is uppermost, CPR can still be done with the dog on the other side too so if you are ever concerned that moving the dog may have adverse effect on a spinal damage, then leave the dog as you find him and carry out CPR on that side.

ARTIFICIAL RESPIRATION

If the dog is **NOT** breathing but **DOES** have a pulse, you need to perform artificial respiration. Artificial respiration is **NOT** the same as CPR (CPR is compressions on the heart AND breaths), artificial respiration is just breathing for a dog who still has a heartbeat as follows:

Mouth to Nose Rescue Breaths

1)   Lay the dog on his right side with his back towards you, legs pointing away.

2)   Extend the neck and tilt the head backwards.

3)   Pull the tongue forward and to the side (poke the tongue out behind the fang)

4)   Hold the muzzle, "clamping" the tongue between the teeth.

5)   Breathe 5 breaths down the nostrils

(NB. for small breeds, puppies and cats you should put the whole of the muzzle in your mouth & breathe gently to avoid doing any damage to the lungs)

6)   Watch the chest rise as you blow, take your face away from the dog's muzzle and watch as the chest falls again before your next breath (do this 5 times in total)

7)   You are aiming to take a breath every 3 seconds or so

After the 5th breath, commence manual respiration as follows:

1)   With the dog in the same position, place your flat palms over his ribs and push down about 1/3 of the depth of the chest – we are NOT aiming for the heart, but merely to squash the air from the lungs (N.B. for small breeds, one had may be enough)

2)   Remove your hands and count to 5 as you allow the ribs to spring back to their usual position, the lungs to re-inflate and the chest to rise.

3)   Continue by rhythmically pushing the chest down, removing your hands and then counting to 5, repeatedly for about 1 minute.

4)   Check to see if the dog has commenced breathing for himself/still has a pulse

5)   If he still has a pulse but is not yet breathing for himself, continue pushing down on the chest & counting to 5 for up to 20 minutes, checking every 2-3 minutes to see if there has been any signs of recovery.

6)   If he does not have a pulse by the time you check, commence CPR.

CHAPTER 3: SHOCK & THE "BIG STUFF"   PG

SHOCK

When people think about canine first aid, they tend to think about things like how to do CPR and artificial respiration – the "big ones", if you will. In actual fact, probably the most serious and potentially life threatening situation you need to be able to spot and treat is shock.

In a nutshell, medical shock is the body's response to a lack of oxygen. What this means is that any situation that lowers the oxygen level can make an animal go into shock.

The kind of things that can trigger it include;
Choking (because if he can't get any air in, his oxygen level goes down),
Drowning (because the lungs fill with water rather than with air),
Crushing injuries to his ribs/chest (if the ribs can't expand, the lungs cant either),
Pain or fear causing rapid breathing

Blood loss. (When somebody "*bleeds to death*", it's not the lack of blood that kills them; it's the loss of all that oxygen the blood was carrying).

If you think your dog is showing signs of shock:

<u>Temporary Treatment:</u>

1) Quickly lay him on his back
2) Manually hold up his back legs to get the oxygenated blood to his brain ASAP.

<u>Shock Stabilisation Treatment:</u>

1) Find a board strong enough to take his weight and lay him on it. It's better to think about what you could use as a board NOW rather than later when you actually need it. Many things can be used, obviously dependent upon the size/weight of the dog, from a tea tray or baking tray, through to the tray in the bottom of

your dog's crate or even the parcel shelf from the rear of your car.

(N.B. Although it's tempting to think that an ironing board will do the job, we are really looking for a board that is short in enough to be used as a stretcher but also to fit into your car.)

ALWAYS lie him on his right hand side in case he deteriorates and requires CPR.

2) Wrap him in a blanket/towel, securing him to the board with it.

3) Place cushion/rolled up jacket under the board, directly under his hind legs.

4) Tilt him sufficiently for the blood to be encouraged to flow toward his brain (4-6").

5) Phone your vet ASAP to meet you at the surgery.

6) The board will act like a stretcher for carrying him to and from the car & it will allow you to invert his body sufficiently to aid the blood flow to his head.

(N.B. Without the board, his body would just sag in the middle, make it difficult for him to breathe and also not be physically tilted)

7) Once at your car, either keep the dog inverted on the board or, if your back seats fold down and are not quite flat, then placing your dog with his bottom on the higher end will do the same job perfectly.

8) If you are in the middle of nowhere, simply laying the dog on uneven ground so that his head is down-hill will help massively, or use your lap to lay his back half across so that his rear end is elevated.

9) If you are near your car, you may be able to use the parcel shelf as a stretcher to carry and tilt your dog. Because it fits into the car, you will be able to use it to tilt and treat the dog en route to the vet too or, as above, lie the back seats down.

10) DO NOT use hot water bottles to warm your dog as this will cause the blood to rush to the specific warm area provided by the water bottle and hence it will be taking it AWAY from the brain where he needs it. Simply using layers and blankets and jackets is the best way to warm him up.

11) Monitor him constantly and be ready to step in and perform CPR or artificial respiration should the need arise.

The Signs and Symptoms of shock are as follows:-

Early Signs	Secondary Signs	Late Signs
Rapid Heart Beat	Increased Heart Beat	V. Increased Heart Beat
Bright Red Gums	Gums Pale or Blue	Gums White or Mottled
Pounding Pulse – Easy To Find	Pulse Faster but Slightly Less Strong	Pulse Rapid - Thready/Weak
Shallow Breathing	Breathing More Shallow	Lack of Respiratory Effort
Dog Responsive but Unsettled/Whining	Dog Lying Down, Refusing to Get Up	Pulse Very Difficult to Detect
Paws Warm	Paws Cold with Intermittent Shivering	Not Focusing
Eyes Reactive	Eyes Wide/Staring	Eyes Glazed
		Coma/Death

ELECTRIC SHOCK – ELECTROCUTION

Electric Shock is a serious business whether you are a human, a dog or any other living being come to that. With pets who like to gnaw such as rabbits or rats for example, or with puppies and adolescent animals or perhaps those "entertaining" themselves due to separation anxiety, it can be a real worry. The most usual source of electrocution comes when a domestic cable is chewed through by an unsupervised pet, with disastrous consequences but there are other causes such as faulty wiring, a direct lightning strike or even coming into contact with live power lines or sub stations (if power lines are down due to a storm, please ensure you stay WELL away).

Sometimes, it might be that you weren't actually there when the shock happened and as such, you may need to get your detective's hat on to work out what has happened – particularly as with more mild or moderate electrocution the evidence may not present itself for up to a couple of days after the event. If you have any queries that an accident has happened, you need to refer to something called Signs and Symptoms.

Signs & Symptoms:
Signs are something that you can see for yourself, even if the animal is unconscious.

Symptoms are things that we can only see by the behaviours of the animals to alert us to how they are feeling inside. Armed with these two aspects, we can then put the story together. You should check:

Where is the animal? Is he near a cable or power source? If he is near the cable, is it damaged? Can you see any burns on the animal? (remember to look for an entry and exit wound) Does the animal look scared or is acting out of character or hiding away? Is he drooling or reluctant to eat/drink in which case is his mouth damaged? Is he unconscious or dead in the vicinity of a damaged cable or power supply? Is he breathing normally? Is his heart rate normal? Are his gums the normal colour ie baby pink?

Electric Shock has levels of severity from:

* **very mild** such that you would get from static

* **mild to moderate** which could elicit burns or ulcers to the part that connected with the power supply

* **severe** which would affect the internal organs (brain, heart, lungs etc) and could cause death

If the electrocution is severe and the lungs have been affected, you may not see the signs for as much as a couple of days. The lungs can fill with fluid due to the damage making it incredibly difficult for the dog to breathe. This poor breathing will reduce his oxygen levels which, in essence, is why the dog is in shock (medical definition of shock is anything that causes lowered levels of oxygen). If the heart has been affected you may discover an irregular heart rhythm or a heart attack, the reduction of oxygen from which can cause collapse and a deterioration in brain function or, sadly, death.

What should you do?

If you think your dog has been electrocuted it is very important to keep a cool head and work through your steps in a safe and methodical manner – if you do not keep yourself from harm's way, you will be no use to your pet. To do this, we use the Primary Survey mnemonic; DRABC:

D = Danger – make it safe for you and the dog including:

* switch off any power supply
* if you cannot switch it off, knock the dog away from the supply with a wooden object
* if you cannot knock your dog away, alert the emergency services ASAP
* if you are outdoors, alert any traffic to your presence
* secure any other dogs you have with you so that you can help
* muzzle the injured animal to protect yourself

R = Response – check your dog's level of consciousness

A = Airway – tilt the head back, extend the neck and pull the tongue forward

B = Breathing – check that the dog is breathing

C = Circulation – check for a pulse/heartbeat

TELEPHONE YOUR EMERGENCY VET RIGHT NOW

If circulation is present but **NO BREATHING** – perform artificial respiration - (see previous blog)

If there is **NO CIRCULATION** – perform CPR (see previous blog)

Place the dog on your jacket or blanket to carry him carefully to your car and transport to the vet. If you have somebody with you, commence your CPR or AR immediately while your friend phones the vet and continue the procedure during the journey to the vet's office while your friend drives.

If there **IS circulation & breathing**, place your dog on his side and elevate his rear end slightly to encourage oxygenated blood to flow to his brain and heart, and then perform a secondary survey as follows:-

Check for the **4 B**'s ie Bleeding, Breaks, Burns and Bruises: starting at the head and checking down the body from chest, spine, ribcage, stomach, thighs and finally legs. If you have any concern at all that your dog has suffered an electric shock, please contact your vet immediately for an urgent appointment.

If you notice burns on your dog, you can treat those immediately while you wait to see the vet:

- run the affected area under cold water for a **MINIMUM** of 10 minutes, or until the skin is cold – ie, if after having run the burn under cold water for 10 minutes there is still any heat left in the burn, you must continue until such time as all the redness and heat has left the wound

- When you have finished cooling the burn, it is perfectly fine to keep it covered with a moist clean dressing to keep the skin cold and wet.

- You can use cling film which will do the same job PROVIDED YOU ARE 100% SURE THE WOUND IS COLD. If you use cling film and there is any heat left in the wound, you will merely keep the heat in and cook the wound still further.

- If the dog will not allow you to do this and refuses to stand for 10 minutes with a running hose over it (no surprise there), you can try placing ice cubes or frozen peas in a clean, wet, tea towel. Place it over the affected area, again for a minimum of 10 minutes. If the skin is exposed, drape a towel over the area before applying the ice pack so as not to damage the skin tissue.

- Remember that the fur might well be masking the size and severity of the burn too and it is often necessary to cut away the fur to expose the area so you can see more clearly what you are dealing with. Burns are very painful and it is often sensible to apply a makeshift muzzle to ensure your own safety

**ALWAYS REMEMBER TO MONITOR
BREATHING AND HEART RATE
AND BE READY TO STEP IN WITH CPR IF REQUIRED.
SEE YOUR VET AS SOON AS POSSIBLE.**

CARRYING A LARGE BREED DOG

Carrying a large breed dog is not for the faint-hearted! For those of you who haven't met me, you may not know that I am only a little person ... in fact, probably just 5ft 3" tall even if I stretch up to my tippy toes. My husband Mike, 6ft 2" refers to me as a hobbit and in all honesty, he does have a point. My dogs, however, are not small by anybody's standard, being 27" to the shoulder and weighing in at around 40 kg each.

They are, however, trained to walk alongside me, on my own, very nicely without a head collar and rarely give me a moment's trouble – but that's on a good day. The question is, what would I do if it all went horribly wrong and I was all alone, just me ..... the hobbit?

We all know the kindest, most caring way to carry an animal is safely in your arms with one hand under their bottom for support and another under their chest for stability.

That said, however, should you ever think your dog is in shock and you need to carry him, then the position should be inverted with one arm around their waist, just above the hips, and another under their front legs at the chest with the DOG'S HEAD DOWN. This position, crazy at it looks, has many beneficial points:

1. The airway is open so if the dog vomits, he will not breathe it in and choke
2. The tongue is lolling forward, again keeping the airway open
3. They have the vital warmth and comfort of being close to you
4. The oxygenated blood is channelled, with gravity, towards the brain where he needs it

Now imagine that the dog you are carrying is larger than you can comfortably manage to carry in the usual manner as above. What then? For me as the tiny owner of three large dogs, the question has come to mind more than once. How would I move such a heavy, large animal on my own? Could I carry him by myself? Probably not, but I could make a stretcher and drag him along.

The following is how I would go about making a stretcher for a larger dog. I know it's not ideal, but if you are on your own and in the absence of any professional "kit" to utilise, it's about the best we've been able to come up with. Thank you to my darling, ever-patient Rain-Bob for co-operating in the demonstration – he must think I am completely and utterly crackers.

1. Remove your hoodie and unzip it
2. Turn the arms inside out and slot a branch up inside them (I'm improvising here with a couple of rolls of wrapping paper, just for demonstration purposes, but anything long & stable would do)

3. Place the dog on top of your hoodie

4. Pull the drawstring on the hood tight and secure to make a pocket for his bottom
5. Zip the dog up in the hoodie, head sticking out of the waistband end

6. Use the sleeves, stabilised with the branches, and drag the dog

I sincerely hope the opportunity to put this into practice never presents itself to you, but at least if it does you will have a plan on the back burner rather than being left in the lurch.

CHOKING & the Heimlich procedure

If your dog is choking, first try to see if you can sweep the mouth (without getting bitten!) and remove the object. If you can see the object, please try to put two fingers over the hump at the back of the tongue and "sweep" round and forward to get the object out.

Please DO NOT try to "pinch" the object as the object will skid away from you and go further down the throat (a little like trying to pinch a moist bar of soap on the edge).

If you cannot, then administer Firm Back Slaps between the shoulders and around the rib-cage to try to dislodge the blockage.

As with humans, back blows work best if the dog's head is **BELOW** the level of the diaphragm so if the ordinary back slaps have not worked, raise the dog's back end by hooking one arm under his hips and raising him up like a wheelbarrow (if you have a large breed dog) or by holding him upside down around his waist with him taking his own body weight on his front paws if you have a medium breed.

If you have a small breed dog, try holding him upside down just above the hocks and administer the back blows while gravity is able to help you. If this does not work, proceed to the Heimlich manoeuvre.

Abdominal Thrusts (Heimlich Manoeuvre)

If the backslaps have failed to help dislodge the blockage, you can proceed to the abdominal thrusts (sometimes referred to as the Heimlich Manoeuvre). Please be aware that this procedure (on a human or a dog) is very dangerous and you should ALWAYS seek professional attention if you have had to perform this due to the small but very real risk of a tear or possible internal bleeding.

Make a fist with one hand in such a way that the first joint on your thumb creates a point.

If you have a large breed dog, then simply straddle over your dog facing his head, so that your knees grip him just in front of his back legs - For a medium breed, have the dog sitting and facing away from you.

Place your arms through and under his front legs tipping him backwards so that his front legs leave the ground.

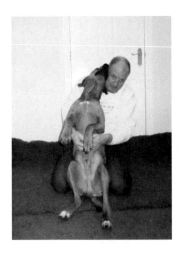

For small breeds, you need to be standing or kneeling, holding the dog against you as per the picture below.

Fit your fist in the soft hollow of your dog's chest just where the two sides of his ribcage meet and form a triangle.

Place your other hand flat up against your fist and administer 5 fast little digs upwards and diagonally, whilst squeezing with your arms against the ribcage itself. It is not important to do the digs with a lot of power, more that you do them as very quick bursts.

Your aim is to gently "poke" the diaphragm with your thumb joint to cause a spasm type cough from your dog and hopefully expel the blockage. If this does not work, revert to the back slaps and then back to the Heimlich Manoeuvre again.

So, the procedure is:-
Check & sweep the mouth
Administer back slaps
Administer Heimlich manoeuvre

Repeat this procedure 3 times. If you are still unsuccessful after the 3rd time, 'phone your vet immediately and tell him you are on your way and continue the procedure if possible while en route. Even if you DO clear the blockage, you should still see your vet as there may be damage to the throat or mouth, internal damage because of the Heimlich Manoeuvre or possible shock due to overheating while struggling and oxygen deficit.

If your dog becomes unconscious:
revert to either CPR (if the heart has stopped)
or Artificial Respiration (if the heart is still beating)

DROWNING

Today's tip tackles the steps to take if your dog has been involved in a drowning/water based emergency.

Begin by using your DR.ABC assessment method:-

D = Danger (Is it safe?)
R = Response (Is he responding to you?)
A = Airway (Open his Airway, pull his tongue forward & clear his mouth of debris.)
B = Breathing (Is he breathing for himself?)
C = Circulation (Does he have a pulse?)

1) Hold a **small** dog just above the hocks on the hind legs to allow as much water as possible to drain from the lungs. Ideally, for around 30 seconds or so.

2) If your dog is a **large breed**, lay him on his side with his head as low as possible and pick up his back legs to tilt him as much as you can to allow the water to drain, again for a good 30 seconds.

3) Clear any debris from his mouth to make sure his airway is clear.

4) Hopefully, he should start to breathe for himself.

5) If he does, ring your vet to let him know you are coming straight over.

6) If he does not take a gasp by himself as the water leaves his lungs, give him 5 mouth-to-nose rescue breaths and then start your **artificial respiration**.

(See our artificial respiration blog)

7) If he does not take a breath and has no pulse, commence **CPR**.

(See our CPR blog)

8) **Remember**, whether he begins to breathe or not, 'phone your vet as soon as possible for further advice due to the possibility of what's known as secondary drowning.

BITCHES - BITCHES, THEIR CYCLE & SEASONS

When you first get a female puppy, any thoughts of them reaching sexual maturity is way off in the distance but from the age of around 5-7 months of age, a female dog is generally considered to be mature. There is of course considerable variation within the different breeds with the larger and giant breeds maturing more slowly. So although it is normal for a bitch to have her first season around the 6 month mark, it is perfectly normal for it to happen much later – even up to 2 years old in some cases.

When she is very first "on heat", it is not uncommon for this first cycle to go completely unnoticed by the owner as the duration of the cycle from start to finish may be much shorter the first time around and also few of the external signs may be visible.

Once maturity is reached, then it is normal to have two cycles or "seasons" per year, but each dog has her own cycle and for some the norm may be every 7-9 months – once again, this is very much down to the individual bitch and is totally normal.

We can pretty much divide the oestrus cycle into four sections – all with medical names i.e. Anoestrus, Pro-oestrus, Oestrus and finally Metoestrus, but for ease of understanding, we'll just call them parts 1,2,3 and 4.

Part 1:
This first part of the cycle is where there is pretty much nothing going on within the reproductive tract and the phase lasts for about 3-4 months or thereabouts, depending on the full length of her entire cycle. She will show no signs or changes and male dogs will have no sexual interest in her.

Part 2:
The next phase lasts for around 10 days or so and is the beginning of her "heat" period. You will notice her vulva begin to swell up (this can be quite marked as time goes on) and she will produce a clear then blood stained discharge from her vagina. She may become nervous or "grippy" with you and need reassurance and comfort. This is the phase where she starts to become desirable to the boys …. but, she is not yet ready for mating at this point and will not allow it to take place, regardless of their persuasive efforts!

Part 3:
Phase 3 lasts for around 10 days or so too. This part of the cycle marks the beginning of the receptive stage – the stage at which she is most receptive to a dog's advances.

FOR THOSE WISHING TO AVOID A PREGNANCY, STAGE 3 IS THE MOST "DANGEROUS" TIME AND THE TIME TO KEEP YOUR HAWK EYE FIRMLY ON HER AND ANY LOCAL LOTHARIOS.

During this phase she will continue to produce a red discharge from the vulva but the consistency of the discharge will likely change and become more bloody and less watery in appearance and then stop. During this time the bitch may become more alert and urinate more frequently as she broadcasts signals of her impending willingness to mate.

Ovulation will usually take place within the first few days of this phase, so if we take the start of phase 2 as day 1, then ovulation should happen on or around two weeks following day 1. The time at which she ovulates will be the time she is happy to accept a male "suiter" and the time at which mating is most likely to be successful. It is important to keep in mind that each bitch is unique and her cycle can only be estimated.

Part 4:
Because hormonal changes take place during stage 4 irrespective of whether the mating was successful or not, a simple blood or urine test to confirm pregnancy is not possible. It is simply a waiting game followed by a visit to your vet to confirm that the bitch is indeed in whelp.

If a successful mating does not take place, phase 4 of the cycle will last for around 2-3 months. During this phase, the uterine wall thickens and outwardly there are no visible signs. A bitch can experience hormonal fluctuations and these peaks and troughs can result in a false or "Phantom" pregnancy.

BITCHES - PHANTOM PREGNANCIES

Sometimes a bitch may appear to be pregnant, but then not produce any puppies. This can be something that is referred to as a false or "Phantom" pregnancy.

As we mentioned yesterday, a bitch's cycle is split into four parts and a Phantom pregnancy can result after the phase where she ovulates. Hormonal changes occur at this time and, if she does not fall pregnant, these changes can mimic the appearance of a pregnancy when in fact none exists. While this condition is fairly common in many bitches and is considered a normal phenomenon, it can cause some really marked symptoms which make the bitch very unsettled and can worry her owner too.

The changes we see are likely to start several weeks following the ovulation part of her cycle and they can continue for several months. Some bitches do seem very prone to Phantom pregnancies with them occurring after each of their seasons when they have not been mated. So, what symptoms are we looking for to alert us that a Phantom may be taking place?

* Nest Building is often seen at the outset of the Phantom

* She may appear skittish and nervous, being spooked by things that normally cause no problems at all.

* Her levels of obedience may seem off as if she is being naughty and just not listening to you.

* Often the bitch may decide that one of her toys, usually a furry one but not always, is her "baby". She will treat it as if she truly believes it to be a puppy and will therefore become very possessive of it.

* Physically, her teats will begin to swell and the mammary glands will fill with milk in readiness for feeding her "baby".

* She may show uncharacteristic temperament changes such as aggressiveness, loss of appetite, restlessness or lethargy.

* In very rare cases, there may even be symptoms suggestive of whelping itself.

Treatment:
In mild cases, it is not really necessary to give any specific treatment at all, save the patience and understanding she may need. It is said that simply keeping her exercise levels up and her brain engaged will be of great assistance in getting her through it.

However, with more severe cases various drugs can be administered to help such as those which will encourage the milk to dry up or even those which prevent the bitch from coming into season in the first place. These drugs will stop the season and, in particular, the ovulation part of the cycle, and hence the hormone fluctuation will be diminished.

Another option is to have the bitch spayed. Spaying can be done as an open surgery where the ovaries and uterus are removed, or even in some cases as a "keyhole" procedure which is a less invasive surgery and is said to have a faster recovery time. Which procedure is best for your bitch should be discussed with your vet.

It is important to remember that spaying of a bitch cannot be carried out while a Phantom pregnancy is on-going as this would likely cause the signs of the false pregnancy to continue even after the surgery.

BITCHES - VAGINAL DISCHARGE & PYOMETRA

Vaginal discharge is not actually a condition in itself, but rather the indication that something is wrong with either the reproductive tract or the urinary tract. There are many possible causes for this problem:

Uterine Problems:

* Uterine infection called pyometra – in bitches which have not been spayed.
(This is more likely to happen with older or middle-aged bitches) Bitches who have been spayed can also suffer from what is known as "stump pyometra", where there is infection of the remaining stump of the uterus.

* Abortion, miscarriage or birth of puppies

* Endometritis (inflammation of the lining of the uterus)

* Uterine cancer (rare)

Ovarian Problems:

* Ovarian cysts or ovarian cancer (both of which are rare)

Vaginal Problems:

* Infantile vulva (where the vulva is not protruding as far as would be considered normal, and the skin around it becomes sore with dermatitis – especially if the bitch is over-weight)

* Juvenile Vaginitis (seen in sexually immature bitches, before their first season). This problem usually disappears by itself as the bitch matures.

* Injury resulting from mating – an excessive yelp or cry during the mating may be heard

* Infection following mating

* Vaginal prolapse

* Vaginal cysts and tumours

General Causes:

* Normal secretion due to hormonal cycle in an un-spayed bitch

* Hormonal cycle in a spayed bitch which has any fragment of ovarian tissue remaining.

You may be able to get an indication of the cause for the vaginal discharge from the symptoms you see associated with it:

Inflammation of the vagina
Change in shape, distortion or swelling of the vulva
Pink tissue protruding from the vagina
"Scooting" the rear end along the ground to scratch the irritation
Frequent licking of the area (if so, fit a Buster collar to avoid further irritation)
Cloudy discharge coming from the vulva
Yellowish or yellowy-red persistent vaginal discharge

If you are concerned about any of the above symptoms, you should see your vet. Be aware that he is likely to ask you the following questions so remember to check out dates etc before you go:-

What did the discharge look like? (cloudy, red, yellow etc)
How long has the discharge been present?
Has she been mated recently and if so, when?
Has she been spayed and if so, when?
If she has not been spayed, when was her last season?
Is the dog well in herself or has there been lethargy, increased thirst, vomiting, weight loss?

Pyometra:

Pyometra literally means pus in the uterus. It is a common and very serious condition of un-spayed bitches and can occur several weeks after a season. This condition often causes vaginal discharge, which may be yellowish or red/brown in colour, although occasionally the bitch may be suffering from what is known as "closed pyometra" where the cervix is tightly closed and does not allow any drainage of pus to the exterior)

<u>Warning signs of pyometra to look out for are</u>:

Older, un-spayed bitch
Recent season
Drinking and urinating more than usual
Possibly a vaginal discharge
Abdominal swelling
Poor appetite
Lethargy
Occasional Vomiting

If your bitch has any vaginal discharge, it is always wise to have it checked out properly by a vet, as leaving it could result in rupture of the uterus and life-threatening peritonitis and/or septicaemia in serious cases.

BITCHES - MASTITIS

Mastitis = inflammation in the mammary gland.

Mastitis is usually caused by an infection which has entered via the teat, through a skin wound caused by a puppy, or via the bloodstream.

The teat and breast tissue will be warm and may be swollen and tender. If the mastitis is more severe, there may be loss of milk production or possibly a brownish coloured milk.

Because severe mastitis is very painful indeed, the bitch is unlikely to allow suckling from the effected gland and, in very severe cases, may refuse to allow any suckling at all.

With the more severe cases, the bitch may also have a high temperature, be off her food and possibly even require an intravenous drip.

Treatment
Warm compresses and gentle exercise can help relieve the discomfort of mastitis but, in more severe cases, antibiotics may be necessary. Drugs to help lower the temperature and ease the discomfort and pain of the gland can also be given.

It is important to bear in mind that should antibiotics or other drugs be given to the bitch, the puppies must be hand-fed or weaned.

BTICHES – ECLAMPSIA

Eclampsia (often known as milk fever) is a serious disease caused by calcium deficiency which may occur in late pregnancy or, more usually, after the puppies are born, when the milk production is at its peak. It is more common amongst smaller bitches who are nursing large litters or bitches who are feeding big, healthy, fat puppies really strongly.

Symptoms
The initial symptoms are general restlessness and panting. Symptoms can progress to nervous twitches and shivering. There may be evidence of difficulties with co-ordination, collapse and muscular spasms.

Always watch for the early tell-tale signs and take the bitch to the vet immediately, day or night, without delay. This is a life-threatening illness and **SHOULD NOT** be underestimated.

Treatment
As stated above, emergency treatment is required for this condition. An injection of calcium will be administered by your vet and, if treatment is prompt enough, a dramatic improvement should be seen.

Prognosis
Following urgent treatment for eclampsia, the outlook is good. The puppies should either be fed artificially or, if slightly older, be weaned to prevent the mother's calcium supplies being depleted still further.

In small dogs or those expected to be carrying larger litters, it may be useful to give calcium supplements in late pregnancy and throughout the lactation period, but these supplements should be stopped once the puppies are weaned.

CHAPTER 5: BITES & STINGS   PG

ALLERGIC REACTIONS & HIVES

There are many things that can trigger allergic reactions and hives in our animals - everything from food or medication that doesn't agree with them, bee stings, wasp stings, nettle rash, vaccinations, flying ants, biting "critters" in the grass or undergrowth and even licking toads!

Sometimes there might be a soft swelling on the face, paws or muzzle after rooting about, and if your dog has a short coat, then he might even get some raised blotches on his body too.

The reaction can be very itchy and often the dog can scratch and rub at himself until he bleeds.

Nettles, skin irritation & homeopathy

For a nettle rash or a general skin reaction, we merely bathe the area with cold water or use icepacks. You can also try a homeopathic remedy which is 1 tablet of Urtica, 4 times daily for 2 days.

Whether its medication, food, toads, frogs, wasps or bees, it's not really a very serious problem for most dogs and is certainly not life threatening unless they either have a severe allergic reaction, they react by going in to Shock, or if they are stung on the mouth/throat area. Any of these situations may cause the windpipe to swell up and make it really difficult to breathe and if the airway swells up too much, it might even cut off the breathing altogether and suffocate the animal, so remember to treat severe allergic reactions and a sting to the mouth or throat as an emergency.

If the dog begins to go in to shock, it is vital that you get it to your vet ASAP.

Always remember to ring ahead and let the vet know that you are on your way so as not to arrive only to find that he/she is out on another call.

If possible, while en route to the vet, monitor the breathing rate (how many breaths are they taking in a 10 second period), what is the heart rate and gum colour - it's advisable to check when the dog is well to see what is NORMAL for him so you are able to detect if things are going badly.

Position the animal with his rear end raised to encourage oxygenated blood towards the brain and keep him warm and calm. With shock, TIME IS OF THE ESSENCE.

An antihistamine is required to counteract the allergic reaction, but please DO NOT give Piriton or any other antihistamine unless it has been prescribed FOR YOUR DOG by your vet. (In the UK, we always use Piriton - not Piriteze or any other type of antihistamine. In other countries, Benadryl may be given but this is not appropriate in the UK due to the ingredients in our version). If you know what dosage and what medication would be suitable, as previously prescribed by your own vet for this animal specifically, then giving antihistamine will help the symptoms to subside.

You may need to give another dose every 6-8 hours for a couple of days as the reaction may flare up again. If the reaction is more severe still, then only a trip to the vet for an injection of high dose steroids and, as any swelling to the windpipe can be a life threatening situation, please 'phone ahead to let your vet know you are on your way and go straight over.

Please keep in mind that not all dogs (dependent upon their history or medication they may be on, or their specific breed) may be safe to use Piriton. Some dogs who fall into the herding varieties such as Border Collies, Shelties, Old English Sheepdogs etc could have a genetic defect called MDR1. If they do, then administering a drug such as Piriton can be incredibly dangerous and should be avoided at all costs. If you do not know if your pastoral breed dog is MDR1 positive or not, a simple cheek swab sent off to a genetic lab for DNA testing can put your mind at rest one way or the other. Check out our blog on MDR1 just in case you want to read more about this mutation.

If you do not have any antihistamine or your vet has not previously prescribed this for your dog, you can give them high doses of Vit-C and Nettle drops as it works as a natural antihistamine. Administer at least 2000-3000 mg of Vitamin C every 4 hours as it is water based and 30-40 drops Nettle drops.

BITES & STINGS - BEE & WASP STINGS

In the summer and early autumn, stings from bees and wasps are an occupational hazard for a dog. Because they like to roam about investigating the undergrowth and hedgerows whenever they can, I suppose it's inevitable that they'll come across the odd sting or two.

Maybe you might notice the actual moment when they are stung, or perhaps you might just see the reaction they have to it. Sometimes there might be a soft swelling on the face, paws or muzzle after rooting about, and if your dog has a short coat, then he might even get some raised blotches on his body too.

Often the bee or wasp may actually be on the ground when your dog passes by resulting in him or her getting stung on the paw or pad if he steps on it. If this happens, you may not be able to see the stinger or any "injection site", but you will see how the dog is acting. Typically, you may hear a yelp (if they're as much of a big girl's blouse as my lot) or perhaps they may be limping. Often when a dog limps we think they have damaged their joints or bones or may be even their nails but sometimes it can be a bite or a sting causing the problem. You may see them nibbling at their foot as if it is itchy, rather than actually painful. This uncomfortable itchy feeling could make them try to scuff or scratch their pad along the surface of the floor to try to scratch the itch, a little like the action of wiping their feet.

Whether it's wasps or bees, it's not really a very serious problem for most dogs and is certainly not life threatening unless they either have a severe allergic reaction or are stung on the mouth/throat area. Either of these situations may cause the windpipe to swell up and make it really difficult to breathe and if the airway swells up too much, it might even cut off the breathing altogether and suffocate the animal, so remember to treat a sting to the mouth or throat as an emergency.

Otherwise, treating stings is really quite straight-forward. If the dog has been stung by a wasp, there will be no stinger left behind. In the case of a bee, although some species do not leave their stinger behind, it likely that you will actually be able to see the entire stinger still stuck in the dog and possibly even still pulsating. Our goal is to remove the sting from the dog and then neutralise the protein strand that makes up the stinging sensation.

Never squeeze the stinger as you remove it. This may inject further painful venom into the dog. Instead, use a sharp edged piece of plastic such as a credit card and scrape the sting off on a diagonal in one swift movement.

If you are unsure as to whether it was a bee or wasp that did the stinging, it's important that you do not try to neutralise the venom as if you pick the wrong antidote, you will in fact make the sting even more painful. In this case, you can bathe the affected areas in cold water or use ice packs for around 15 minutes to reduce the swelling and irritation.

If you DO know which type of sting you are dealing with, then so far as neutralising the sting goes, the best way to help you remember which sting needs which treatment is to pair up the initials as follow:-

Bee Sting = **B**icarbonate of soda.

A bee sting is acidic, so you need to use something alkaline to neutralise its action and the best thing for the job is Bicarbonate of Soda (many toothpastes are bicarb based so they are often a good choice too)

Wasp Sting = **V**inegar (well, I reckon 2 **V**'s look like a **W**)

A wasp sting is alkaline and so we need to bathe it in a dilute acid solution to neutralise the effect. A good source of dilute acid is vinegar, or you could use lemon juice too. It wouldn't be the first time I've resorted to squirting Axl outside a Fish and Chip shop with a bottle of Sarson's vinegar when he's been stung!

A cold compress or ice pack will help ease the irritation and, if the dog has been prescribed an antihistamine such as Piriton before, you may use this to help with any discomfort. Piriton can be re-administered 8 hours later if necessary. Please **DO NOT administer Piriton if it has not been prescribed for your animal previously by a vet.** For some dogs, the active ingredient in the medication can actually be more dangerous than the reaction you are treating and in some cases may prove fatal so please do check with your vet BEFORE you need it, and keep it in your doggy first aid kit if he is happy for you to use it with your dog.

BITES & STINGS - SNAKEBITES

The Common Adder, or Viper, is the only venomous snake in the British Isles. Most Adder encounters happen during their active season which is between March and October. They have a dark "zig-zag" stripe along the back and their background colour varies from grey or white in the male, right through to shades of brown or copper in the female. They can grow up to around 60 cm long.

Generally speaking, dogs usually get bitten on the head or neck, and less often on the limbs, because they tend to stick their head's in to have a good investigate!

1)   The injected venom causes a severe swelling
2)   In the centre are two small fang puncture wounds
3)   Venom produces excitement/trembling/staggering/shock
4)   Later there may be depression, collapse and even death is possible.

Treatment: Time is of the essence

1)   Phone ahead & get to your vet ASAP for treatment
(dog should be kept quiet and exercise reduced to a minimum – carried if possible)

2)   Your vet will administer treatment with anti-venom or other and usually an antihistamine. If you carry this yourself and it has been **PRESCRIBED BY YOUR VET** for this particular dog, giving an antihistamine such as Piriton ASAP will help)

3)   Clean with soap & water (**ONLY** if this does not delay getting to the vet)

4)   Applying an ice pack should **ONLY** be attempted when excessive delay in getting to a vet is unavoidable.

 Application of a tourniquet is no longer practiced by most professionals.

5)   Again, if time is not wasted in doing so, applying a thick paste of activated charcoal (AC) to the affected area has been shown to be incredibly effective. If you walk regularly in an area known to have Adders, then carrying AC with you for just such eventualities is a good idea.

6)   Monitor for signs of shock and be ready to administer CPR if required

DO NOT incise the bite or attempt to suck out the venom!

Grass Snakes:

Grass Snakes are non-venomous, but they still bite if they feel threatened.

There will be little swelling from the bite and the clinical signs above caused by the Adder venom do not occur. There will be

<u>not</u> be the visible double fang marks as in an Adder bite, but instead you will see a U-shaped set of teeth imprints.

Although, as I've already said, there is no poisonous venom with a Grass Snake, their bite can still cause infection, so the wound should be cleaned thoroughly with soap and water to prevent bacteria penetrating the tissues.

Monitor the wound for any signs of infection or any change in your dog's behaviour.

BITES & STINGS – NETTLES

We have covered various allergic reactions in previous blogs including bees, wasps, toads and caterpillars. Don't forget that when Spring has sprung and new growth appears throughout our countryside and hedgerows, it's nettle season which can really irritate your dog, particularly his paws if he runs through a patch on his walk. As with the treatment for Bees (an acidic poison) and Wasps (an alkaline poison), the key thing to remember when attempting to treat nettle stings is that the poison which makes up the nettle "venom" is made up of an acidic compound. In order to soothe and neutralise the effect of that acid sting, you will need to apply an alkaline solution to help calm and treat the irritation. Alkaline preparations such as bicarbonate of soda or toothpaste will certainly sooth such an irritation as the alkaline counteracts the acid in the nettle sting.

If you notice your dog has been affected while you are still on your walk, look around to see if you can see any Dock leaves. It is very usual to find both Nettles and Dock living in close proximity to one another.

Dock contains a natural remedy for the Nettle sting. Simply crumple and crush up the dock leaf in your hand and rub the juices it lets out over the paws. The sap is not, as people think, an alkaline but merely works because it is cool and moist and soothing on the skin.

As soon as you get back from your walk, if you think you have been in contact with nettles:-

1. Wash the area (be that the pads, the whole paw, or even if you notice raised bumps on the legs or other parts of the body) with soap and water as soon as possible to relieve the stinging sensation. Nettles are covered with tiny hairs which act like minute rods of glass which scratch the skin and deliver the acidic poison. Washing with soap and water in this way will help to remove these small glass hair filaments.

2. Make up a paste of baking soda and water and carefully apply it to the affected areas (or smear on some toothpaste).

3. If possible, try to prevent the dog from scratching or rubbing the itchy areas as this will merely aggravate the sensation and make it itch more.

4. If your dog has been prescribed Piriton antihistamine BY YOUR VET, then it is safe to give a dose to your dog. Should you find that the reaction goes down and then recurs, you can repeat the dose suggested by your vet six hours later should this be necessary.

5. Pay close attention to your dog's airway and if you feel his breathing is in anyway compromised by the allergic reaction, please call your vet immediately for emergency treatment.

BITES & STINGS - TOADS/CATERPILLARS

Some species of toad secrete a toxic substance on their skin. This passes into the mouth of any dog that picks up the toad to play with it.

Certain types of longhaired caterpillar can also produce similar irritants and even anaphylactic reactions in severe cases.

Signs & Symptoms of a severe allergic reaction to look out for include:

* Swollen eyes
* Swollen mouth & tongue
* Swollen throat making breathing difficult
* Raised spots which make the coat stand up in tufts
* Itching
* Major drooling & Pawing at the mouth
* Red/inflamed gums
* Vomiting
* Convulsions
* Heart attack

Please be aware that if the allergic reaction is so severe as to become anaphylactic shock, you will also see all the signs and symptoms associated with ordinary shock too ie:-

Early Signs	Secondary Signs	Late Signs
Rapid Heart Beat	Increased Heart Beat	Heart Rate Increases
Anxious/Agitated	Gums Pale or Blue	Gums White/Mottled
Bright Red Gums	Lethargy/Weakness	Weak Pulse
Shallow Breathing	Breathing More Shallow	Glazed Eyes/Not Focusing
Pulse Easy to Find	Pulse More Difficult to Find	Coma
		Heart Attack
		Death

If the reaction is due to toad secretion, wash around the muzzle, nose and the mouth if possible. A water spray is ideal for flushing out the mouth, but do not let the dog swallow any water. Rinse the mouth from the side and in a forward direction. If this is not possible, use a wet cloth and wash the tongue as best you can with clean water.

If a caterpillar is the culprit, you should still try to wash the dog's tongue and mouth but remember to protect yourself with gloves in case any of the caterpillar hairs are still on the dog as they could cause a reaction to you too.

If you can find the caterpillar (and if the dog hasn't 'munched him up' so that he is unrecognisable!) either bring him with you to the vet so he knows what has caused the reaction or simply take a good, <u>clear</u> photograph for him to work from.

Contact a vet if the dog is in discomfort – he may need antihistamines to reduce the swelling WHICH SHOULD ONLY BE PRESCRIBED BY A VET, to ensure they are safe for your dog to take and if so, THE CORRECT DOSAGE.

N.B. Only give antihistamine prescribed for the particular dog in question by the vet.

If the reaction is severe, please telephone immediately to seek urgent veterinary attention & monitor for signs of shock. Do not just turn up at the veterinary office as he may be out on another emergency or in theatre when you arrive – you MUST let him know you are coming so they are ready and waiting to treat your dog immediately.

Remember to watch the dog for 24 hours in case the reaction recurs.

BITES & STINGS - JELLYFISH

Currently in the UK we are experiencing a high influx of jellyfish (and therefore jellyfish stings) to our Coastline. Although the majority are not dangerous, some are, so here's our guide to jellyfish treatment – for both ourselves as well as our dogs.

Before we go any further, the advice below in no way mentions (and in fact would certainly discourage) us from urinating on the casualty! So, now we have that out of the way, please read on.

Jellyfish have tentacles and it's these tentacles that do the damage. They are covered with nematocysts, known as stinging cells, which have a variety of functions including sticking to surfaces and wrapping around objects, penetrating surfaces or secreting proteinaceous toxins.

Prevention

If you think there is any chance of your dog meeting a jellyfish whilst on a swim, they need some protection. The tentacles of a jellyfish will sting as they come into contact with the skin – it's not the pressure of touching that initiates the sting, but rather the chemical on the skin (this is why divers in and around Australia for example will usually wear tights (pantyhose) to try to protect their bare skin. Our dogs then are basically safer than we are, although we can spread petroleum jelly on any exposed skin, including the footpads, abdomen, nose, testicles, and eye rims to keep the venom from penetrating to the skin.

Signs & Symptoms:

Below are listed the most common signs and symptoms of a jellyfish sting, although it is important to note that only some and not all may be present.

* Heavy, very itchy rash with burning sensation.
* Nausea
* Vomiting
* High blood pressure follows
* Fever
* Confusion
* Shock
* Heart and respiratory problems
* Death

N.B. Jellyfish stings can react differently based upon the species they belong to.

- For the vast majority of jellyfish stings (on humans or on our dogs for that matter), treatment would be to soak or rinse the area in vinegar for 15-30 minutes to stop the nematocysts from releasing their toxins. If you do not have vinegar available, rinse in sea water or 70% alcohol.
- **Do not use fresh water** as this will cause toxins to be continued to be released.
- **Do not rub** the area as this will irritate the area still further.
- Wear gloves to remove tentacles or, if you don't have any, use a shell, a stick or a pair of tweezers. DO NOT touch the tentacles

with your bare hands, even if the tentacle is no longer attached to the jellyfish itself.

- Make a paste of baking soda to apply to the area or you can use shaving cream.
- Shave the area with a razor or credit card to remove any adherent nematocysts.
- Reapply vinegar or alcohol. The shaving cream or paste prevents nematocysts that have not been activated from releasing their toxin during removal with the razor.
- Rinse eye stings with saline solution readily found in first aid kits for both humans and canines.
- For stings around the eyes, take a towel and soak it in vinegar the carefully dab the skin around the eyes ensuring that you **Do Not place vinegar directly in the eyes.**
- For stings to the mouth itself, we can use 1/4 strength vinegar. Simply mix ¼ cup of vinegar with ¾ cup of water and use a medicine syringe to irrigate the mouth. Do not allow the dog to drink or swallow the solution (for humans, gargle and spit out the solution).
- Monitor for signs of shock and be ready to commence CPR if required.
- Transport to your Vet ASAP.

- Seek medical assistance immediately if you are stung by a **box jellyfish**.
- While you are waiting for medical help, **and before attempting to remove the tentacles,** flood the area with vinegar to soak the tentacles for **10 minutes or more** , or until medical help arrives.
- Keep as still as possible.

- If you do not have any vinegar available, soak with salt water **NOT fresh water**

Vinegar is the correct treatment for anything **except the Portuguese Man O War** (commonly called bluebottles). Portuguese Man O War are usually found in warmer waters and as such I think it would be unlikely to find them in the UK.

However, should you come in to contact with a Man O war, the treatment would be hot water, followed by ice. It is said that water of a temperature of 102 degrees will be helpful but that of 120 degrees would be better. Therefore, as most of us rarely have a thermometer to hand, it is suggested that asking the casualty to put their limb in as hot water as they can stand and then gradually raising the temperature is the best way to achieve this.

N.B. Please be sure not to burn your casualty by using water that is of too high a temperature.

This is a surprisingly solid, large jellyfish. The bell is shaped like a dome and has a ghost white colour with purple/blue lobes around the margin. It has eight solid oral-arms that resemble a cauliflower but no tentacles.

Size:
Up to 1m in diameter. These have been as up to 80 cm in

diameter and weighing 35 kg

Distribution:
Forms dense aggregations in coastal areas (Rosslare, Tre Madoc and Carmarthen Bays) during summer months. Some individuals sighted or caught in the Irish Sea and off the South coast of Ireland during the winter.

Sting:
No tentacles but can cause irritation.

TREATMENT FOR WOUNDS & BLEEDING

Before you treat any type of bleed/wound, you should always go through the **SEEP** checklist, to ensure you take all the right steps in the correct order. Treating a bleed relies heavily on things like the application of pressure, and the positioning of the animal's injured limb as bleeding will slow down it if has to go "uphill" against gravity.

The **SEEP checklist** is as follows:-

S=Sit or lie
(sit for a head or shoulder injury, lie down for a leg or paw injury with paw raised)
E=Elevate
(raise the wounded area above level of heart)
E=Examine
(see exactly what's going on to categorize the wound and also looking for foreign bodies)
P=Pressure
(place pressure directly on the wound unless there is something protruding in which case use pressure AROUND the object rather than on top of it)

We would treat the 5 most common canine flesh wounds as follows:-

Laceration (Rip or Tear)
This wound doesn't bleed as much as some, but it is likely to be dirty with particles of debris in it. Therefore, work through your **SEEP** checklist then, after around 5 minutes of direct pressure on the wound, provided the bleeding is well controlled, clean THOROUGHLY to remove any grit, rust, glass particles or debris with warm water, saline and/or sterile wipes. If the wound is caused by a bite, then extra care should be taken to irrigate and

clean the wound (until you are bored stiff!!!) to make sure it is actually clean. If the bleeding is NOT well controlled, apply a pressure bandage by wrapping the wound with several layers of gauze and then using vet wrap, an elastic bandage, duct tape, or masking tape over it to maintain pressure. Remember not to wrap so tightly that you compromise the circulation to the limb.

Incision (Sharp Slice)

This wound is usually very clean but does bleed a lot as, if it is deep, it may gape open. Therefore, work through your **SEEP** checklist. If blood seeps through your dressing, apply another pad directly on top of it. If after dressing number 2 you are still not able to control the blood loss, ring your vet immediately for further advice and notification of your intention to come to the surgery, apply a pressure dressing as above. As this wound is likely to be clean, there is no need to waste time (and blood) trying to clean it. If the blood loss is severe, slightly raise your pet's back end to increase blood flow to the head. Keep your pet warm with a blanket if cold. If your pet is hot, cool down with cold compresses to the chest and abdomen.

Puncture (Stabbing or Standing on Pointy Object)

DO NOT remove any object that is penetrating the animal. This object may be stemming blood flow as it blocks the hole, preventing infection getting in and may also cause more damage to the tissues as it is withdrawn. Work through your **SEEP** check list as above, this time applying your pressure AROUND the penetrating object. Treat for shock by raising your pet's back end as above.

Amputation (Partial or complete severing of a limb)

We deal with amputation in two sections:

− firstly treatment of the dog and secondly treatment of the amputated limb)
1) treat the dog using **SEEP**
2) treat for shock
3) ring your vet

− to treat the severed limb, act as follows:-
1) collect the amputated limb
2) wrap in waterproof covering – ie cling film/plastic bag
3) wrap in tissue or light bandage to protect it
4) place **ON** top of frozen peas/ice **DO NOT** PUT COMPLETELY IN ICE
5) if no ice available, place in cold milk bottle (with limb in waterproof bag)
6) transport pet & severed limb to vet urgently.

De-Gloving Injury (Flap of skin or creased skin wound)

1) Muzzle dog
2) Sit or Lie as appropriate
3) Elevate limb
4) Examine wound
5) Replace skin flap if possible

6) If skin is wrinkled rather than an actual flap and therefore cannot be repositioned, cover with plastic (cling-film or clean poo bag) or a moist dressing if plastic unavailable
7) Apply pressure dressing to the wound
8) Phone the vet
9) Transport to vet immediately
10) Monitor for signs of shock en route to vet

With any of these injuries, it is important to get your dog to the vet ASAP but please remember to **PHONE AHEAD** of your arrival. To turn up unannounced may cause more delay if there is no vet on site at the time you arrive or if the clinic is shut. To phone ahead gives them the opportunity to meet you there and administer treatment immediately.

BLEEDS & WOUNDS – VET WRAP

Vet Wrap – In an ideal world, I would love for every single one of you to have a well-stocked first aid box.

Obviously, it's not normal to carry everything but the kitchen sink around with us on our walks though, so if you only have ONE piece of first aid equipment, make it a roll of vet wrap. It is so versatile and can be used for so many purposes including application of a pressure dressing to stop a severe bleed, a support bandage for a sprain/strain, a dressing on an awkward shaped part of the body due to its adherence to itself, a muzzle for a fearful/dangerous dog, a spare lead should you come across a stray or injured animal or should you lose your own lead on a walk – not to mention the fact that you can use it on yourself if you need it too.

A small roll of vet wrap in your back pocket has saved many a scary moment. In a 3 month period, I used mine as a lead for a stray dog, to bandage Axl's paw when he got a freezer burn to his pad on a walk in the ice and also as a bandage on Rain's stopper pad when he sliced it on a thorn in the undergrowth a mile from home. If I had not had it with me on any of these three occasions, things would have been decidedly more tricky to deal with.

If you don't know what vet wrap is, it's a stretchy bandage that has a kind of light rubbery coating on it so that although it is not actually sticky, it will grip and adhere to itself when applied so that you have no need for tape or safety pins or knots or anything.

Remember when using vet wrap on a limb, due to its stretchy nature, each time you wrap it round it will get tighter and tighter so it's vital not to pull too hard or you will cut off the blood supply to the limb beyond where you're bandaging.

A good tip is to unroll as much as you think it is going to take you to bandage the area and then roll it back on to the rest of the roll LOOSELY. This will mean as you come to apply it to the dog, you will not have to pull so hard to get it off the roll which, in turn, means you are less likely to wrap it too tightly on the dog.

When you are finished, make sure you can get your finger EASILY under the top and bottom of the dressing and that pressure is only being applied directly to the injury itself. It's incredibly easy to apply vet wrap too tightly. I would much rather your dressing was slightly too loose than even remotely too tight, so please look at the dressing you've done and if you are at all unsure of yourself, ALWAYS release it slightly to err on the side of caution.

Remember to keep checking the dressing because as an injured limb swells up, the dressing will become tighter, even though it may well have been perfect to start with.

Remember also that vet wrap does get a little tighter when it gets wet so if you have used it and then walked about in a wet environment, please keep a close eye on the pressure and release it if it does increase too far.

Apart from sliding your finger under the dressing, you can also squeeze the limb where the vet wrap is. It should have some give

in it:-
* If it feels very firm under your hand then it is too tight.
* If the skin above or below the dressing is bulging, it is too tight.
* If the paw or limb beyond the dressing is swelling, it is too tight
* If the limb feels colder than the other comparable limb, it is too tight.

If you are using the vet wrap to stem a severe bleed, any colour other than black is a good choice – with the black dressing the blood won't show through so clearly should the bleed not be controlled and you may be unaware that your dressing needs changing or altering.

Another point worth noting is that for reasons I'm not quite sure of, the black vet wrap does not adhere to itself nearly as well as all the other colours in **cold weather**. Therefore, if you are considering using it as I did to fashion a make-shift bootie for your dog if it gets a freezer burn, any of the other colours are much more efficient for doing the job. The black will tend to unravel and fall off in cold temperatures.

The vet wrap can be applied directly over a bleeding injury in a first aid situation although it is better if you can apply a wound dressing first. That said, if you are in the middle of nowhere with no first aid kit, a roll of vet wrap alone will definitely save the day.

BLEEDS & WOUNDS – DOG BITES

Firstly let me say that a dog bit really should be seen by a vet due to the extreme likelihood of bacterial infection and requirement of antibiotics.

Before you treat any type of bleed/wound, you should always go through the **SEEP** checklist, to ensure you take all the right steps in the correct order. Treating a bleed relies heavily on things like the application of pressure, and the positioning of the animal's injured limb as bleeding will slow down it if has to go "uphill" against gravity, i.e.

S=Sit or lie the dog down
(sit for a head or shoulder injury, lie down for a leg or paw injury with paw raised)
E=Elevate
(elevate the wounded area above level of heart)
E=Examine
(see exactly what's going on)
P=Pressure
(place pressure directly on the wound)

BEFORE you try to help your dog, please remember that he is likely still to be very scared with adrenaline racing through his body and probably in a fair bit of pain.

ALWAYS MUZZLE YOUR DOG before addressing his injuries or you may well wind up having to treat yourself for a dog bite too! If you haven't already done so, it's a good idea to get your dog used to accepting a muzzle BEFORE you need to use one so that the muzzle itself does not ramp up the stress levels. If you are unsure how to introduce your dog to a muzzle using positive reinforcement techniques, there's a brilliant video to show you how. Just go to your search engine of choice and type in "Rhodes 2 Safety Muzzle Acceptance".

Dog bites are usually classed either as puncture wounds, if the tooth has penetrated the skin or as a laceration if the skin has been ripped or torn by the tooth

Lacerations
Lacerations don't usually bleed as much as say an incision, but the wound is likely to be dirty with bacteria deposited from the dogs teeth within in. Therefore, work through your **SEEP** checklist as above then, after around 5 minutes of direct pressure on the wound, provided the bleeding is well controlled, we can commence cleaning the injury.

It is important to clean the wound thoroughly either with warm water, saline (salt water solution), sterile wipes or a micro bacterial cleansing solution such as Hibiscrub if you have it. Remember, if you are using Hibiscrub it is imperative to dilute the solution down to a ratio of 1:10, until it only just has a tiny tinge of pink to it. If the solution is too strong it will actively sting the wound and be uncomfortable for your dog. Ideally, Hibiscrub should only be used on topical problem areas or wounds that are completely clotted and sealed.

If, after a good clean, the wound does not appear too bad and the flesh has not actually been torn, merely keep an eye on the wound to make sure there is no sign of any infection (ie no oozing, weeping, bleeding, swelling or heat after a day or so)

Once you've cleaned the wound and the bleeding has stopped, provided that the wound is not huge, gaping, or has flesh hanging off, you can leave the injury undressed. You can use a natural remedy like Manuka honey applied to the wound to help it to heal (so long as Rover doesn't want to lick it off!)

It is unlikely, unless the bite is very serious, that the vet will stitch the wound. Leaving the wound open is preferable so as not to trap any bacteria from the tooth within the wound, which may turn into an abscess later on. Don't be surprised if your vet chooses not to suture the injury even if it does look a little grizzly.

If the bleeding is quite serious and you find that blood seeps through your dressing, apply another pad directly on top of it. If, after dressing number 2 you are still not able to control the blood loss, apply a pressure bandage by wrapping the wound with several layers of gauze and then using vet wrap, an elastic bandage, duct tape, or masking tape over it to maintain pressure. Remember not to wrap so tightly that you compromise the circulation to the limb. If you notice that the limb beyond the pressure dressing is swelling up or beginning to feel colder than the other limbs, you MUST release the pressure ASAP.

N.B. If the wound is on the neck, near the windpipe or on the chest, remember not to bandage tightly as this would inhibit breathing. Better to apply and maintain pressure by hand.

If the blood loss is severe, slightly raise your pet's back end to increase blood flow to the head. Keep your pet warm with a blanket if cold. If your pet is hot, cool down with cold compresses to the chest and abdomen.

Treat for shock by raising your pet's back end as described in our blog on shock.

Puncture Wounds
A puncture wound resulting from a dog's tooth during a bite may look small in diameter but it might actually have caused injury to underlying structures and be very deep – possibly even puncturing a main artery/vein.

Work through your **SEEP** check list as above, and if the puncture wound is deep, pack it before applying your pressure dressing.

With both the laceration and puncture wound, it is essential to seek veterinary help.

Even if the wounds do not appear to be huge, it is imperative that they are cleaned thoroughly and examined professionally. Apart from the possible danger of damage to underlying tissues or structures, it is likely that your dog will require a course of antibiotics, anti-inflammatory drugs and painkillers too.

With a serious bite, please remember to '**PHONE AHEAD** of your arrival. To turn up unannounced may cause more delay if there is no vet on site at the time you arrive or if the clinic is shut. Phoning ahead gives them the opportunity to meet you there and administer treatment immediately.

BLEEDS & WOUNDS – SPLIT EAR TIPS

This morning while on our walk I was wondering what I would put in today's blog. Axl, my trustee Rhodesian Ridgeback side-kick, must have been reading my thoughts because no sooner had the thought crossed my mind, than he came up with the answer for me. Now that he's an "agility nut", he loves to leap and jump over as many fences as possible and this morning was no exception. He charged at a fence but didn't realise that above it ran a length of wire, tacked to the top rung. Thankfully it was not barbed wire, but there was a sharp point sticking out none the less.

Now don't ask me how he managed it, but after he'd jumped the fence he'd put a tiny nick in his right ear tip and therefore, today's blog is about bandaging the more tricky bits of your wriggly canine!

As you know, when dealing with bleeding we always employ the S.E.E.P. checklist so that we get everything in the right order and don't miss any steps out:

S = Sit or Lie (which ever position allows the bleeding bit to be elevated)
E = Elevate (raise the wound to slow down the bleed)
E = Examine (check what type of bleed you have & if there is anything stuck in it)
P = Pressure (Applied directly to the wound itself so long as nothing is protruding)

Now usually, with most body parts this would be easy enough, but with Axl's long floppy ears, it's a little more tricky to elevate them – so here's how we treat a split ear tip.

1) Apply a wound dressing over the ear tip and hold firmly in place with microporous tape

2) Fold the ear so that it lies across the top of the dog's head

3) Hold the ear in place on top of the head with a Buff neck warmer or the leg of a pair of tights, like a snood.

(When using a pair of tights, please make sure you select a size big enough for the breed of dog you have. There is no point in using "petite" stockings on a Ridgeback as they would be too tight and be both uncomfortable and restrictive for his breathing/swallowing. Ridgebacks definitely require a "large" or "extra large" size of stockings/tights.

Leave the ear and dressing in place like this for at least 5 minutes to give the blood time to clot.

4) Remove the dressing and replace the ear into its normal position and then re-apply the Buff or stocking to keep the ear pressed to the side of the head to prevent re-opening if the dog should flap his head (at least 60 minutes).

A small split in the ear tip should be controlled fairly well using this method – you'll need to keep the stocking in place for an hour or so.

If the ear refuses to heal, you can of course opt for a veterinary glue to "stick" the wound together. There are several on the market that are recommended for veterinary use only. The monomeric formulation forms a thin, waterproof adhesion to bond/seal tissue in a variety of injuries.

For a more severe split, it is likely that it may be necessary for your dog to wear his fashionable new look for as much as a week or two, even after the bleeding has stopped, to prevent the split re-opening again. Make sure the split is really nicely healed before you allow him to stop wearing the stocking.

Other ways to help a stubborn ear to heal include sticking a large fabric Elastoplast on both sides of the ear with them extending beyond the ear tip then sticking them to each other. The old fashioned fabric plasters tend to stick very well both to the ear and to each other, creating a reliable dressing that shouldn't fall off.

There is also something you could invest in called a "No Flap Ear Wrap" which is pretty expensive but if you have tried everything else, this may well be your only other course of action. I am informed by somebody who struggled with this problem for a year that this REALLY works.

BLEEDS & WOUNDS - SPLIT TAIL TIP

If you have a breed with a lovely long, waggy tail, you may well have encountered the nightmare that is a split tail tip or "Happy Tail". Usually, as a result of some seriously exuberant wagging, the tail may come into contact with a stationary object such as the door frame or wall and when "thwacked" with great force, a split can appear in the tip which then bleeds and showers the walls and ceiling with gory red spatter ... all that red spray often looks worse than it is, as if an axe murderer has rampaged through your house. So, what should you do?

Once again we need to re-visit the '**SEEP**' technique that I've mentioned so many times before in other blogs ie, **S**itting or lying the dog down, **E**xamining it so we know what is going on, **E**levating it (for a short time just holding it up should suffice) and putting **P**ressure on it with a wound dressing to stop the bleed.

Again, after around 5 minutes, the tip should have begun to clot but this wound will need protecting for some time to prevent it opening up every time they wag and show their affection to you. Fold a wound dressing around the tip of the tail and hold it in place right from the tip to a fair way up the length of the tail with a strip of vet-wrap to cushion the tip of the tail. The vet-wrap will need to go a good distance up the tail to prevent the dressing flying off with each and every swish of the tail. Keeping the dressing on can be quite a challenge and if your furry pal is making this tricky, see our blog on preventing them licking wounds and picking stitches which, hopefully, may help you get around this problem.

After a couple of days, the wound should have begun to heal quite nicely but there is still the very real risk of it re-opening with each wag. A good method to try is to insert the tip of the tail into a tube just wide enough so that it's not quite touching the tail too much (something like a couple of inches of foam pipe lagging/insulation from a DIY store, or the shaft of a plastic syringe for example for smaller breeds) or better yet, a foam hair roller with the outer "grippy" bit removed.

The important thing is that whatever tube you choose, it should have an open end rather than being completely sealed. We want the air to be able to circulate around the tip of the tail to help it heal and so making sure there is a hole at the end will allow it to breathe as well as protect it from further wagging incidents.

If the tail refuses to heal, you can of course opt for a first aid super glue to "stick" the wound together. There are several on the market that are recommended for skin use. The monomeric formulation forms a thin, waterproof adhesion to bond/seal tissue in a variety of injuries. This type of glue is ideal for skin closure, sealing broken nails and generally used as a "quick fix" and will usually stay on for around 3-4 days. It should not be applied to an actively bleeding/open wound.

Please DO NOT use regular super glue that you can just pick up on the high street. These types of glues work with an exothermic reaction which basically means they give out heat as they stick – enough heat in fact to burn the tissues of the tail. This is why we recommend only the appropriate first aid grade versions.

Often, keeping the tail from wagging is the only way to give the injury time to heal. The best way we have found to accomplish this is to secure the tail between the legs (not TO the leg itself). There is something I've seen that you can buy to do this called, I believe, a "Tail Bandit" ... but this is the R2S cheap as chips version:

First, find yourself a length of ribbon or bandage (probably about 2 meters in length for a large breed dog) and a keyring. Loop the ribbon through the keyring as per this picture:

Next, pass the ribbon around the tail and slot it through the keyring to secure it to the tail itself without pinching the tail hard or cutting off the circulation:

Next, stand the dog and bring his tail between his legs with the ribbon coming up and over his back just in front of his hips (be sure NOT to tie the knot on the dog's spinal area ... always better to tie it slightly over to one side to prevent any discomfort of the knot pressing on his vertebrae)

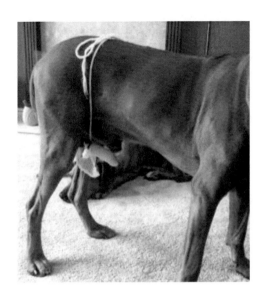

Keeping the skin as healthy as possible is the quickest way to get it to heal. A tried and tested method to help the skin remain healthy once the wound has closed up was sent to me from Yvonne Bowker ... a Ridgeback owner of many years' standing and with a lot of experience in treating split tail tips. Yvonne's "insider info" is as follows:

1) Wash the affected area and gently clean off any scabby bits with warm salted water.
2) Dry thoroughly.
3) Use Udder Cream or Bag Balm, (available from farm/equine supply stores)
4) Gently massage cream onto affected area
5) Cover with sterile gauze or cotton
6) Wrap from tip to root of tail with Vet Wrap, moulding to the shape of the tail
7) Change 2 x per day and treat as above

BLEEDS & WOUNDS - INTERNAL BLEEDING

After an accident where there has been significant trauma, such as a road traffic collision or fall from a height, or perhaps when our dog has a serious disease or infection, internal bleeding can develop.

When we see blood from a wound, we know instinctively that we need to stop the bleeding as quickly as possible so we apply pressure to the wound and dress it with a bandage. That's not so easy if the bleeding is INSIDE the dog. You can't exactly put a plaster on a bleed if you can't see the wound.

So, what do we do?

Well firstly, you must ask yourself what it is that alerts you to the possibility of an internal bleed? Maybe we saw the accident happen, or we know our dog has been unwell. This might tip us off to the possibility but what can you as an owner do to detect whether that is actually what is happening?

Signs:
Blood is supposed to travel around the circulatory system feeding oxygen to our organs. If the blood leaves the body, it takes oxygen with it and the animal will start to slide into shock. With internal bleeding, although the blood is not actually leaving the body, it isn't travelling around the circulatory system as it should be, and hence it is not delivering the oxygen where it is needed.

Signs you might see to alert you to this are:-

Early Signs	Secondary Signs	Late Signs
Rapid Heart Beat	Increased Heart Beat	V. Increased Heart Beat
Bright Red Gums	Gums Pale or Blue	Gums White or Mottled
Pounding Pulse – Easy To Find	Pulse Faster but Slightly Less Strong	Pulse Rapid - Thready/Weak
Shallow Breathing	Breathing More Shallow	Lack of Respiratory Effort
Dog Responsive but Unsettled/Whining	Dog Lying Down, Refusing to Get Up	Pulse Very Difficult to Detect
Paws Warm	Paws Cold with Intermittent Shivering	Not Focusing
Eyes Reactive	Eyes Wide/Staring	Eyes Glazed
		Coma/Death

Apart from the above signs, the key and most obvious sign as to whether or not your dog has internal bleeding might be that it is possible to detect the bleeding, just by feeling his tummy/abdomen with the flat of your hand.

Gently place your palm on his tummy and roll it from wrist to finger tips. Don't take your hand off in between presses, don't poke him with your fingers and don't slap his tummy – just "roll" your hand gently 3-4 times and see what it feels like.

A normal tummy should feel soft and squidgy (you can feel your own tummy when you are lying down and relaxed to see how it should feel – whether you've "eaten all the pies" or whether you've been down to the gym every night for six months, your tummy should be soft). It should have the texture of a raw steak.

If, when you roll your hand on the tummy, it feels hard and tight and doesn't squidge much under your palm, then this can often indicate internal bleeding within the abdomen. As the blood fills the space, the tummy swells and doesn't feel so soft. This has more the texture of an over-cooked or "well-done" steak. This was, in fact, the deciding factor for me personally when I had to make the decision to take my Labrador to be put to sleep following an illness in her old age.

Obviously, we cannot bandage this type of injury, so we need to act fast. The first thing to do is to put him in the correct position for treating shock. Although we cannot stop the bleeding, we can minimise the effect that the blood loss will have on the dog.

IT IS VITAL TO GET YOUR DOG TO A VET
Remember to 'phone the vet immediately and tell him what you suspect BEFORE you set off to the clinic. The dog MUST be seen as an emergency. This CANNOT wait.

<u>Temporary Treatment:</u>

1) Quickly lay him on his back

2) Manually hold his back legs up in the air to get the oxygenated blood to his brain ASAP.

Shock Stabilisation Treatment:

1) Find a board strong enough to take his weight and lay him on it.

The board I found which would be suitable for treating my big Ridgebacks in such a situation turned out to be the lid off my son's toy box. If you have a small breed dog then perhaps a chopping board or the tray you have your supper on may suffice. With a larger dog, then maybe the tray in the bottom of his crate or even the parcel shelf of your car, if it has one, may do the job admirably.

N.B. Always lay him on his right hand side in case the shock gets worse and requires CPR.

2) Wrap him in a blanket/towel, securing him to the board with it.

3) Place cushion/rolled up jacket and put under the board, directly under his hind legs.

4) Tilt him sufficiently for the blood to be encouraged to flow toward his brain.

5) Phone your vet ASAP to meet you at the surgery.

6) The board will act like a stretcher for carrying him to and from the car & it will allow you to tilt his body sufficiently to aid the blood flow to his head.

(N.B. Without the board, his body would just sag in the middle and not be physically tilted)

If you have rear seats that can be folded down, you might find that they don't go ENTIRELY flat. If this is the case, you can lay the dog so that his bottom is towards the higher end of the seats, thus treating him for his shock all the way en route to the vet.

TREATMENT PROTOCOL

There are lots of places a dog could get a burn from, and several different types of burn too, from hot burns (caused by coming into contact with anything hot including flames, boiling water and even the sun), cold burns (typically ice or frozen metal), chemical burns (from anything that can get either onto the dog's skin or be licked off), friction burns (usually as a result of coming to an emergency stop on their paws or being dragged along a road surface such as may happen in a road traffic accident) and electric burns (caused by electric shocks).

Remember in hot weather, particularly if your dog has pale skin, light coloured fur or only thin hair coverage on the muzzle and on the ear tips, sunscreen should be applied to prevent sunburn. A high factor, waterproof, child-friendly lotion is recommended and, if possible, one without fragrance so as not to encourage the dog to lick it off. If your dog does manage to get himself sunburnt, use the tips below to cool the burn just as you would any other type of burn.

* CAUTION * If his burn is on the muzzle, be very careful not to drown or choke your dog by running cold water across his nose and muzzle. Better to use a cold ice pack gently to help cool and soothe.

The golden rule is that if skin dries, it dies, and so if your dog gets a burn, you must:

1. Run the affected area under cold water for a **MINIMUM** of 10 minutes, or until the skin is cold – therefore, if after having run the burn under cold water for 10 minutes there is still any heat left in the burn, you must continue until such time as all the redness and heat has left the wound.
2. When you have finished cooling the burn, it is perfectly fine to keep it covered with a moist clean dressing to keep the skin cold and wet.
3. You can use cling film which will do the same job PROVIDED YOU ARE 100% SURE THE WOUND IS COLD. If you use cling film and there is any heat left in the wound, you will merely keep the heat in and cook the wound still further.
4. If the dog will not allow you to do this and refuses to stand for 10 minutes with a running hose over it (no surprise there), you can try placing ice cubes or frozen peas in a clean, wet, tea towel and keeping it in contact with the affected area, again for a minimum of 10 minutes. Always ensure you have a barrier between the ice and the skin.
5. Remember that the fur might well be masking the size and severity of the burn too and it is often necessary to cut away the

fur to expose the area so you can see more clearly what you are dealing with. Burns are very painful and it is often sensible to apply a makeshift muzzle to ensure your own safety. We can go through the **S.C.A.L.D.** check list to assess the severity of the burn as follows:-

S = Size – how big is the burn? Any burn bigger than 1" square on a large dog needs treatment from a vet. Therefore, with a small breed, obviously this size guide will be considerably smaller. Be on the safe side and always seek veterinary advice if your dog has been burned, however small.

C = Cause – what caused the burn? Some burns are more serious than others for example if the burn was caused by a chemical, not only do you have the burnt skin to deal with but also the possibility of a poisoning if the chemical manages to make its way into the dog's blood stream. You also have the added likelihood that he may have ingested some of the chemical while licking it to remove it from his fur. With chemical burns your MINIMUM time under the cold running water DOUBLES to at least 20 minutes to ensure you flush the chemical from the layers of the skin completely.

A = Age – how old is the dog? Very young, elderly, frail or recently ill dogs need urgent attention

L = Location – some places on your dog are more dangerous than others. If any of the following locations are damaged then I would always seek veterinary attention immediately:-

Muzzle,
Eyes,
Nose,
Windpipe/Throat,
Ribcage,
Pads,
Genitals.

D = Depth – how deep is the burn? A full thickness burn will be oozing, bleeding and very wet. This is an emergency situation. You should apply a cold wet dressing to the burn, ring your vet and tell him you are coming to the surgery immediately.

Remember, all the while you are treating your dog and his burns, please be on the look-out for signs of shock, which are much more dangerous than the burn itself. Should your dog start displaying any of the shock signs, stabilise him with his rear end elevated, keep him warm, ring your vet and then continue to treat the burn once you have his shock under control.

If you are **ever** in doubt as to the severity of a burn, please **'phone your vet immediately for advice**.

BURNS – COLD BURNS

Cold Burns: There are 5 main categories of burn that we need to be aware of, not just the ones caused by flames or hot cups of tea and in fact, some burns are caused by the opposite of heat! The 5 include:

Hot/Thermal
Cold
Chemical
Friction
Electrical

As we in the UK are currently moving towards our colder part of the year, in a previous blog we discussed how best to avoid burns arising from cold/icy surfaces and also chemical burns such as those derived from salt gritting. Today, we need to look at what you should do if your dog is unlucky enough to develop an ice burn.

A burn occurs when skin comes into contact with a surface significantly hotter or colder than that of the body temperature. Extreme cold such as that experienced by a dog's paws when walking on packed ice or deep snow as the paws are pressed down by the dog's body weight, can cause damage to the skin and underlying tissues. The heat in the paws is transferred to the colder surface, taking it away from the body tissue.

The dog may experience symptoms of burning, pins and needles or itchiness, causing them to chew at their feet or do "zoomies" around the carpet to try to scratch them and ease the itching sensation. The tissue may appear white, blistered or even open and bleeding if the surface of the pad has been burnt away and torn off as it has stuck to the ice beneath. The pads may be numb in the area where they are very cold and it might be that the dog is unaware of the damage.

Obviously, if you know your walk will be involving lots of snow and ice, then prevention could be better than the cure for example using boots to protect the pads or simply slathering on a good protective barrier such as Musher's paw wax.

As soon as you notice that your dog has an ice burn, immediate and appropriate treatment is absolutely essential.

- Take the dog indoors as soon as possible or, at the very least, try to seek shelter if you are unable to get home immediately.
- Watch for other signs of hypothermia such as shivering, stiffness, pale gums, anxiety, disorientation or collapse and keep the dog warm with layers of blankets, jackets etc. Do not immerse the dog in HOT water to warm him as this may very well send him into shock as his blood tries to make its way to the extremities of his body and in doing so, moves away from his brain and vital organs.
- If you are unable to get home, wrap the affected areas using sterile dressings ensuring that you have removed any "snowballs" from between the toes. (A great tip for breeds with hair between the pads and toes or feathers up their legs is to spray the fur with baby oil before your walk which will prevent the snow/ice from sticking to the fur. I've also heard of people using Mane and Tail conditioner to really good effect too)
- We need to warm the area immediately which can be done by immersing the affected paws in LUKE WARM water. It is very important to ensure that the water is just tepid to begin with, such as you would use for a new-born baby. Anything other than JUST warm will feel burning hot to the dog and cause further damage.
- Once the paw begins to warm through, you may start to add small quantities of hotter water and bring the water temperature up gradually.
- Once the temperature has risen, it should ideally be maintained at around 104 to 108 degrees F and as the warmth of the water transfers to the pad, the wound will begin to heal (in exactly the opposite way that using cold water to a hot burn will stop the cooking process and heal the area).

- Please remember that as you warm the paw, itchiness, a burning/pins and needles sensation and even swelling may occur so it is vital not to proceed with the warming procedure too quickly.
- Telephone your vet and ask for advice and guidance. It might be that your dog will need an appointment to be seen by a professional if the size of the burn is extensive, if the damage is deep or if your dog is very young, old or frail.
- If the wounds are not extensive, keep them moisturised with Sudocreme, Aloe Vera, Aveeno or Manuka Honey to encourage them to heal.
- Keep the area covered, clean and waterproof when the dog goes out for toilet breaks until the surface has begun to heal.

BURNS - FRICTION BURNS

When you have a fast moving, athletic dog who loves to chase or race or turn on a sixpence, friction burns to the pads are an occupational hazard. People tend to think of burns merely in the capacity of being caused by something hot, like a flame or boiling water, but there are several different types of burn that your pet can sustain including:-

Hot burns
(caused by anything hot ie flames, boiling water the sun),

Cold burns
(usually due to ice or frozen metal),

Chemical burns
(from anything either on the dog's skin or has been licked off)

Electric burns
(caused by electricity during a shock)

Friction burns
(usually as a result of coming to an emergency stop on the paws or other skin surface)

The golden rule is that if skin dries, it dies, and so if your dog gets a burn, you must run the affected area under cold water for a **MINIMUM** of 10 minutes, or until the skin is cold – therefore, if after having run the burn under cold water for 10 minutes there is still any heat left in the burn, you must continue until such time as all the redness and heat has left the wound. When you have finished cooling the burn, it is perfectly fine to keep it covered with a moist clean dressing to keep the skin cold and wet. If the dog will not allow you to do this and refuses to have either a hosepipe cooling the wound or is unable to stand in the case of friction burns to the pads, for 10 minutes in a pool of cold water), you can try placing ice cubes or frozen peas in a clean, wet, tea towel and keeping it in contact with the affected area, again for a minimum of 10 minutes. Remember that if the burn is on skin beneath the fur, it might well be masked and therefore difficult to determine the size and severity of the burn. It is often necessary to cut away the fur to expose the area so you can see more clearly what you are dealing with. Burns are very painful and it is often sensible to apply a makeshift muzzle to ensure your own safety.

We can go through the **S.C.A.L.D.** check list to assess the severity of the burn as on our previous Burns blog.

Remember, all the while you are treating your dog and his burns, please be on the lookout for signs of shock which are much more dangerous than the burn itself. Should your dog start displaying any of the shock signs, stabilise him with his rear end elevated, ring your vet and then continue to treat the burn once you have his shock under control.

Extra Tip for Flyballers
When competing at flyball, our dogs can often experience friction burns due to the sheer speed of their runs and turns. They do more than one run in a session so its a great idea to treat their pads between runs if you get the opportunity. Simply using an ice pack or cold compress to the pads for several minutes after

each run can greatly reduce the incidence of friction burns. If you want your dog to run and compete for you all day, its imperative that you take care of his paws and cooling them between the sessions is a very pro-active step to take.

If you are **ever** in doubt as to the severity of a burn, please **phone your vet immediately for advice**.

BURNS - CHEMICAL BURNS

Chemical burns come in all sorts of guises – from our dogs sticking their noses into substances in the garage or garden shed, finding "dumped" chemicals in the undergrowth on our walks, on their paws if they walk through a spilt liquid on the floor or pesticides sprayed on a farmers field, or may be even with something as seemingly innocent as walking along a salt/gritted road in the winter.

Anytime that you become aware of a chemical burn, the faster you are able to deal with the problem, the less damage will be inflicted on the animal.

It is advisable that each time you walk your dog where there is the possibility of him walking on salted/treated roads, always clean and rinse the paws thoroughly (including between the toes and pads) when you return to the house. Many people who know their dogs are sensitive advocate the use of lavender in the cleaning water to help soothe the skin.

Once the paws are clean, they should be dried off as normal and inspected to ensure that the surface of the pad is not damaged in any way. If the skin is not broken but you sense there may be any kind of irritation, it's a good idea to wash the foot a little more to ensure you prevent absorption of the salt any further into the layers of the skin. Savlon, Aveeno oatmeal moisturiser and Aloe Vera are excellent preparations to apply to the skin to soothe and help repair any damage – but please try if possible to stop your dog licking it off (a pair of children's socks will probably come in very handy here!)

Even if the salt has not actually damaged the pads, the dog's natural instinct will be to lick and groom the feet to remove any residue. Such a high quantity of salt being ingested is very dangerous indeed – even more so for smaller dogs – so please make sure that his feet are cleaned way before he has a chance to clean them himself. Please remember that the salt levels will build up in his body each time he goes out on a treated road (THIS PROCEDURE SHOULD ALWAYS BE APPLIED FOR OUR FELINE FRIENDS WHEN THEY'VE BEEN OUT TOO!)

If the chemical that has caused the burn is toxic or corrosive for example an acid, it is vital that the dog's mouth be rinsed out too, from the side and across the tongue if possible, without the dog swallowing any of the solution. You can use wet flannels to wash the tongue, rinsing them in FRESH water between each wash to ensure you are diluting any chemical in the mouth. If you suspect that your dog has ingested any chemical, please seek immediate veterinary advice urgently as your dog may be poisoned as a result. (See blog on Poisoning).

Treating a Chemical Burn:

The golden rule is that if skin dries, it dies, and so if your dog gets a burn such as from a flame, something hot or friction for example, you must run the affected area under cold water for a **MINIMUM** of 10 minutes. This minimum time **DOUBLES** to at least **20 minutes** in the case of a chemical burn. You should continue to rinse and irrigate the surface of the tissue until you are positive you have not only cleaned the surface, but have also water-logged the layers of the dermis so that none of the chemical remains below the surface.

Please only ever use fresh running water to clean the area – **NEVER STAND A PAW IN A BOWL** to wash off a chemical – If you try to wash the substance from the paw while in a bowl, all you will do is dilute the chemical throughout the entire contents of the bowl and then be soaking your dog's foot in a chemical solution.

Remember that if the burn is on skin beneath the fur, it might well be masked and therefore difficult to determine the size and severity of the burn. It is often necessary to cut away the fur to expose the area so you can see more clearly what you are dealing with.

Burns are very painful and it is often sensible to apply a makeshift muzzle to ensure your own safety.

Go through the **S.C.A.L.D.** check list to assess the severity of the burn as per the previous Burns blog.

Remember, all the while you are treating your dog and his burns, to be on the look-out for signs of shock, which is much more dangerous than the burn itself. Should your dog start displaying any of the shock signs, stabilise him with his rear end elevated, keep him warm, monitor his breathing, gums and heartrate, ring your vet and then continue to treat the burn once you have his shock under control.

BURNS - SUNBURN

It's important to remember that even the most innocent of situations can result in sunburn or burns of one type or another. There are 5 main categories you need to be aware of and they are: Hot (or "thermal"), Cold, Friction, Electrical and Chemical. When we think of HOT burns, we usually think about fire or may be spilling a hot drink but we should also be thinking about thermal burns from the sun – particularly if your dog has a pale coloured, sparse or short coat.

The breeds most commonly affected are:-

- Pitbulls
- Dalmatians
- Boxers
- Weimaraners
- Greyhounds
- Chinese Crested Dog

The areas most at risk from the sun are the top of the muzzle where the fur is shorter and less dense, the nose itself, the ear tips and also the underbelly – especially if your dog is a real sun-worshiper who likes to lie out and catch those rays! Basically, anywhere with little or no fur to protect it is a danger area for your pooch.

Don't forget, their eyelids can also burn and if you have a dog with little or no pigment in the eyelids, you could always consider something like the Doggles Protective Eyewear which are just special doggy goggles.

Sunburn doesn't look like human sunburn – yes, it can be red and sore as you'd expect but often it might be that the skin looks dry and leathery, cracked or even turns white, so please don't dismiss these changes out of hand as they may well be telling you that your pet could do with a little more protection.

If you know your dog likes to sunbathe, particularly if he is pale-coloured, then protecting him BEFORE he goes into the sun is a sensible idea. You wouldn't let your kids play out all day in the sun without applying sunscreen, so please get into the habit of doing the same for your dog.

But which sunscreen should you choose? We've already said that protecting the muzzle and nose is very important but you know as well as I do, if you apply any cream or lotion to his nose, that tongue is going to be out immediately to lick it all off, so it's important to choose a sunscreen that is fragrance-free (in an effort not to attract his licking lizard), waterproof (so that if he does lick, at least SOME of it may manage to stay on) and finally and perhaps most importantly, non-toxic.

Many human adult sunscreens have Zinc Oxide in them. This is a toxic chemical for your dog, particularly if ingested in large quantities. That being said, we must consider the size of our dog too and realise that what is not a particularly large quantity for a large breed dog, would be a massive amount for a toy breed.

There are specific doggy sunscreens on the market and though designed for dogs, I'm very sad to say that many of them still have ingredients which are not good for our furry friends and as such, it's pretty difficult to find one that would suit. You are perhaps just as safe to use a mild and sensitive sunscreen designed for babies instead – again go for fragrance free and waterproof if possible and always aim for a high factor such as factor 30 or above.

But what do you do if you discover your dog has already been burned by the sun? Well, usually for a burn we would apply cold running water for at least 10 minutes and that's fine for say, the underbelly, but what do you do if it's their nose that they've burnt? There is no way your dog is going to allow you to pour cold water over his nose is there (poor little sausage will think he's being water-boarded!)

If possible, hold a cold compress or place an ice pack on a light damp cloth on the nose being careful not to block up the nostrils as you try to help. Another option is to take some frozen peas and lay them on a sheet of cling-film. Lightly spray with water so they stick together to make a cold sheet, one pea deep. Have the dog lay with his head across your lap and then gently raise his head up and more specifically the injured area of the nose.

Cover with a damp sling or clean tea-towel leaving the nostrils peeking out, and then drape the cold "pea-film" over the top of the sling. Because it is damp, the sling will not stick and because the peas do not weigh very much, your dog will hopefully be able to tolerate the gentle cold feeling on his muzzle.

For other parts of the body, simply applying a cold, wet towel after you have cooled the burn will help – if skin dries it dies, so if we can keep the skin moist, it will prevent further damage.

For underbelly burns, bathing your dog in cool water will really soothe him. You can also try adding colloidal oat flour to the bath or colloidal oatmeal bod-wash, which will help soothe the burn and prevent itching and further damage to his skin surface by scratching the itch. Remember, if you are going to bathe your dog in cool water to help ease the burn, do not use shampoo as this will irritate the skin – especially if the wound is severe.

Applying Aloe Vera, or Witch Hazel to the area once cooled will also help soothe him but please be aware that if the burn is full or partial thickness rather than merely just superficial, or if he shows any signs of discomfort or pain, he will need to see a vet. Often, it is difficult to tell just how big a burn is because the dog's coat obscures your view, so if you are in any doubt as to the severity of the burn, please have him checked over professionally. It might well be that the vet will need to shave off his fur to be able to treat his wound, possibly with a solution of Silver Sulphadiazine. If it is more severe, he may even need to hospitalise him and keep him on a drip to prevent him going into shock, so please do take all burns very seriously.

CHAPTER 8: CONDITIONS   PG

EPILEPSY, FITS & SEIZURES

Fits and Seizures can occur when brain cells malfunction and abnormal nerve signals spread throughout part of the brain in an uncontrolled way. The most common cause of fits/seizures/convulsions in dogs include:

EPILEPSY
This is the most common cause.
The first fit normally occurs before age 3 if true epilepsy is the cause.
Fits in young dogs may often be epilepsy but can also be due to other congenital problems such as abnormalities in liver blood supply, hydrocephalus or Distemper.
It is inherited in certain breeds (including German Shepherds, Golden Retrievers and Dachshunds).

Other common causes of seizures and fits are:-

Other diseases
Brain tumours
Poisons
Infections
Hyperthermia (over-heating)
Traumatic injury to the head

There are various medical treatments available to help with the frequency and severity of seizures and once your dog has undergone assessments and tests, these can be prescribed by your vet if deemed appropriate.

There are also other homeopathic treatments that can be tried and it is suggested that many of them can help reduce the number of episodes that the dog experiences. Such things as Viscum Album 30c straight after a seizure, for example, is said to reduce the effects and possibly the onset of another. You might also want to try Coccolus in 6c given twice weekly which I have had very good reports of, particularly for dogs with "absence" type episodes, though these are anecdotal and not something I have tried personally.

Recognising stages of Epileptic Fits

BEFORE THE FIT

After a while, owners may be able to discover their dog's particular triggers that bring on a fit, which can be very varied and unique to each animal. Such things as a specific food, a vaccination or even lack of sleep or stress caused by a couple of days' back-to-back strenuous mental activity can be enough.

Usual signs that a fit may be on the way include a slight abnormality in the dog's behaviour including restlessness, pacing, and anxious behaviour, panting or whining and seeking comfort. Many dogs are actually aware that a fit is imminent and may come to "tell" their owner that something is not right.

The most common time for dogs to experience fits is when they are at their most relaxed so often this means very late at night say around midnight, or early in the morning say around 5 or 6 AM. That's not to say, however, that fits cannot occur at other times of the day.

FIT/SEIZURE

Sudden onset of the fit with the dog losing coordination and sometimes consciousness. Falling to the floor. The limbs extend and become quite rigid, often including the tail. Breathing may stop for a few seconds which can be extremely frightening for the owner, although it is good to remember that it is very unusual for a dog to die during an epileptic episode.

"Paddling" movements, shaking or vibration of the muscles in the back limbs may start. The dog may appear to be trying to hang on to the floor with his front paws, almost as if it the room may be spinning as you might feel after consuming large quantities of alcohol yourself. He may chatter his teeth, lick his lips, drool, bark and be unable to lift up his head because of a stiff neck. At this stage he may lose bladder and or bowel continence. It is usual for this phase of the fit to continue for 5/6 minutes.

AFTER THE FIT

After about 5 minutes the symptoms will start to subside and the dog will begin to return to his normal self and consciousness. It may take from a few minutes to up to an hour for the dog to regain himself again totally after which time he may wish to sleep or even feel very hungry due to the amount of energy the fit has used.

When we think about Epilepsy and Seizures, we tend to think about the full blown fits where the legs and body spasm violently as the electrical impulses go through the muscles. While this can be how the fit looks, it's not always the way and sometimes it can be more of a partial seizure where perhaps just the front end "judders" or the back end, or the head.

The first thing to say is
Don't Panic.
It looks worse than it is.
It won't last long and generally speaking the dog will feel no pain at all.

What should you do?

* Remove any obstacles such as tables or chairs, and move them away from fires/radiators.
* Be sure their face is not obstructed by the way they are lying – if necessary remember to extend the head and neck to keep the airway clear – NB, take care to watch your fingers as often dogs will "chomp" or chatter their teeth and may bite you by mistake.
* Dim any bright lights and if possible cool the area.
* Remove children from the room and keep the environment calm and quiet.
* Remove any other animals as sometimes they can attack the fitting dog.
* If the fit takes place outside, ensure that you have the animal in a safe place and, as he starts to come around, ensure you have him on the lead or have a firm grip on his collar. Occasionally, when they regain consciousness, they are confused and disorientated and it is not unheard of for a dog to pelt off at top speed through fear and with no regard for his own safety.

Remember to check the time at the very beginning of the fit so you know how long it has been going on. Time is a very subjective thing and it is easy to get confused about how long the fit has taken if you don't have a definite time noted down.

The fit should last no more than around 5/6 minutes. If the animal is still fitting at the 10 minute mark, you must ring the vet immediately for further advice.

Because it is likely that the dog's temperature will go up with the extreme muscular activity and also the effect on his brain and central nervous system, it's a good idea to soothe him during and following a seizure by applying cold wet towels/flannels to the back of the neck, the top of his head and along the spinal region.

After the fit has subsided and the dog is bright and conscious again, offer him a portion of his usual food (around a third of his daily allowance) as he may well be very hungry due to all the calories burned up during the fit. You could also try offering natural yoghurt with a spoon of honey in it – a welcome treat that will help replenish his calories quickly.

If it is possible, it's a good idea to video the episode to show to your vet at a later date as describing all the signs is often very difficult to do accurately when you are frightened for your pet.

<u>** NEW **</u>
I have recently come across a new technique called Ocular Compression which stimulates the Vagus nerve and is said to help minimise the fits and in some cases even prevent them. See our blog for Ocular Compression

CONDITIONS - OCULAR COMPRESSION FOR FITS

Ocular Compression is a technique hoped to help dogs with epilepsy. We do cover fits and epilepsy in a separate blog which I recommend reading in conjunction with this one.

Many people try very hard to minimise the amount of drugs or chemicals they use with their dogs, be that in the form of vaccinations or medication. If your dog has seizures fairly infrequently, you may prefer not to go down the medication route for him because, as is always the case with drug therapies, there may be side effects caused by the medication itself that are less than satisfactory.

Recently I came across something called Ocular Compression, a technique used to stimulate the Vagus nerve. This stimulus is used in an effort to "shut down" the random signals being sent to the brain during a seizure and it is thought that it could reduce the severity of the episode or possibly even inhibit the fit from taking place at all.

Such an approach could be used by itself for less severe cases or possibly side-by-side with medication for more acute conditions. It is very much in its infancy and something really quite new so I will be looking into this technique further but it does look like something that could help our furry friends who suffer with such episodes.

Below is a link which will give you an overview of the technique itself and a better of understanding of just how it is proposed to work. I hope you find it as interesting as I did. If you do think this could benefit your dog, I would suggest speaking to your vet to ask his opinion and for guidance on how you might be able to administer this technique safely yourself.

This is something that we have been using very successful with Rain, our middle Ridgeback and certainly for him, we find it useful in reducing the longevity and violence of the actual seizure. It takes a while to perfect how hard to press for best effect, but it's certainly something I would advocate looking in to.

http://www.canine-epilepsy.com/Ocularcompression.html

CONDITIONS - HYPOTHYROIDISM

The thyroid gland is found in the dog's neck. The prefix "Hypo" is Latin and means low, under or not enough. Hypothyroidism then is a condition resulting when the thyroid gland is not producing enough hormone. It is a problem with the immune system where it attacks the thyroid gland, destroying the tissue and results in a deficiency of thyroid hormone.

It's not always easy to spot when a dog is hypothyroid as there is a myriad of signs and symptoms that they could exhibit or, conversely, they may show only one or two. More confusing still is the fact that some other conditions can cause low levels of thyroid hormone as well, and this can muddy the waters further.

Hypothyroidism is a very common hormonal problem, usually affecting dogs from around 4-7 years of age, but it can occur much earlier in some cases. Dogs which have been spayed or neutered are slightly more likely to suffer from hypothyroidism and some breeds in particular are more prone to it including the Rhodesian Ridgeback, Doberman, Golden Retriever, Airedale, Irish Setter, Dachshund, Poodle, Boxer and Miniature Schnauzer.

Symptoms: – please remember not all are likely to be present, perhaps just one or two

Lethargy and a general "can't be bothered" mentality.
Dull/Depressed/Old before their time temperament.
Susceptibility to the cold – perhaps seeking out warm places in which to lie.
Weight gain, even when the food intake is reduced.

Poor coat condition including dullness, dandruff, poor hair growth rate.

Hair-loss, especially over the shoulders.

Hair-loss, on the tail which may become quite bald and rat-like.

Symmetrical patches of hair-loss, particularly on the flanks and inner thighs.

The skin may thicken and becomes darkly pigmented, particularly on the inner ear.

The paws and ears may seem cool to the touch compared with non-effected dogs.

The heart rate is often slower than normal.

Skin folds on the face may increase giving a "tragic expression".

Infertility can be a problem in entire dogs.

In severe cases, there may even be facial paralysis on one side.

Diagnosis:

Because there is such a varied list of possible signs, diagnosing hypothyroidism is not always straight forward and other things may be considered before this condition. Blood tests to assess thyroid function can be done to ascertain if anything else is going on under the surface.

Treatment:

If hypothyroidism is confirmed, then simply giving thyroid replacement therapy in a tablet or drops is all that is required. Frequent blood tests are necessary to keep a close eye on the thyroid level once medication is started and the dog will have to remain on treatment for the rest of his life. The outlook for hypothyroid dogs on treatment is very good, although it may take a while at first for things to get back to normal with skin conditions and hair loss taking a little longer to improve. With thyroid replacement therapy, their quality of life and life expectancy should be unchanged.

P.S.

Since writing this blog, I've learned of another rare symptom of hypothyroidism – one I can only describe as "kicking its own butt". Yes, I know this sounds funny and like I'm joking but honestly, I'm truly not. So, rather than try to explain it all, Ill merely copy you the message as it came across to me, written by the actual woman who's dog experienced it. I'd NEVER heard of it before but will certainly bare it in mind in the future.

Laurie writes "ok, this was a new one on me so I thought I would share.

I have a 10.5 year old Ridgeback Male that passed his OFFA testing years ago. He had no signs at all of any thyroid issues... but he did start kicking his own butt.

Not kidding. About 4 weeks ago, he started lifting his right back leg up when he walked, like a twitch. The foot went up so high, it basically kicked his butt. No other issues. He has slowed down but he is a big dog and 10.5 years old. He deserves to slow down.

It started just once or twice a day I noticed it, and by 2 weeks he was doing it a lot. I asked around, I looked on the Internet... finally, I found hypothyroidism neuropathy.

No other signs of Thyroid problems. No hair loss, no rash, no weight gain, no loss of muscle. Just butt kicking.

So, I took him to the vet. They ran complete blood work including chemistry profile, CBC, and T4. The T4 came back low normal (1 when 1-2.5 is normal). They sent more blood work out and sure enough, his TSH was very high.

He has been on Thyroid meds now for over 10 days and he stopped butt kicking when he walks, now only does it when he moves too quickly.

We expect him to make a complete recovery from his Butt Kicking issues... (sorry too funny not to add that). Anyways, it was a new one on me. Over half of my older RR's end up on Thyroid meds. It is just that way. They live longer than the Thyroid gland was meant to function. But none so have had any neuropathy issues.

Laurie Anderson
AndyboyRidgebacks.com

CONDITIONS - LARYNGEAL PARALYSIS

Laryngeal Paralysis or GOLPP is thought, at least in some breeds, to be inherited as an autosomal dominant trait. It is perhaps something you've not heard of. Do you have an older dog? Have you noticed he is a little short of breath nowadays? Is his breathing a bit raspy and noisy or perhaps faster than normal even when he isn't doing anything? Has his back end gone a little weaker and the muscles seem less defined than they once were? Old age right? Well, I confess that this condition hasn't really been on my radar until the last year or so either, primarily because until then I'd never had a dog who'd suffered with it .... or had I? Because a lot of the signs and symptoms are usually associated with old age anyway, I'm sure there are a whole lot more dogs with this condition than have ever been professionally diagnosed so it's certainly worth taking a look at to see if any of this sounds familiar to you.

I'd like to thank the amazing members of the Laryngeal Paralysis (LP) Support Group on FB, and in particular the lovely Jo Field, for all the help, advice and incredible information in putting this blog together. In my experience, these guys know more about this condition than most of the professionals out there so if any of this blog is ringing bells for you, you could do a lot worse than start your research and questions there.

Although, as per the title of this blog, I will be concentrating on the Geriatric Onset Laryngeal Paralysis Polyneuropathy, there is a version that effects younger dogs too and this can be brought about by parasitic infection amongst other things.

This is quite a "meaty" subject which I'll try to put as simply and in as layman's terms as I can as it truly is fascinating. So, here's the science bit

Laryngeal (pertains the to the larynx or the "voice box" as it is often known)
Paralysis (the loss of the ability to move (and sometimes to feel anything)

In essence, Laryngeal Paralysis is when a cartilage in the larynx (usually on the left side) stops working properly and this can cause difficulties with swallowing and breathing .... but its sooooooooooo much more than just that. It is actually a single part of a bigger condition called GOLPP (Geriatric Onset Laryngeal Paralysis Polyneuropathy) which basically means the condition happens in old age and has many nerve type facets to it. I hope you're still with me!

The reason this condition has so many signs and symptoms wrapped around rather than just breathing problems appears to be its link with the Vagus Nerve. This nerve is pretty much the nerve that runs our entire bodies and all the different systems within it - a "super-nerve" if you will. Because it is instrumental in how virtually every part of the body works, if it is damaged then the effects can appear in many different areas - and this is why it is known as a Polyneuropathy). I noticed Axl went deaf very suddenly about the same time as he started demonstrating signs of LP and I'm now wondering if this is connected too! To flesh out more about what the Vagus nerve is and does, check out an article by DogDiscoveries.com called I am your dog's Vagus Nerve

LP is said to be "idiopathic" in nature which really means they have no idea what has caused it. Likely, it has been triggered through some kind of damage to the left side of the larynx, possibly through a knock, a jerk or even just the pressure of the sudden lunge on a collar. For this reason, teaching your dog a good loose-leash walking technique and using a harness will help reduce the chances. If you are looking into getting a harness for your dog, please choose one with an anchor point on the chest and on the back to give you the control of "steering" your dog that reins give when riding a horse. See our blog on harnesses.

There are other possible reasons for such breathing difficulties which should also be considered such as growths, abnormalities or thyroid conditions etc, but the only way to get a definitive diagnosis of the condition is to have a scope put down his throat so that all the structures internally can be seen. However, this in itself can come with its own risks due to the need for sedation, so many people opt not to go for this until their hand is forced, particularly if their own vet is reasonably confident of the diagnosis based on all the signs and symptoms your dog is presenting with:

Signs & Symptoms of LP

Coughing

Gagging

Yacking (as if trying to bring something up from the throat)

Change in the bark (either quieter or perhaps a more husky quality to it)

Licking the air or the forelegs (this could indicate acid reflux)

Increased anxiety

Noisy breathing known as Stridor (sounds like sawing wood, or living with Thomas the Tank Engine!)

Hind end weakness/muscle wastage

Sudden respiratory crisis (a bit like an asthma attack)

Faster breathing rate for no apparent reason

Living with LP

Eating can be a very hazardous occupation for an LP dog. If any of the food or water manages to get into the lungs rather than the stomach due to the damaged laryngeal fold, aspiration pneumonia is a very real possibility that can prove fatal. For this reason, many LP dog owners opt to hand-feed their dogs, particularly after tie-back surgery, standing up. If you feed your dog raw, then roll the food into meatballs in your hand and pop them down his throat, standing up, with his head at about a 30 degree angle. Personally, I use a spoon and kind of "quenelle" the meat and he takes it from the spoon. If you feed your dog kibble, then you can try soaking the food in a little water so you can make balls from that too. This way, the food tends to go straight down the throat without particles breaking off and going where they shouldn't.

Perhaps the most important thing to remember is how much of an impact the heat and humidity will have on an LP dog. The best way to think of it is, if you are WARM, then he is HOT. If you are HOT, then he is BOILING. Certainly, I have seen a massive deterioration in Axl over this past summer which, for the UK, has been ridiculously warm and now that the weather is back to its normal rubbishy self, he is markedly improved. When it is hot, it makes them stress. When they become stressed, the tissues of their airways swell up making the calibre of the airways narrower making it more difficult to get oxygen in which in itself is very stressful. This is a vicious circle. A dog will pant to try to cool down and rid himself of excess heat. If the atmosphere is humid, then this method of cooling is even less effective and the vicious circle becomes even worse.

Heat Management:

Balance any exercise he is doing with how hot it is making him become, and reduce accordingly.
Walk in the cooler parts of the day (a good tip for ANY dog guardian)

Invest in an air conditioning unit for the home to help during the summer months

Use cool coats (soaked in water frequently to insure against the sauna effect)

Wipe down with a cool wet cloth over the ears, belly and armpits/groins

Use iced treats such as frozen yoghurts

Cool mats for them to lie on can really help too

Surgery:

LP is a progressive condition. It will deteriorate but at what speed depends entirely on the individual dog. All you can do is watch, monitor and keep them as comfortable as possible. When the time comes that their quality of life is an issue, then perhaps you might consider surgery as an option. This is something that is not to be undertaken lightly and is probably more towards the end of the progression of the illness rather than early on.

For some dogs, surgery is not an option and for their owners this can be especially worrying. Though still in research stages, there is encouraging evidence that the use of a human antidepressant could actually be beneficial. The drug Doxepin is used to treat problems such as depression and anxiety. By chance, it was given to a vet's dog to treat something completely different and, completely unexpectedly, this had the side effect of helping the Flat Coat Retriever's breathing problems substantially. Since then, many other dogs have been tried on this drug, the effects of which vary from dog to dog and seem possibly to be dependent upon the severity of the damage to the larynx with cases where there is total paralysis likely to see no improvement at all. Studies into this drug are still on-going, but if your dog is not a viable candidate for surgery, this may be something worth talking to your vet about.

Tie-Back Surgery:

This form of surgery takes one of the laryngeal folds (usually the left) and ties it back with sutures. It does come with a certain element of risk because, as we age, cartilage becomes more brittle which means it can cause surgery to fail during or after the procedure. There is also the risk of Aspiration Pneumonia which happens when food or water "goes down the wrong way" and enters the lungs instead of the stomach. The folds in the larynx are there to stop this from happening but, because this surgery ties one of these folds back, AP is always a risk that should be on your radar. That said, I've seen numerous success stories with this procedure where dogs have gone on to live very full, happy, healthy lives with a new vigour for walks and exercise again, often resulting in increased muscle mass and tone and reversal of rear end weakness.

There is another surgical procedure where the fold is removed entirely or lasered. This also runs the risk of AP as well as the possibility of the fold growing back. I cannot comment any further on that procedure as I do not know anybody who has had this undertaken.

If you do decide to go down the surgical route, it is imperative that you research the professional who will be carrying out the procedure for your dog. Make sure the specialist you are referred to has carried out the technique many, many times. This is not a procedure to be done by your local vet unless he is fully certified in it ... to put this in to perspective, in the US a vet who is a Board Certified Surgeon will have carried out the procedure in excess of 300 times to get his certification. You want a vet who "knows his onions"!!!

Exercise:

Because of the change in their ability to exercise, your ever evolving role through this condition is to repeatedly find a "new normal". If you notice your dog is lagging behind on his usual walk, perhaps hesitating not wanting to go, or maybe just sniffing around a lot rather than actually walking, this may well be what is known as displacement behaviour - ie behaviour he is doing to distract away from what you are asking of him ... and what he is reluctant to do. You will have good days and bad days. You do not NEED to finish a specific distance every day; a 20 minute WALK one day could well be 20 minutes of just sniffing around in the hedgerow for 100 yards the next ;)

Their abilities will change and you need to be inventive to keep their bodies and brains as active as possible, which in turn will hopefully slow down the progression of the condition.

Professional Maintenance Assistance:

McTimoney physiotherapy
Acupuncture

Daily Stuff at Home:

Walking purposefully over poles. Proprioception (ie knowing where their feet and legs are) is great for their coordination. When they have to pick up their feet to clear a pole or low bar (this should be no higher than the hock) it makes them use their muscles (and muscle memory) in the correct way. Walking over the poles should be done slowly and specifically. This is down to the need to make very purposeful, definite movements and the slow walk achieves that for him. We do this for 5 minutes, twice a day.

You can try shifting his weight from one leg to another. I tend to stand behind Axl and gently sway him one way then the other so he has to shift his weight and his balance and use the muscles on both side of his flanks and back end to stay up right (for about a minute each morning).

Another good core and rear-end strengthening exercise is to use a wobble cushion. Teaching them to step backwards onto the cushion will not only mean they are using their awareness of where their feet/legs are, but also the movement of picking the foot up and placing it backwards is great. Add to this the need for stability and weight shifting on the cushion and you have a triple-whammy! Depending on the size of your dog (you'll want a big 'un for a Ridgeback!!!), there are lots of good versions available, some specifically for dogs such as Paw Pods and other things by Fit Paws or you could even use a wobble cushion designed for humans. Please ensure that the surface is non-slip to give your dog confidence when standing on what is already a very unstable surface.

You can try introducing mats with different textures on them and do foot targeting work.

You could pinch their toes/pads gently so the sensation travels up to the brain and completes the circuit.

You could use hair bobbles or vet wrap around their hocks to remind them where their legs are.

And of course you could trot them over a ladder or trotting poles to help with their coordination too.

There are lots of ways to help your dog and keeping his brain and body active will help keep him happy and healthy for longer. If you decide to go down the surgical route, there is every chance it will be successful and give your dog many more happy years with you too.

VITAL HOMEWORK:

Please take the time to learn 3 things about your dog:
What is his normal heart rate
What is his normal breathing rate
What is his normal gum colour

These three things will alert you if he is starting to go into crisis. The sooner you spot it, the sooner you will be able to get him the help he needs. Last November, when I was blissfully unaware that Axl had any problems whatsoever, his breathing changed in the middle of the night from his usual 3 breaths per 10 seconds to 20 breaths. I rushed him to the vet at 3am and he was diagnosed with Aspiration Pneumonia.

We were lucky … he got through it, I learned about LP and we changed his life accordingly. He has been hand fed, standing up, ever since. This week, 10 months later and one day before his 12th birthday, the same thing happened. His breaths were up to 10 times in 10 seconds and I was taking no chances. Off to the emergency vet and this time we were lucky enough to catch it at the bronchitis stage. After a couple of days of anti-inflammatory pain killers and antibiotics, he was much more like himself. If your dog has LP, you have my total empathy. If I can help, just ask but please check out the Laryngeal Paralysis (LP) Support page on FB because a more informed bunch of people you could not wish to find.

CONDITIONS -
HYPOGLYCAEMIC COLLAPSE (LOW BLOOD SUGAR)

Hypoglycaemic Collapse – Insulin is produced naturally in the body to control and regulate the amount of sugar in the blood. Dogs who suffer with diabetes AND those dogs who are worked very hard such as gundogs, working huskies, agility and flyball competitors etc, use up their calorific reserves quickly and if not replenished, this can result in hypoglycaemic collapse.

Symptoms to look out for include:-

Disorientation
Hunger
Lack of energy
Head Tilting
Shivering
Seizures
Weakness
Coma
Restlessness

Our aim would be to raise the sugar levels, back to an acceptable level.

If the hypoglycaemia is only fairly **mild**, giving the dog a meal of its regular food should be enough to raise the levels.

If the hypoglycaemia is **moderate** in nature, then their regular food with the addition of a sugar-containing food (ice cream is great) can be given.

Small dogs (1 tsp ice cream)

Medium dogs (2-3 tsp)

Large dogs (1-2 table spoons)

If, however, the hypoglycaemia is **severe**, then a more proactive course of action should be taken to raise the sugar levels ASAP.

If unconscious:-

– Rub small amounts of the ice cream on the gums and in cheek pocket.

– **DO NOT** put too much in the mouth as this may choke the dog.

– **DO NOT** put your fingers into the mouth if fitting as you may get bitten.

– Call your vet for guidance and advice
.
– If the dog continues to fit or does not come round quickly, take him to the vet immediately

For working dogs such as gundogs, huskies, agility and flyball dogs who are actually doing a job of work throughout a specific day, then often giving a calorific substitute throughout the day can keep the energy levels up to an acceptable level without the worry of hypoglycaemic collapse. A good one that I've used myself when competing in agility tournaments with Axl is Kronch Pemmikan from Denmark. It smells fishy but looks like a slab of chocolate, but it actually consists of 58.5 per cent crude fat being made from salmon, fishmeal, barley, maize, brewer's yeast, sugar beet, garlic and numerous vitamins and minerals.

Pemmikan reaches its full effect after about an hour. Because of this, it's probably a good idea to split the daily ration into several small portions to keep a constant performance. The manufacturer's recommendation is that beating and picking-up dogs should be given no more than two squares during the day. Axl being a large Rhodesian Ridgeback had a square between each of his 4 agility runs, ie 3 in a day and it really pepped him up.

CONDITIONS - HEART DISEASE & FAILURE

Seen more usually in middle and old age, this is the most common problem to affect our beloved canine companions. This disease is particularly prevalent in small breeds such as Chihuahuas and even more frequently in Cavalier King Charles Spaniels, but that is not to say we may not come across heart valve degeneration in large breeds too.

When taking your dog for a routine check-up, your vet will check him over with a stethoscope to listen to his heart beat. He may pick up a murmur in the sound the heart makes and this is down to the way the blood is rushing through the distorted valve. However, just because your dog has a murmur doesn't always mean he will go on to develop heart disease. In fact, some dogs never go on to show any signs of chronic heart disease at all.

Symptoms –

Early signs to look out for include:

* coughing (often during or after excitement or exercise)
* breathlessness,
* reduced ability to partake in any exercise activity (or indeed even the wish to try)
* abdominal swelling
* stopping while out on their daily walks
* restlessness during the night

More severe signs to look out for include:
* fainting
* collapse

Because the heart is a pump, if it becomes damaged and is less effective, some of the blood may "dam" backwards and cause fluid retention in the chest which, in turn, is the reason for the coughing and breathlessness. Fluid may also accumulate in the tummy causing the appearance of swelling.

Diagnosis
Various tests may be carried out to diagnose the precise form of heart disease and these include x-rays, ECG and possibly an ultrasound scan.

Treatment
In the earlier stages of the disease, it is often possible to manage the condition quite effectively with drugs. This medication will help to ease the workload on the heart and prevent fluid accumulation in the chest, thus making it more comfortable for the dog to breathe.

Sadly, this condition is not curative, but many dogs do go on to live a number of years with a good quality of life when the heart failure is being well controlled with drugs and careful management. As the disease progresses, drug doses may be altered, diet may be reduced and exercise cut back to a more manageable level.

All dogs are different and their rate of progression with this condition is also unique to each dog – some managing a good many years with a perfectly reasonable quality of life, whereas others may deteriorate more rapidly. It is important to keep stresses to a minimum, administration of medication to a tight regular schedule and day to day routine as predictable and calm as possible.

As you would expect, the costs with such a condition due to the drugs and tests required can very quickly become high and consideration needs to be given to this aspect of care too.

CONDITIONS: CANINE LYMPHOMA – A NEW REPORT IS OUT

Canine Lymphoma is one of the most common forms of cancer experienced by our canine companions – it's very aggressive and has a poor prognosis. Nothing strikes fear into our hearts quite like the word cancer. Although treatments and therapies are getting better and cures and life expectancy are on the up, still our first reaction on hearing such a diagnosis is complete horror.

Often, the first indication that something is wrong is when the dog is brought to the vet because he has developed some hard lumps. At this point, he is usually not showing any signs of illness other than these lumps which are typically not painful for him. These lumps are, in fact, enlarged lymph nodes. In most cases, it is preferred to treat the dog with a combination of chemo and radiotherapy.

With any luck and fingers crossed, we are hoping things could be about to change, as veterinary professionals look at tackling canine lymphoma on another level.

K9Magazine.com have a monthly on-line magazine which covers all kinds of topics and this month they have published a new report which will tell you about lymphoma and how it can affect your dog as well as how vets are looking to use an old technique in a brand new way. With such a frightening condition, it's good to know as much as possible, particularly if you are going through this with your own dog.

http://www.k9magazine.com/canine-lymphoma-special-report/

CONDITIONS - MENINGITIS

Today's blog comes out of a situation experienced by a good friend of mine and her dog over the past six months. I say six months because this is how long it has taken for a fair few very experienced veterinary professionals to finally get to the bottom of this problem and come up with a diagnosis – a delay probably due to the fact that meningitis is a fairly uncommon problem in dogs. For my friend, and more importantly her dog, it has obviously been very distressing but finally, her beautiful girl has been diagnosed as having this condition.

Unlike humans, the most common form of meningitis in dogs is called "Aseptic Meningitis" and it does not seem to have an infectious cause. In fact, it is not known why it occurs but its appearance is more common among larger breeds of dogs, effecting them USUALLY (but not exclusively) between roughly 4 months and around 2 years of age.

Symptoms:
* Depression
* Not wanting to move around very much
* Exhibiting signs of severe neck pains
* Exhibiting signs of reluctance to allow you to touch their head
* Not wanting to have their head moved up, down or to the side (even gently)
* They may appear hunch-backed and walk very stiffly

The above signs may come and go (for my friend, her dog suffered intermittently for a full 6 months before getting to the bottom of the problem with the symptoms returning acutely and then abating repeatedly). Often, when examined by the vet, all of the dog's nervous reflexes appear normal.

It will be necessary for your vet to carry out various tests to confirm a diagnosis of meningitis and, as this is quite a rare condition, it may not necessarily be top of the list when confronted with the symptoms. Indeed, it was originally thought that my friend's dog had damaged her neck while playing with her other dog in the park, as it was during this play that she first yelped and elicited signs of pain. More likely as it transpires, she had already contracted meningitis and the play hurt her already uncomfortable head and neck areas.

Tests to diagnose Aseptic Meningitis (or Infectious Meningitis which although a very rare disease would cause the dog to be very sick indeed) include taking X-rays, blood samples and a spinal tap of the fluid in the spinal cord to be analysed. Where there is any doubt, prompt referral to a veterinary neurologist for further testing and perhaps an MRI scan may also be necessary.

Treatment:

It would be necessary to administer a prolonged course of steroids (usually something like Prednisolone) to treat a case of Aseptic Meningitis and a low dose of medication would need to be continued, even after their recovery, for a further two months or so. This continuation of the steroidal treatment is to prevent the patient relapsing once it has seemingly recovered.

CONDITIONS – CANINE AUTISM

Is it a real thing? Am I making it up? Have I lost the plot?

Autism in humans is something I'm sure you've heard of. It's something we are starting to understand more and more these days, thank goodness, but what exactly is it?

Autism is a spectrum disorder (meaning that it has a wide variety of symptoms) that affects the person for all of their life. There is no cure – just coping strategies and methods to help manage the condition. In a nutshell, it affects the individual's ability to understand and communicate with the world around them, be that people, animals, sounds, movement, new, familiar or different situations. As with anything, everybody is unique and it's certainly not a case of "on size fits all" so we find that different people react differently and have an array of sensitivities or triggers.

So is it just humans that suffer with this condition? While the science is as yet unproven, there is a building acceptance that other animals can experience it too from Mice to Apes and really when you think about it, why is this surprising? We ourselves are, after all, merely another species of animal. When I mention canine autism to people initially, their first reaction is usually to laugh and assume I'm kidding. I'm not. And when you begin to see the signs and symptoms mirrored in your own dog, you do start to question the various behaviours they are exhibiting as possibly not just "naughty" but perhaps a learning difficulty of sorts.

Dogs learn very early on in their little lives – we tend to say the key initial "learning window" is between about 8-16 weeks of age. At this stage your puppy is like a sponge; learning new things every minute of the day and familiarising himself with people, places, noises, activities etc all the time (be that a washing machine, a TV, a knock at the door, noisy shopping trollies at the supermarket etc etc). To socialise your dog and introduce him to lots of new challenges early on can make such a difference in his mental development and his ability to cope in later life. If dogs are NOT introduced to such stimuli in this early stage of development, it can very often result in a fearful, timid, aggressive or reactive dog. Often, we may assign a dog's "naughty" behaviour to a lack of socialisation and while it MAY indeed be the case, sometimes, there is a little more to it – your dog could actually be suffering with Canine Autism.

There is lots of talk and conjecture about just what causes autism (both human and canine autism for that matter) and the jury is out as to whether it is genetic, causal (linked to things such as vaccination), autoimmune problems or even environmental factors.

As I say, each dog is different but symptoms can be things such as being over or under reactive to sounds. Perhaps the slightest bang sets your dog off, puts him on edge or, conversely, perhaps he actively seems to ignore sounds seeking the safety of turning a blind eye to them rather than facing whatever they denote?

Maybe he appears overly aggressive or pushy when playing – I've heard it described as like having no "off switch" and not understanding where the boundaries of play end and those of aggression and violence begin, with a desire to WIN at all costs.

Sometimes, it's the movement of the dog that can give the first clue that there may be problems. Are they clumsy, tripping or slipping more than you would expect? Do they seem uncoordinated in their movement with a seeming disconnection between the activities of their front half and their back end?

Do they struggle with touch, eye contact or closeness with people or other animals? Often they may seem at ease with a person or situation and then suddenly get a look in their eye that tells you they are not coping, are unsure of what is going on and then freak out to get away from the situation, seemingly for absolutely no reason at all.

You may find they are very reactive and then suddenly the moment has passed and they are not at all reacting to the situation, a little like they've forgotten what they were worried about. This can be very confusing for them and for us. One minute they are perfectly happy with a new dog or playmate but the next time they meet, they can have a completely different reaction to the self and same dog.

Also, as yet unproven, there appears to be a possible link between those dogs who exhibit signs of Canine Autism and those who develop epilepsy – the incidence of the link does appear to be quite high. Some CA sufferers report an incidence of gastro-intestinal problems too, especially "leaky gut" syndrome.

So, are there ANY upsides? Well, it can be a double-edge sword. Many people report that their special C.A. (Canine Autism) dogs are super clever, being able to learn and carry out tasks after being shown just a few times when "normal" dogs would need much longer. This quick ability to learn and take things in is quite a talent but it is also worth noting that the short term memory for other things can be quite debilitated too. For example, a new person comes to the house and you carefully introduce them to your dog until he seems happy enough with the situation. The person is in your home for say, an hour, mixing and talking to your C.A. dog and then pops to use the toilet, leaving the room and going out of sight. Two minutes later when he returns, your dog may well have absolutely no recollection of who the person is or that he has, in fact, ever even met him, resulting in you having to reintroduce them all over again.

All the above is just an over view. As you'd imagine, it's a very complicated and involved subject but something worth bearing in mind if you have seen these type of behaviours demonstrated by your dog.

Further Reading
The following article was written by Angela Stockdale and from about half way down the page, she begins to talk about autism. If you think any of the points raised above sound familiar to you and your dog, have a little read through Angela's article as it really does explain things beautifully. It might be that rather than trying to correct or "cure" your naughty dog, he may simply need a different approach and the implementation of some good coping strategies to help him (and you) adjust and deal with the world around you.

CONDITIONS - MDR1 GENE & COLLIES

The MDR1 (or Multi-Drug Resistant protein gene protects the brain by ensuring that any harmful chemicals are transported AWAY from the brain. In some dogs who are members of the herding varieties such as Collies and Australian Shepherds, a mutation in this gene causes extreme reactions to various drugs including Ivermectin (found in some heart worm medication), Loperamide (found in things like Imodium for diarrhoea) and several others including pesticide treatments. The mutation causes the gene to be defective and makes it difficult for the dog to remove these drugs from the brain, leading to a build-up of toxins. As a result, the dog may experience problems of a neurological nature such as seizures, incoordination, or even death.

All our characteristics are derived by our genes – one copy of which we get from our mother and the other from our father. Dogs that have two copies of the mutation will display a sensitivity to these types of drugs. It is also worth noting that they will pass on one copy of the mutation to any potential offspring, so it is important that dogs are tested before entering a breeding programme.

Dogs that only have one copy of the genetic mutation may still react to these drugs if they are administered at high doses and they also have a 50% chance of passing on the mutation to their puppies too.

Breeds affected by the MDR1 mutation (frequency %)

Breed	Approximate Frequency
Australian Shepherd	50%
Australian Shepherd, Mini	50%
Border Collie	< 5%
Rough Collie	70 %
English Shepherd	15 %
German Shepherd	10 %
Herding Breed Cross	10 %
Long-Haired Whippet	65 %
McNab	30 %
Mixed Breed	5 %
Old English Sheepdog	5 %
Shetland Sheepdog	15 %
Silken Windhound	30 %

The drugs fall into 3 categories – class A, B and C:

CLASS A

DO NOT USE in dogs with MDR1 defect.

An affected dog (-/-) carries two MDR1 gene mutations, having received one from each of its parents. It will also pass on a mutant MDR1 gene to its offspring.

MDR1-affected dogs are likely to experience drug toxicity following normal doses of the drugs listed here:

Anti-Parasitic drugs:

Ivermectin substances: Diapec®, Ecomectin®, Equimax®,Eqvalan®, Ivomec®, Noromectin®, Paramectin®, Qualimec®, Sumex® & Virbamec®

Doramectine substances: Dectomax®

Moxidectine substances: Cydectin® & Equest®

Loperamide substances (anti-diarrhoea): Immodium®

Metronidazole (Flagyl ®) – general antibiotic

CLASS B

Toxic reactions have been known to occur so only use under the close supervision of your vet

Cancer treatments (Cytostatics): Vinblastine, Doxorubicine, Paclitaxel, Docetaxel, Methotrexate & Vincristine

Glucocortisoids (steroids commonly used to treat auto-immune diseases): Dexamethasone

Immuno-suppressants: Cyclosporine A

Heart Glycosides: Digoxine & Methyldigoxine

Anti-Arrhythmics (heart problems): Verapamil, Diltiazem & Chinidine

Pain control: Morphine & Butorphenol

Anti-Emetics (sickness/vomiting): Ondansetron, Domperidone andMetoclopramide

Antibiotics: Sparfloxacin, Grepafloxicin & Erythromycin

Antihistamines: Ebastin, (although safe for most dogs, Piriton should be queried when dealing with MDR1 positive dogs)

Tranquillisers & pre-anaesthetic agents: Aceptomazine (ACP) & Butorphenol

Other drugs: Etoposide, Mitoxantrone, Ondanestron, Paclitaxel, Rifampicin

CLASS C

Can be used safely providing the correct dosage is given.

Stronghold®, Advocate® & Milbemax® can be used only in the recommended application and dosage.

The importance of knowing your Collie's MDR1 status cannot be over-emphasised, as you never know when he or she may require surgery and/or drug treatment. If your dog is known to be affected, you will at least be in a position to inform your vet of the dangers of certain drugs, by printing off the information.

There are two laboratories offering DNA tests for MDR1 – Laboklin Laboratories of Manchester (UK branch of the Laboklin Company of Bad Kissingen, Germany).

UK lab: www.laboklin.co.uk
Germany lab: www.laboklin.de

Animal Genetics is another lab that does this test. There are clinics with reduced rates throughout the year. You can find out more by contacting Pastoral Breeds Health Foundation: www.pbhf-dog.com

The test is carried out using simple buccal (cheek) swabs, which you can easily do yourself.

Testing is also available in the US where you can simply send for a kit to take a cheek swab and sent it off to the lab: www.horsetesting.com/Canine/Canine-sample-kit.asp – I understand that the cost is in the region of $55

CONDITIONS - DERMOID SINUS

You may have heard of something called a pilonidal sinus. This is a problem that humans can experience and some people also refer to dermoid sinus' in dogs as a pilonidal sinus too. However, a true dermoid sinus is actually a neural defect.

As a puppy grows in the mother's womb, there is a connection between the puppy's skin and the spinal cord. This connection separates during the embryonic stage and the tract is closed off. This is what SHOULD happen. With a dermoid sinus, however, this separation from the skin does not fully take place and the tract may either remain connecting the skin to the spinal cord, on occasion actually wrapping itself right around the spinal ligaments, or perhaps the tract does not travel the full way to the cord and instead ends in a blind sac (this version of the defect is slightly less dangerous to remove). Until the puppy actually goes to theatre, it is impossible to tell the full extent and severity of the sinus.

If you were to look inside the sinus or "tract" as it is often referred, you would find a similar construction to that of the surface of the skin ie hair follicles, sebaceous glands and sweat glands too. Because of this, the tract is designed to drain itself and remove any debris but should this get blocked, it is very easy for the tract to become infected. This is very serious indeed as it can cause meningitis and in some cases myelitis, which is an infection of the spinal cord itself. Obviously, such infections can be life-threatening and the dog may experience spinal pain, rigidity and high fever.

Breeds known to be affected include my own particular fancy, the Rhodesian Ridgeback and the Thai Ridgeback. That said, please don't think that only "ridged" dogs can suffer with this condition. Not only can it appear in "ridgeless" Ridgebacks, but it has also been known to affect other breeds including, but not restricted to, the Kerry Blue, the Shih Tzu and the Boxer (and some cats too!)

Some people believe that this condition involves many genes to bring it about. Others lean more toward the idea that the genes need to be carried by both parents in order for the condition to occur. Regardless which theory is correct, in view of the hereditary nature of dermoid sinus it is generally accepted that no animal which either has this condition, or carries the gene for it, should be entered into a breeding programme.

So, what does a DS look like? How do you detect one and, if you find one, what should be done?

Well, DS can appear anywhere at all through the length of the spine from the top of the neck, all the way down to the bottom of the tail. (On very rare occasions it has been detected behind the ear, under the ear towards the jaw and even on the front of the neck, but these are few and far between in comparison.) It can appear as a single lump, or multiple lumps, anywhere on that dorsal midline. In breeds such as the Rhodesian Ridgeback where such a condition is known to be a possibility, a good breeder will make sure that the bitch is given folic acid for at least a month before she is mated, and then for the whole of her first trimester of pregnancy, as research has shown this supplement to help reduce the incidence of this defect occurring. The pups, when born, will be checked two, three or even four times before they go off to their new homes to make sure that no sinus is present. If it is, this will be assessed to elicit the severity of the DS and then most likely operated on, generally at between 12-14 weeks of age. The puppy will then be "endorsed" which means that the breeder will put a stipulation on the puppy's pedigree to say that it should never be bred from and it will be sold as a pet only, with the cost of the puppy reflecting only what has been necessary to rear it.

If the puppy DOES NOT come from an experienced and well respected breeder – say perhaps from an accidental mating, a less knowledgeable source or a puppy farm for example, there is a good chance that the breeder may not have looked for this defect and it may well go undetected. As this is such a rare condition, there are cases where even a vet may miss the detection of it having never seen one before – another good reason to get your puppy from somebody who really knows their breed and knows what they are looking for. It might not be until months down the line that the sinus becomes blocked and/or infected and then the problem rears its head, sometimes with life-threatening results.

At first, the problem may appear as a small lump. Perhaps it could be mistaken for an insect bite, snake bite or a cyst resulting from rough play with the pack. You may notice a small "puncture" on the cyst or even two or three, leading you to think that it is indeed an insect bite. In the case of DS, the tract may become so infected that it swells up massively with little or no improvement from the use of antibiotics. At this stage, surgical intervention as quickly as possible is the only option.

So is there any way that you could detect a dermoid sinus for yourself if you have the worry that this may not have been picked up?

Checking for DS

It is important to check from the nobly bump on the back of the skull, right down to the tail along the midline of the dog. Support the puppy in one hand and take the dog by the scruff with your thumb and forefinger. Carefully pull the skin upwards towards the nose and then downwards towards the tail. Make sure you pull the flesh but do not move your hand. If there is a DS present, it may show itself as a "dimple" in the flesh where the connective tissue pulls against the skin:

As you gently pull the flesh up or down, you may be able to feel the sinus slip through your fingers and feel like a noodle attached from the skin to the spinal cord or possibly a thinner, small string-like structure. Systematically, move your examining point down the entire length of the midline repeating the procedure over and over. When you arrive at the tail, it may be too difficult to hold enough skin to check in which case simply pushing the flesh to one side and the other, and up and down, should have the same effect. If it is a very short DS in the tail area, you may simply find that the skin remains in situ and doesn't move at all.

Please bear in mind that if a dog has previously been diagnosed with a dermoid sinus, it is advisable that injections or microchipping in that area, at the top of the neck or the shoulders should be avoided, and instead placed slightly to the side. Occasionally, reactions of such injections can cause a swelling which looks very similar to DS.

Often, by about day 5-6 after surgery, there may be increased swelling as fluid builds up at the wound site and around the neck. In some cases, it is necessary to insert drains into the site at the time of surgery to help with the safe drainage of fluids, although some vets prefer to put up with a "lumpy neck" for a week or so in the belief that the fluid will be reabsorbed by the body naturally and prove better for healing in the long-term.

* The bottom line with this awful condition is to be aware.
* Know your breed and any possible problems associated with it.
* Check that your vet knows what he is looking for when bringing your puppy home.
* Get your puppy from a breeder who has done all the relevant health checks and

KNOWS THEIR ONIONS!!!

CHAPTER 9: DIGESTIVE TRACT

DIGESTIVE TRACT - FLATULENCE (FARTING!)

All animals suffer with excessive wind or "gas" from time to time, just like humans do. For the most part it's a bit whiffy, funny or possibly even embarrassing but generally, all part and parcel of living with a dog. I'm sure most of us would simply open a window or add a quick squirt of air freshener to combat it.

So, what is flatulence? Well, just as with us, when food in the gut is digested, it produces gas naturally. This gas accumulates until finally it has to be expelled to relieve that bloated feeling in the abdomen – hence the "fart" (sometimes noisy like a motorbike and sometimes what my son refers to as the S.B.D. – silent but deadly!)

There are several causes of flatulence from feeding things that you know will cause it (you KNOW baked beans or sprouts are a pretty explosive food stuffs for you and if you feed them to your dog you can expect the same outcome), to feeding poorer quality dog foods and foods not really designed for our dogs. The amount of excess gas they suffer can also be, in part, down to the way your dog eats. If you have a "gulper" who swallows air with every mouthful, it stands to reason that the extra air he has consumed will need to come out somewhere.

Each dog will suffer with flatulence to varying degrees and some may get it excessively. If you feel that your dog has been more smelly than normal, or been this way for a prolonged length of time, please check with your vet to make sure that nothing more serious is going on.

So, is there anything we can do to help our Furry Farticus?

Firstly, let's look at his level of exercise. Does he get plenty? A well exercised dog generally produces a lot less wind at home. Exercise helps the digestive tract to work and move freely. A good transition through the gut while they're out will result in much of their excess gas being expelled out in the fresh air, rather than in your home.

I'm sure you've noticed how many people go for a nice walk in the fresh air after their Christmas lunch. There is no coincidence that after a large meal, stuffed with sprouts and other veg, many of us find that a brisk walk is the best way move things along and prevent that bloated feeling.

Another good tip is to always feed the best quality dog food you can afford, whether that's a raw diet you put together yourself, a processed raw food or a kibble. Always check on the packaging – the better the quality of the ingredients, the better he'll feel on the inside and the better he'll look on the outside. We all like a naughty take-out now and again, but think how you'd feel if that was all you ever ate? Sluggish, poor skin, slow digestion and generally out of sorts with yourself.

If your dog does hoover up his food quickly with huge gulps of air, there are a couple of things you can try in order to reduce this. Firstly, there are specific dishes you can buy with nobbles in the bottom which makes it more difficult for your dog to wolf down his dinner. By slowing him up, you also reduce the amount of gulping and hence the amount of air he swallows.

If you don't want to go to the expense of buying a specially designed product for this, you can always just use an up-turned bowl or ramekin in the bottom of the dog's bowl. He will then have to eat around the ramekin, pushing it out of the way to get to his food, which will have exactly the same outcome – much slower eating.

You might also try splitting his meals into smaller portions. For example, if you usually feed at supper time, try giving half his daily allowance at breakfast and the other half at supper – in really bad cases you might even try splitting it into three. Smaller portions, little and often, will produce less gas build up for him, and less pong for you! I actually do feed my guys three times a day. They enjoy eating as often as they can and don't seem to notice that they are getting smaller portions than usual.

Try giving a charcoal biscuit a couple of times a day. The charcoal will filter the gasses in the gut and "neutralise" them. While charcoal will likely not reduce the amount of wind, it will certainly make it sweeter on your nostrils!

Another thing to try is giving a spoonful of natural yoghurt after their meal. Apart from the obvious benefits of the calcium, natural yoghurt also aids digestion due to its probiotic properties. Assisting the digestion in this way can also reduce the build-up of gas.

If all else fails ………. JUST DON'T LIGHT A MATCH

DIGESTIVE TRACT –

SWALLOWING THINGS THEY SHOULDN'T ... and things "hanging out" the other end.

Dogs do tend to wolf down anything and everything – and not all of the things they try to consume are good for them! Sometimes they manage to swallow the most inappropriate of things ranging from socks and pants, through to needles and thread and a myriad of dodgy things in between.

If you know that your dog has swallowed, say a pair of your favourite undies or your kid's sports socks, the best course of action is to try to get them to be sick ASAP before the item has a chance to become lodged in the gut.

Always speak to your vet when inducing vomiting for foreign objects – if an object has sharp edges or is jammed, vomiting could be dangerous so speaking to your vet immediately is a must.

To induce vomiting (within 30 minutes if possible):

using washing soda crystals – for large breeds use a piece about the size of a walnut and scale down accordingly) It is handy to prepare an ice-cube tray with the washing soda crystals already made up so that if you need them in an emergency, you can simply pop one down without delay. (The crystals should be mixed with a little water to form into a thick paste and then used to fill the individual ice-cube compartments)
or
using salt/mustard – 1 tablespoon diluted in to ¼ cup of warm

water

It is also possible to use hydrogen peroxide 3% 5-10 ml via syringe to the back of the throat – this procedure can be done twice if necessary but one should be careful that the fluid goes down the throat and is not misdirected into the airway, choking the dog. However, this technique is not something I personally would wish to administer. It is very dangerous and I would not recommend it.

Always have your dog checked out even if you have been successful in getting him to vomit, just in case there has been damage to his throat, airway or gut.

If you are unable to get the dog to vomit, 'phone your vet and take him in immediately to have the dog examined professionally. He will likely be given an emetic (drug to make him sick) by the vet in the hopes that the item will be safely expelled. If, however, this does not work for him either, then your vet may decide that surgery is the safest option.

If you notice something hanging from your dog's mouth, or his bottom, say a piece of sewing thread or fishing line, PLEASE RESIST THE URGE TO PULL IT!

Because you are unaware of just how long the thread or line is, it might actually be caught within the dog's gut or intestines and pulling on it could do him serious damage.

Likewise, if there was a needle or fish hook attached to the line when it was swallowed, you could well be risking serious internal damage by tugging on the line or thread.

Without exception, a situation such as this requires a trip to the vet. Your vet will need to x-ray your dog to ascertain whether there is a needle or hook attached and if so, it will need to be removed carefully by your vet, likely under anaesthetic/surgical guidance.

N.B. regarding Nyla-Bones: I have recently been made aware of an incident regarding Nyla-Bones, specifically the ones that smell of liver and bacon. My friend's dog swallowed one of these bones whole, presumably because the liver and bacon smell made him think it was real food. When she took him to the vet it was found that Nyla-Bones DO NOT show up on x-rays. Due to the size and shape of the bone, inducing vomiting in this particular case was not recommended and he had to undergo stomach surgery instead as an emergency procedure – so PLEASE be careful with them. The best advice would be to only allow your dog to have them under your supervision.

If you notice a fish hook in your dog's mouth, perhaps caught in his lip or tongue, it is important to remove it as quickly as possible before it causes further damage or distress to your dog.

If the hook has gone right through the skin, restrain the dog (a second pair of hands is a good idea for this) and take care not to get yourself or your assistant bitten in the process.

Use wire cutters to cut off the barbed end of the hook and then retract the straight end of the hook, ideally pulling in the direction it was going.

Remember to clean the wound with a mild antiseptic once you have removed it.

If the hook is embedded in the skin, DO NOT try to remove the hook yourself. Your dog will need to see a vet who will be able to remove the hook for you, likely under sedation.

DIGESTIVE TRACT - COLITIS IN DOGS

Colitis is really uncomfortable and unpleasant – and it doesn't just affect us humans. Your dog can suffer with this too and it has many causes. So, what actually is colitis?

The colon is part of the intestine and is responsible for doing things like collecting the fibrous parts of the diet that the dog isn't able to digest properly, storing stool (poo), absorbing water and also extracting any extra nutrients that haven't already been taken out during digestion.

The word colitis when broken up into its Latin parts literally means inflammation ('itis') of the colon ('col') and can relate to either the large or small intestine.

Colitis can come on suddenly (sudden onset colitis) which is considered an "acute" condition or it can take place over several months and be episodic or "chronic". If you suspect that your dog has episodic colitis, please see your vet for further investigation and treatment as this can be anything from a change in diet to hard-core medication.

Recognising the Signs & Symptoms of Colitis
If you don't know the symptoms to watch out for, your alarm bells won't be ringing when they should be, so here's the sort of things to be aware of:

Number one is the appearance of the stool itself. Commonly the biggest sign is diarrhoea – hardly a surprise that this would be the main thing on your list (and probably a difficult one to miss!!) On the other hand, it may be more of a slimy consistency rather than full-on watery diarrhoea or perhaps seem normal to start with and get more runny towards the end of the stool.

Presumably, as the good and responsible dog owner that you are, you will go straight over to pick up the poo. You may notice that it seems more slimy than usual, or coated in a mucus, and in a lot of cases you may also see fresh blood in the poo too.

Next, we look at how the dog behaves. When your dog goes to relieve himself, you may well notice that he has to go all of a sudden. This urgency to poo, often with lots of straining and pushing rather than the usual behaviour is a strong indicator that something is not right. Overall, we would not expect your dog to have any actual weight loss.

Causes

Causes for colitis can be anything as mundane as simply scavenging something that doesn't agree with them, a change in their usual diet or perhaps the introduction of a food that is too rich, an intolerance or allergy to something in their diet, a stressful situation like the move of house, introduction of a new dog to the family, change in routine etc and these type of causes usually result in the "sudden onset" form of colitis.

Treatment for such sudden attacks would obviously include feeding a more agreeable diet if you know what initially caused the trouble (particularly if you have a "bin-raider"), helping the dog as best you can to acclimatise to the new situation in their lifestyle, or perhaps looking at the diet to pinpoint if there is a particular element to it that could be causing the intolerance. Increasing the fibre in your dog's diet can help dramatically to get him over the episode too – such things as bran or unsweetened pumpkin flesh in their meal can really help.

If the condition goes on for months rather than days, and is "chronic" in nature, then it is important that your vet is able to get to the bottom of the problem and diagnose the cause so that appropriate treatment can be given. Causes for this type of colitis range from parasitic triggers such as Whipworms and also problems with the dog's ability to produce digestive enzymes in the pancreas. Your vet may opt simply to treat the dog for Whipworm first and, if this does not work then perhaps look at taking stool samples to look at under the microscope or even more invasive investigations such as a biopsy or colonoscopy (placing a camera up into the colon to see what the lining itself actually looks like – just as we do with humans suffering this condition).

Once the vet has ascertained what is going on, he will decide on a treatment plan and this can be anything from various different anti-inflammatory medications, a high fibre diet specifically designed for colitis, a steroidal approach or may be what is called an elimination diet. An elimination diet is one where the dog is fed only one specific food for around two months to see if there is any change to the condition. This approach is tried with various foods until the trigger intolerance is detected and can therefore be avoided in the future.

DIGESTIVE TRACT - WHICH FRUITS ARE SAFE TO EAT?

A lot of dogs do like the odd piece of fruit. They enjoy a taste of something sweet from time to time, just as we do. When it's hot, feeding your dog some frozen fruit can be a really good way of cooling them down while giving them a tasty, low calorie treat too. When they are teething as puppies, chewing on something like a piece of frozen carrot or broccoli can be very soothing indeed, but which fruits are OK and which could cause problems?

There is a world of difference between the word "safe" and the phrase "won't cause any reactions". Simply put, just because a food stuff is "safe" doesn't mean that your dog may not experience alteration in his bowel habit as a result (he may be windy or even "loose" – a little or A LOT) so if you are thinking of introducing fruit to their diet, then please do it gradually to prevent any digestive discomfort to Rover, or any unwanted "poopy presents" for you!

FRUIT	SAFE or NOT
Strawberries	Yes – if your dog shows signs of allergies, do not feed strawberries again as they are known to be allergenic in some dogs.
Raspberries	Yes
Water Mellon	Yes – though rind could cause intestinal blockage if not chewed well enough. If in doubt, leave the rind out. Seeds should be fine provided there are only a few. Again, everything in moderation so if you miss a couple when cutting the slice, don't panic.
Apples	Yes. Many people quote that the seeds are

dangerous. Well yes, they do contain trace elements of cyanide but the levels are incredibly low and in the same way as one would not expect an apple seed to kill a human, the odd seed or two, or apple core now and again won't hurt your dog either. As with anything, common sense should be applied and care taken that the dog doesn't eat very many pips.

Bananas	Yes – great squashed into a Kong and frozen
Oranges	Yes
Raisins	No – can cause kidney failure
Grapes	No – can cause kidney failure
Cherries	No – can cause cyanide toxicity if eaten in large quantities
Avocado	No – can cause vomiting
Peaches	Yes – provided you remove the pit which could otherwise become blocked in the digestive tract
Pineapple	Yes – can also be good at dissuading coprophagia (eating poop). Poop produced when an animal has been eating pineapple is a lot less appetising apparently!
Macadamia Nuts	No – can cause a total paralysis reaction which may last for 24 hours, and may at worst, prevent the animal from breathing.
Kiwis	Yes
Lemons	Yes
Blue Berries	Yes

DIGESTIVE TRACT - SWALLOWING GLASS/SHARP OBJECTS

So you're just starting to cook supper and as you take a glass bowl from the fridge, it slips through your fingers and shatters all over your kitchen floor. The glass is broken and splintered into a squillion pieces, each one coated with the juices of your marinated chicken. The smells waft through and quick as a flash, your dog appears from nowhere trying desperately to snag himself a taste of the action. You shout for him to "leave it" as quickly as you can but he has a tongue like the tentacles of an octopus and is already slurping at the juices.

Were you quick enough with your shout?
Did he swallow any glass splinters?
If he did, what will happen as they pass through his digestive system?
What should you do now?????

This is exactly the situation that faced one of our followers recently. She was advised that she should give lots of stodgy foods like bread and or porridge and (what might appear quite surprising) cotton wool balls soaked in cream. Off the back of her ordeal, she got in touch to ask me to write a blog for you guys ... just in case.

Before I write any blog, I always try to research a topic in quite a bit of depth so that I can give you the most up-to-date information available. On researching this subject more thoroughly, however, advice in this regard differed widely from vet to vet and I found two very different schools of thought on what should be done in such a situation, and in particular with regard to the "cotton wool ball" technique.

Obviously, the most important thing is to speak to your vet ASAP, as how likely it is that surgery will be required is largely dependent upon the size of the object that has been eaten. Shards of glass or porcelain larger than say a £1 coin would fall into this category.

DO NOT make the dog vomit. There is always the chance that further damage could be done on the way back up, so that's a definite no-no.

Firstly, call your vet ASAP to explain the situation and see what course of action they advise. It might be that they'd like to admit the dog or possibly merely for you to watch him at home. This decision will be made dependant on several factors including:

* the object (and size) of what has been swallowed,
* the size and character of dog,
* whether the owner is able to observe the dog closely,
* whether the practice would be able to deal with the situation on site, or whether a referral elsewhere might be required etc.

So what about this technique of swallowing cotton wool balls soaked in milk, cream or peanut butter? The rationale behind this technique is that the cushioning provided will pad any sharp edges and protect the gut during transit. Any small shards of glass or bits of plastic etc. would get caught up in the cotton wool and hopefully just pass through, without incident.

I myself would be wary of using something non-digestible, however, as I fear this could prove problematic and could actually cause a blockage in its own right. Other, safer, ways of padding a sharp foreign body are things like porridge, bread, sauerkraut and mashed potato, shredded cabbage and spaghetti – in essence anything high fibre that won't break down completely in the digestive tract and can wrap itself around the sharp points. Mix it with something stodgy, gloopy and voluminous. You might also try brown rice or canned pumpkin flesh but make sure that you get the plain pumpkin rather than the sweetened variety for making pumpkin tarts/pies.

If you do decide to go down this route, the important thing is to observe the dog very carefully indeed, and to be able to get him to the vet if any signs of trouble occur.

Thank you to Elizabeth Halliday for suggesting the topic for today's blog, and to vet Rebecca Kohnke for all her help with the information contained in this blog – Rebecca, you're a star!

DIGESTIVE TRACT - XYLITOL (ARTIFICIAL SWEETENER)

Recently I posted a slight amendment to our advice on dehydration, notably that it is no longer advisable to give your dog Dioralyte as a salts replacement therapy. The reason for this is that the ingredients in this treatment have changed – where some time ago it was perfectly safe for dogs, it now includes something called XYLITOL which is known to be extremely toxic for them.

When I posted this information on our Rhodes 2 Safety Facebook page, it soon became apparent that a lot of "dog folk" are unaware of Xylitol, its effects on our furry friends or which products you may find it in – I mean, if you don't know where it will show up, it's very difficult to avoid it, right?

Those of you who know me, will be aware that I have no interest in frightening people witless. I am, however, very keen to equip dog owners with the facts they need to enable their pet to live a long, happy and healthy life. Today's blog is me making an effort to explain more about this additive in a non-scientific kind of way that will make sense to us ordinary, non-medical members of the public. If you feel there is more you would like to know, simply Googling Xylitol will give you a good starting point.

So let's start with the basics. Xylitol is an artificial sweetener additive. It is a natural substance which comes from the bark of Birch trees. It has just two thirds of the calorific content of sugar and because of this it is thought to be good for dental health as it is less likely to cause cavities and decay. This sweetener is often used in diabetic foods, rather than ordinary sugars.

We all know that foods such as chocolate, grapes and raisins are toxic to dogs but it appears most people don't realize that products containing Xylitol may cause even more harm.

As the number of products containing Xylitol grows, so to do the number of canine poisoning cases. The first paper published in a veterinary journal about Xylitol didn't appear until 2004 as compared to the first paper regarding the toxicity of chocolate which came out in 1981.

Xylitol is perfectly safe for people but dogs don't deal with it in the same way we do. For them, it causes the body to release a large amount of insulin. Insulin is normally produced to control blood sugar levels. When insulin is released in this way it causes a sudden drop in blood sugar. This condition is called hypoglycaemia.

Signs of hypoglycaemia include:-
unsteadiness,
depression,
dilated pupils,
in severe cases, seizures and liver failure.

Signs of Xylitol Poisoning:
If a large amount of Xylitol is swallowed, there is a possibility that it may lead to liver failure although this does not always happen.

Symptoms of Xylitol intoxication include:

- Vomiting
- Weakness

- Lethargy
- Diarrhoea
- Loss of coordination
- Collapse
- Seizures

If you suspect your pet has eaten a product containing xylitol and is experiencing any of these symptoms, immediate veterinary care is needed to save your dog's life.

So, how much Xylitol might you find in products that contain it? Well that's a difficult one to answer for two reasons. Firstly, sometimes manufacturers do not list it in their ingredients at all since they consider it to be proprietary information or, if they do, they may not actually say how much Xylitol is in the product; only that it is there. Another problem is that the amounts will vary from manufacturer to manufacturer, product to product and flavour to flavour so there is no real way of knowing exactly what levels to expect. What we do know is that the toxic dose for dogs is 75-100 mg/kg (but due to the differences as noted above, the quantity of xylitol in one piece of gum for instance, ranges from 0.9 mg to 1,000 mg)

Depending on the product, the amounts of Xylitol vary and it's the actual dosage itself that causes the level of toxicity. Toothpaste/Dental Wash, for example may have Xylitol in it but it is in such small amounts that it does not cause sickness (however, some vets have taken the decision to withdraw such products on a "just in case" precautionary basis).

Often, the Xylitol in a product is released by the action of physically chewing. As dogs usually just swallow whatever they find, with very little chewing, this gives us longer to make the animal vomit before the toxins begin to leech out into the stomach. In products such as sweets or mints, it is found in powder form which is quickly absorbed. We might expect to see signs of illness in around 30 minutes or so.

Having said all of this, Xylitol is not right up there with antifreeze or rat poison and, once you work out that this is the cause of your dog's illness, it is fairly easy to treat with supportive treatment such as the administration of fluids with dextrose to increase the sugar levels in the blood. In severe cases, it may also be necessary to try dexamethasone which is a corticosteroid, and glucagon which is a hormone, to reverse the hypoglycaemia.

As we've commented above, the incidence of Xylitol being found is increasing markedly these days. It is used in all sorts of products from gum, sweets, dental rinses, nasal sprays, powdered protein, chewable vitamins, ketchup, yoghurt, throat lozenges, sugar-replacement for baking …. blah blah blah – the list goes on!

DIGESTIVE TRACT - POISONING

Poisoning is scary and it's serious. There are five entry routes by which a poison can enter your dog's system:

* **Ingested** (swallowed)
It might be that the poison is physically eaten by the dog or perhaps it was on his coat and he has licked himself to clean it off and swallowed it in the process.

* **Inhaled**
This would be the case with noxious fumes or smoke from a house fire

* **Pervasion** (Absorption through the skin)
This would usually be if the dog has walked through a substance eg battery acid

* **Puncture wound**
For example if the dog stood on a sharp object such as a dirty nail or needle

* **Eyes**
Any poison/chemical that comes into contact with the dog's eye will absorb into the blood stream very quickly – this is more likely to happen with products applied with a brush if the bristles "flick" the fluid off

With corrosive substances:

1)   Wash the affected area thoroughly (at least 20 minutes)

2)   Prevent the dog from licking the area

3)   Collect a sample of the poison

4)   Ring ahead and go directly to the vet

5)   Monitor for Signs of Shock & perform CPR as required

With non-corrosive substances:

1)   Induce vomiting within 30 minutes if possible

(using washing soda crystals – for large breeds use a piece @ the size of a walnut and scale down accordingly)

or

(salt/mustard – 1 tablespoon diluted in ¼ cup of warm water)

* N.B. – some opinions suggest the use of hydrogen peroxide 3% in a 5 ml dose via syringe but this is a very serious step and NOT something I would advocate.

2)   Wash area to prevent secondary poisoning

3)   Collect a sample of the poison

4)   Ring ahead and go directly to the vet

5)   Monitor for Signs of Shock & perform CPR as required

I've been looking for an advice line you can call if your dog swallows a poison. To be honest, it's proved a little tricky finding a dedicated number just for this service although I did manage to find the following information (strictly speaking it's for veterinary professionals). The general rule seems to be that you should call your vet for advice in such cases but I have to say that if an advice line exists for vets to tell them what to do with regard to poisoning, I'm a bit worried that us mere members of the public have to ask a vet who will then have to ask these guys. That said, if you calling this number delays you from getting your dog to the vet ASAP, then please don't waste any further time.

Anyway, the information for the Veterinary Poisons Information Service is:-
Mary Sheridan House, Guy's Hospital, London SE1 9RT
Tel: 020 7188 0200
Fax: 020 7188 0700
http://www.vpisuk.co.uk

List of common potentially poisonous household and garden substances – as supplied by the VPIS (Veterinary Poisons Information Service)
Anticoagulant rodenticides

• difenacoum • bromadiolone • brodadiolone • coumatetralyl
Ibuprofen • Nurofen • Advil
Metaldehyde • Slug bait
Human oral contraceptives (very low toxicity)
Chocolate / theobromine
Diclofenac sodium (a similar drug to Ibuprofen)
Salbutamol

• Ventolin inhalers
Alphachloralose rodenticides
Paraquat
Wallpaper paste (very low toxicity)
Borax / Boric acid ant killer gels
Bone-meal
Glyphosate based herbicides
Aspirin
Cannabis

Batteries
Bendiocarb • powder ant killers
White spirit / barbecue lighter fluid
Antifreeze
Loperamide • anti-diarrhoea drugs
Bleach
Pyrethrin-based insecticides

Creosote	
Temazepam	

Below is a table illustrating a selection of possible poisons, the effect they have and the actions you should take in a first aid capacity.

While this is by no means an exhaustive list, it should give you good direction that you can also apply to other substances:

Possible substances that could be found in various locations throughout the home that could be poisonous to a dog:

Location:	Poisonous Substance:
Kitchen	Bleach Surface Cleaner, Degreaser, Chocolate, Kettle De-scaler Oven Cleaner Drain Unblocker
Lounge	Plants (Poinsettia)Macadamia Nuts, Fire Lighters, Scented

	Candles/Burners
Bedroom with en suite bathroom	Bleach, Toilet Cleaner, Shampoo, Conditioner
	Shower Body Wash
	Shower Cleaner
	Contraceptive Pill
	Pain Killers
Garage	Antifreeze, Car Shampoos, Windscreen Washer Fluid, Wine/Beer/Spirits
	Paint Thinner
Garden Shed	Pesticides, Lawn Feed, Plant Food, Fertilizer
	Weed Killer
	Path Clearer
	Creosote
	Slug Pellets
Garden	Rhubarb Leaves, Frogs/Toads, Azalea, Cocoa Husks/Mulch
	Daffodil Bulb

	Mistletoe
	Ragwort
	Slug Pellets

Below is the first aid action recommended for a selection of substances, one from each area of the home as listed above:

Substance Suspected	First Aid Action Taken
Surface Cleaner/Degreaser	If the poison is on the dog's coat or paws (perhaps through walking through it), apart from the risk of absorption through the skin, there is also the risk of secondary poisoning due to ingestion of the chemical as the dog tries to lick his coat clean. Signs resulting from poisoning with this type of product include inflamed skin, vomiting, diarrhoea, convulsions and ulcers on the tongue - **Do not** make the dog vomit - Ensure the dog discontinues licking ASAP – Wear gloves when cleansing the contaminant away – Clean in/around the mouth with water – Do not allow the dog to swallow the cleaning water

	– Clean the fur thoroughly with soap/water – Contact the vet immediately – Take bottle to vet for information – Monitor Airway, Breathing, Circulation and be ready to step in and perform CPR or artificial respiration as required.
Macadamia Nuts	Ingestion may result in macadamia nut toxicosis. The signs of this are weakness, hind limb paralysis with the inability to stand, occurring within 12 hours of ingestion. Depending on the quantity ingested and size of the dog, symptoms may also include muscle tremors, joint pain and severe abdominal pain.- Administer an emetic ASAP (Either with a crystal of washing soda or rock salt) – Make a note of the time ingested. – Contact the vet immediately

	– Monitor A, B, C's and be ready to perform CPR or artificial respiration as required.
Aspirin	Accidental poisoning can arise if such medications are not kept safely locked away for puppies, playful adults or bored dogs. Poisonings with medications such as Aspirin can also result if the owner administers the medication incorrectly as a pain-killing medium. Ingestion of Aspirin can result in loss of appetite, depression and vomiting either with or without blood apparent. If the dog is conscious: – Administer an emetic ASAP – if possible within half an hour but certainly within 2 hours. (Either with a crystal of washing soda or rock salt) Regardless if conscious or not:- – Contact the vet immediately – Make a note of the time it occurred – Estimate how much the dog has

	had – Monitor A, B, C's and be ready to step in and perform CPR or artificial respiration as required.
Antifreeze	Antifreeze can be dangerous in three ways either by absorption through the skin should the dog walk through it, say from a dripping car radiator, from secondary ingestion should the animal try to lick his coat clean, and by primary ingestion if the dog should come across the antifreeze itself and lick it (apparently, they just love the taste of it) Antifreeze can cause convulsions, collapse, coma and may even be fatal so swift action is required - Administer an emetic ASAP(Either with a crystal of washing soda or rock salt) – Ensure the dog discontinues licking ASAP – Wear gloves when cleansing the contaminant away – Clean in/around the mouth with

	water
	– Ensure the dog does not swallow the cleaning water
	– Clean the fur thoroughly with soap/water
	– Contact the vet and transport Immediately
	– Make a note of the time it occurred
	– Monitor A, B, C's and be ready to step in and perform CPR or artificial respiration as required.
	Consideration should also be given to the use of VODKA as a possible aid to treatment. Ideally this should be administered intravenously (IV) by your vet but a measure of vodka to drink as a non-prescription treatment to get things underway certainly won't do any harm.
	Please make sure you know how much you have given the dog so you can tell the vet when you arrive as it may alter his dosage and treatment

	of your pet. Also, please take a bottle of vodka with you if you have it, just in case the vet does not have any on site when you arrive and would like to use this method to help your dog.
Slug Pellets	Unfortunately, slug pellets are another thing that often tastes good to dogs. This encourages them to eat them should they come across them in the garden or shed. Signs resulting from ingestion of slug pellets and snail bail include tremors, salivation, convulsions and coma. Slug pellets can, in extreme cases, be fatal to the dog.- Administer an emetic ASAP (Either with a crystal of washing soda or rock salt) – Ensure the dog discontinues licking ASAP – Wear gloves when dealing cleansing – Clean in/around the mouth with water

	– Clean the fur thoroughly with soap/water – Contact the vet and transport Immediately – Make a note of the time it occurred – Monitor A, B, C's and be ready to step in and perform CPR or artificial respiration as required
Frogs/Toads/Caterpillars	Some species of toad and a few frogs are covered with a toxic secretion on the skin. When the dog goes to play with the toad, it inevitably ingests some of the toxins or, on some occasions, the toxins may enter the body through the eye of the dog. A similar reaction can result if the dog comes across a caterpillar. Some species can also cause terrible reactions in dogs should they try to play with them. The resulting symptoms depend greatly on the toxicity of the species of toad and can prove fatal.

Possible symptoms include:
profuse salivation
pawing at the mouth due to pain
red/inflamed gums
vomiting
seizures
convulsions
cardiac arrest.

There may also be an allergic reaction to the toad venom resulting in welling of:

face/eyes/tongue/windpipe

– Use a jet of water to remove the toxin

– Do not let him swallow any water

– Rub the teeth/gums with soft rag & toothpaste

– Call your vet for immediate advice

– If your vet has already told you what   antihistamine he can take, administer this ASAP as per the dosage instructions   you were given previously.

– If not, give high doses of Vit-C and Nettle drops as it works as a natural antihistamine. At least 2000-3000 mg vit c every 4 hours as it is water based and 30-40 drops Nettle drops

– If the dog is convulsing, keep him safe from any obstacles during the fit and   ensure he is cool and not over-heating   due to the energy he is expending while the fit is taking place.

– Make a note of the time the fit began.

– Transport to vet as quickly and quietly as possible.

– Remember that he may be confused and disorientated during the fit, so take care not to get bitten. If his teeth come into contact with anything during the fit, it is likely that he may bite down and clamp his teeth together firmly.

DIGESTIVE TRACT - RAT POISON

In my local area I have recently been made aware of at least 3 instances where dogs have ingested rat poison – sadly, one of those dogs didn't make it.

Since then, another of my friends has found rat poison dumped in the garden after their neighbours took exception to the dogs barking. So, firstly, would you know what rat poison looks like if you come across it?

It's important to be able to spot the signs and symptoms of poisoning if you can and, as I started to do a blog on this very subject, I came across this brilliant information on the www.ehow.com website and honestly, it's so good there is no point in me re-writing it.

This article by www.ehow.com sums it up really well and from it, the following information on the signs to look out for is as follows:-

Pale Gums – Pale gums are a sign of anaemia, a common side effect of rat poisoning. Your dog's gums should be bright pink. If they appear pale pink to white or greyish white, there is cause for concern. Become familiar with your dog's normal gum tone so that you are more easily able to spot a problem.

Drooling – Drooling, especially if accompanied by streaks of blood in the saliva, may indicate poison ingestion. Most dogs drool when they see food or become overheated, but a foamy drool without cause should be investigated. Other toxic conditions cause drooling such as eating toads, in particular can cause foamy drool, but if there is blood present, examine the interior of your dog's mouth. If the source of the blood is not a cut or injury to the mouth, contact your veterinarian.

Sudden Weakness – Fever, muscle tremors and sudden weakness indicate a dangerous condition. The signs of rat poison toxicity are subtle; be alert to changes in your dog's demeanour. If rat poisoning is left untreated, it can cause fatal haemorrhaging and internal bleeding.

Blood – Rat poisons cause internal bleeding and organs may begin to fail. Large amounts of blood in the urine, faeces or vomit, a bloody nose or uncontrolled bleeding from the mouth or anus is a serious sign. Your dog needs immediate veterinary attention at this point. Bleeding – Symptoms begin 72 to 96 hours after ingestion of anticoagulant rat poison. The dog will show bleeding throughout its system. Often blood flows from the nose, ears, eyes, gums and even skin. Urine or bowel movements show blood. Where the dog's skin is visible, widespread bruising often   appears.

Contaminated Rodents – Rats and mice do not die immediately after eating rodenticides. They may live for one to two days, gradually becoming more debilitated. These animals are easy prey for dogs and cats. Often, the amount contained in a poisoned rodent is not enough to kill a dog, but ingestion could cause   illness.

Coughing – The dog might exhibit signs of respiratory distress, such as wheezing and coughing, as its lungs fill with blood. It is not unusual for the dog to cough up blood in an effort to clear its lungs. The dog's gums will appear pale or white from lack of oxygen and excessive bleeding.

Abdomen – The dog's abdomen begins to distend. Upon palpitation it will feel hard and filled with fluid as blood seeps into the abdominal cavity from widespread bleeding of the internal organs.

Collapse – As the poisoning progresses, the dog collapses, too weak to stand or even sit up. The dog might struggle to rise but will be unable even to lift its head as the poisoning progresses. The dog's body feels cold to the touch as shock sets in.

Respiratory Rate – The dog's breathing becomes shallow and may appear slow. As the poisoning progresses, the dog's breathing might become rapid and hollow as the dog gasps for breath. The animal is unable to absorb oxygen due to the abundance of blood and flood within its lungs. Respiratory distress sets in. The dog will quickly loose awareness of its surroundings.

Heart Rate – The dog's heart rate becomes slow and the animal loses consciousness. If immediate medical treatment is not sought, the dog quickly dies.

What To Do –
If you know that your dog has consumed rat poison, induce vomiting. Administer one tea spoon to 1/8 cup of salt water or 3% hydrogen peroxide. Use a needle-free syringe or turkey baster to squirt the solution to the back of the throat ensuring that you

do not do this too quickly or choke him. Follow vomiting with an emergency veterinary visit, activated charcoal and/or vitamin K supplements.

Read more: http://www.ehow.com/list_6563001_symptoms-rat-poison-dogs.html#ixzz2YAT9IOyi

DIGESTIVE TRACT - EATING POO

Eating Poo (or coprophagia to give it its medical term) causes an awful lot of revulsion for the owners of dogs who, for whatever reason, like to eat poo. Because faeces are an easily digestible source of protein or vegetation (mine do love a sneaky mouth-full of horse-poo if they can get it) many predatory species will do this.

Be mindful that along with the fact this habit is more than a little "icky", if the dog eats from a source where the host animal has recently been wormed, not only will your dog be consuming the worms that are ejected but also the drug that was given to the host animal to treat it. For some dogs in the herding varieties, if they have a condition known as MDR1, this can be incredibly dangerous as the drugs used to worm animals can, in some cases, prove fatal to dogs with this condition. (Check out our blog on MDR1 if you have a dog which may fall into this category such as Border Collies, Shelties, Old English Sheep Dogs etc)

It is perfectly natural for bitches to eat the faeces of their pups, and equally normal for a pup to do it out of curiosity (though this problem is often resolved once the puppy is toilet-trained) – and quicker still if you take away the deposit as soon as it arrives.

If an adult dog is eating his own poo however, this is not normal behaviour and so we need to look at what the possible cause for such unpleasant munching could be.

Check the list and see if any of these suit your situation:

- Curiosity – as in puppies, he may just wonder what it tastes like.
- We all learn from our mothers and some puppies copy the cleaning behaviour too. Occasionally this behaviour is carried on as the puppy grows up. Similarly, some bitches continue the cleaning behaviour even after their puppies have gone to their new homes.
- When he was being toilet trained, did you tell him off at any time for going in the wrong place? If you did, he may have decided that he needs to hide the evidence from you to avoid a further scolding.
- Is your dog finding his food a little boring? Perhaps it is just a complete dry diet that you are feeding. If so, you could gradually change it to something more interesting (not too quickly as he may get an upset stomach), or add other things for variety.
- Perhaps he needs a little more fibre to bulk out his diet. Adding in raw vegetables such as carrots can help with the formation of better stools.
- Is your dog hungry? Perhaps he needs a little more to feel satisfied? If his weight is ideal yet he still appears hungry, you could try splitting his meals into smaller portions but feeding him more frequently so he has something in his tummy more often. If you try feeding him an hour before his walk, he will likely still feel relatively full and hopefully not fill up on a poo-snack!
- Could your dog be bored? Often behaviours like coprophagia can denote boredom and a suggestion that a bit more mental stimulation is needed. You could try various games and learning sessions such as clicker training tricks such as taking a bow – check out You Tube to see lots of ways you can stimulate your dog's mind.

- Does he like the taste? This is somewhat easier if he is eating his own poo as you can certainly make sure it is removed as soon as it appears or you could try putting something on the poo that he will find unpleasant-tasting. Sprays such as the bitter apple flavour are available. Another alternative is to add a dietary supplement that may render the faeces unpalatable to him. Try adding two to four tablespoons of canned pumpkin to his meals – although it tastes great the first time around, it apparently is much less enticing when mixed with the poo. Another thing to try is adding some canned pineapple, pineapple juice or spinach to his food as this too has been shown to put a lot of dogs off. Once the dog associates the process with an unpleasant taste, the habit usually stops and the supplement can then be discontinued. Your vet can guide you as to what to use. (Sadly this technique is of no use to you if he is eating poo he finds out on his walks)
- Sometimes it can be due to a vitamin B or K deficiency or it could be a sign of a more serious problem – speak with your vet for more information.

So how do we get him to stop doing it?

- Using some really high value treats (there's no point in simply using his daily kibble if you want him to learn something with enthusiasm – so something like roast chicken or smelly cheese is great) start with some really good recall training so that he knows if you call him, the treat he will get will be way more tasty and special than the poo is.
- Once you feel his recall is consistently good, keep a really close eye on him during your walks, watching out for him finding any

poo and as soon as he does, use your recall command and reward him with an absolute jackpot of your high value treats.

- Always be positive and make the training a happy, fun experience. Use your treats and fun voice to entice him away. If you do not feel he has quite got the idea yet, you can leave a long line attached to him so he doesn't get the chance to make it to the poo in the first place. He will soon get the idea that coming to you for some yummy treats and a happy, rewarding experience is a way better alternative than a mouth full of YUK!
- You'll need to continue to distract him as you get past the poo, so that he'll hopefully forget it was there.

If after trying everything you can, it transpires that your dog just cannot be persuaded to drop the habit and he occasionally manages to get to an unguarded poo before you do, please don't panic. Other than perhaps making him vomit it back again, eating the poo won't actually hurt them (unless as stated above he is MDR1 positive), but you should make sure he is wormed regularly or taking Diatomaceous Earth (see blog if you are unsure about what D.E. is) to combat the parasites he will surely pick up along the way – and certainly you might want to start avoiding most of the kisses from your furry friend

DIGESTIVE TRACT - IS YOUR DOG TOO FAT?

A lot of problems with our dogs can be caused or exacerbated by our dog's weight so, Is Your Dog Too Fat?

As a rule, people who show their dogs in breed dog show competitions such as Crufts here in the UK and the Westminster Cup in the US see other examples of their breed regularly so they know how their dog shapes up. If you are not an expert on the breed or a "show person" (and particularly if your dog is of a rarer breed that you just don't see as often or perhaps a cross breed), you might not be quite so sure as to whether your dog is the right weight for his breed and type or whether he is, in actual fact, too fat.

Each breed has a different ideal healthy shape; for example, dogs such as Whippets, Salukis and Borzois who are intended to run and run should be very lean, whereas dogs like the Rottweiler and the Mastiff are intended to be of a much more muscular and substantial frame (though still not "fat"). The shape of each breed corresponds closely to the job he was originally designed to do but, as a very basic and general rule, you should at least be easily able to feel his ribs and perhaps also see the outline of the last couple. If the pin bones of the hips at the spine are clearly visible and the ribs have absolutely no fatty covering at all, then this is too thin. Conversely, if you cannot even find Fido's ribs beneath the layers of wobbly blubber, then it's time to cut back on the treats and increase the exercise.

If your dog is severely overweight, please speak to your vet before cranking up the exercise regime. It is important that any increase in his physical activity be done in a controlled and safe manner that will not put excessive strain on his heart or joints. His calorific requirements should be tailored to suit his level of activity so speaking to a professional to help you get it right is always advised.

While a dog on the thinner side is always preferable to a chunkier one, WAY too thin is still dangerous for your dog's health. Lack of proper food intake means that the body will not be getting the appropriate nutrition, joints will suffer and the organs will be placed under too much strain and may begin to shut down. All this goes hand in hand with an overall poor body condition which will be clearly visible in the energy levels and behaviour, the dogs coat, the eyes and his general picture of wellbeing.

If you feel he is a teeny bit on the tubby side, reign in the treats and titbits and make sure his diet is suitable for his needs both in content and in amount. If he really is a hungry-nose who always seems to be sharking about for food, perhaps try introducing lower calorie treats like chunks of carrot to fill him up. Look at how often you walk and for how long as well as how much opportunity he gets to chase about and really cut loose. If you really don't feel that you are feeding excessively, perhaps there is an underlying problem causing the weight gain in which case, a consultation with your vet should be your first port of call. An underactive thyroid gland or "Hypothyroidism" can cause your dog to pile on the pounds even though he is fed substantially less.

If he is too thin, does he need more food or could there be any medical explanation for his slender frame? An overactive thyroid gland or "Hyperthyroidism" can cause dogs and humans to drop weight dramatically. There are many other reasons for weight loss too, so please do not delay in seeking a veterinary opinion. If you are feeding your dog appropriately and he still looks skinny, don't feel that you will be judged by your vet as a bad owner. This is his job and a good owner will seek help when they are at a loss to explain such a reduction in body weight. Does his coat look sleek and glossy or does it show signs of sparseness, flaky or scurfy patches or even red/angry bits on his skin? Perhaps you are simply not giving him a large enough quantity for the amount of activity he enjoys, or may be the quality and calorific balance of the food you are feeding is not quite good enough. Every dog is different and just because you may have two or three other dogs of the same breed who get the same amount and look fine, doesn't mean that the same amount will work for every dog – metabolism can mean that calories are burned up more or less quickly and everybody is an individual

DIGESTIVE TRACT - DIARRHOEA AFTER EATING

Usually, when your dog gets an upset stomach or a "runny bum" it's down to them eating something undesirable that they've managed to find on a walk, picking up a bug of some sort or it may be that they've eaten something new that doesn't quite agree with them. Often, when we try to change our dogs over to a different brand of food or to a new type of diet, it may take a while for them to adapt to the new food and this might cause diarrhoea. Perhaps they've been in a particularly stressful situation recently which has resulted in a looser motion.

So, what do you do if this happens to your dog? Well, if you KNOW that you've tried a different food and it appears to have caused the problem, read on. If you HAVEN'T done anything different and yet your furry friend has developed an upset tummy, please read our other blog on Upset Tummies instead.

OK, so perhaps you have decided to change on to a different brand of dog food or maybe you thought it might be nice to supplement your dog's diet with something new, like some beautiful fresh sardines. The fact that she developed diarrhoea after eating the new thing doesn't mean she can't eat it. It merely means that she probably needs to have the new foodstuff introduced to her in smaller portions over a longer period of time until she gets used to them. Certainly things like sardines (which are fabulous for your dog both from the point of view of her coat and her joints) are quite rich and oily, hence this may cause diarrhoea until they get used to them.

If this is the case, and as you KNOW what the cause is, I would suggest that all you need to do is starve her for 6-9 hours allowing things to return to normal as the new food makes its way through her digestive system. If, however, you feel you would like to try to do something to help speed things up, there are a couple of things you could try:

You could try giving a dose of Imodium – it works for us and for them too. However, just a note of caution with this medication if I may: Some dogs react very badly indeed to the active ingredient in Imodium (far worse in fact than the problem you are trying to treat). If your dog is of a herding variety such as a Border Collie, then please check with your vet before giving him this medication, just in case.

An alternative to Imodium and perhaps a safer bet is Pro-Kolin, which helps to provide an immediate response to digestive upsets. It contains probiotic Enterococcus Faecium to help restore the balance of the microflora in the digestive tract, firms up the stools, soothes the gut's lining and also contains prebiotic too.

If you didn't want to go to the trouble of buying a product specifically for the problem (such as the Pro-Kolin above), you could always try adding add a probiotic (such as the live yoghurt type stuff) as this will help her gut to balance and recover. Probiotics are great to add into any diet as a matter of course – whether you're a human or a dog for that matter.

Another thing you could try is to give her canned pumpkin (not the stuff that you find in a pumpkin pie filling with all the sugars and additives in it, just 100% natural pumpkin flesh). Most dogs love the flavour of pumpkin, and it is a unique fibre that regulates the bowel. It will colour the stool, so don't be surprised or worried by this.

Another natural approach is something called Slippery Elm which has properties that turn fluids into a gel and can be helpful in settling a runny tummy – many dog people swear by this and indeed it is something I keep on hand for our lot, just in case.

If by the next meal you are still a little reserved about feeding, rather than reverting to your normal food you could try feeding plain boiled chicken (shredded after it has been cooked) and plain boiled white rice. Both are gentle and will help bind her. The added moisture in the food will also help to keep her hydrated.

N.B. Don't forget to make sure she has plenty of water – diarrhoea will dehydrate a dog quite quickly so it is important to give her every opportunity to drink, even if she is not eating. If you suspect your dog is dehydrated, you can give Dioralyte sachets to help replenish the electrolytes in her system too. Please be very careful BEFORE you give Dioralyte to check the ingredients, as the flavoured sachets (things like black current flavour etc) use the sweetener Xylitol which is, of course, toxic to dogs

If you do not know what has caused the diarrhoea and she is still loose after a couple of days, or if you see blood in the stool, please speak to your vet for further advice and possible investigation.

DIGESTIVE TRACT - UPSET TUMMY

Upset Tummy: You know what dogs are like, very often it's a case of "if it's not nailed down, they'll have a go at eating it!" and invariably, some of the things they eat are not always very agreeable to their digestion. Vomiting and diarrhoea are often the outcome but, confusingly, these symptoms can be caused by many things including mild bugs and diseases or a sudden change in diet. Maybe the symptoms could relate to a more serious life threatening cause, however, and so establishing a diagnosis for the tummy upset is a major consideration.

So, if your dog gets an upset tummy, either with vomiting, diarrhoea or both, what should you do? Well, firstly its important to assess the severity of the problem and take it from there. Treatment for vomiting can range from simply starving the dog and then giving a bland diet (as described below in the treatment for diarrhoea) all the way through to surgical procedures, so it is important to assess the situation carefully:-

Mild Vomiting is described as follows.
Seek a **routine** appointment if these signs fit:-

* Sporadic vomiting/retching (once or twice daily)
* Gradual onset
* Dog behaves much as normal
* Swallows saliva normally
* Abdomen normal size
* Eats as normal

Severe Vomiting is described as follows.
Seek **immediate** veterinary attention with any of these signs:-
.

* Frequent vomiting/retching (more than 4 times daily)
* Sudden onset
* Dog depressed and subdued
* Swallowing problems; drooling saliva
* Abdominal distention (swelling/firmness)
* Will not eat

If your dog has diarrhoea and you know it is down to something he has eaten (say a change in his normal diet or something he has managed to get hold of) then please read our blog specifically on this problem: Runny Bum after Eating

However, if the diarrhoea is unexplained and you think it could be down to a bug perhaps, then the following is our recommended treatment for an otherwise healthy dog:

1. Starve for 12 hours but allow constant access to water

2. **DO NOT** give milk, raw eggs, raw meat or processed human foods

3. Every 3 hours or so, start to introduce small bland meals such as cooked chicken, scrambled egg or fish with equal parts of boiled rice.

4. Gradually start to leave the gap between feeds a little longer and increase the size of the portion

5. After a couple of days it should be safe to start reintroducing your dog's normal food and phasing out the bland diet

NB Large quantities of blood, or poo that appears to be made up just of blood require immediate veterinary attention. Please 'phone your vet straight away and request emergency advice.

DIGESTIVE TRACT - ANAL GLANDS

Before reading this article, please:
DO NOT ATTEMPT THIS PROCEDURE WITHOUT PROPER SUPERVISION FROM A QUALIFIED PROFESSIONAL AS DOING SO COULD CAUSE SERIOUS INJURY.

All dogs have anal glands. They are scent glands under the skin on each side of the dog's anal area (at about the 4 and 8 o'clock positions). The openings to these glands lie inside the dog's body, just inside the anus. As the dog poos, these glands are squeezed and emptied by the pressure of the poo moving past them and out of the body. If this normal emptying process doesn't happen for whatever reason, the glands can get very full and become impacted or infected. This is quite a common source of irritation for many dogs.

Symptoms
* Sitting and dragging their bottoms along the floor, known as "scooting" (often many owners who see their dogs doing this assume it means their pet needs worming).
* Frequent and excessive licking of the perineal area

If these impacted or infected glands become quite severe or develop abscesses, the dog will be very uncomfortable indeed and may scoot, yelp, lick, and be very wary of any approach to their rear end. The dog may also exhibit signs of aggression towards his owner or, in some cases, they may show episodes of hyper-excitability merely due to the fact that they are so uncomfortable that they just don't know what to do with themselves.

Diagnosis

Diagnosing impacted or infected anal glands is a very straightforward procedure requiring nothing more than an internal examination by your vet. However, if the dog is very uncomfortable indeed or in an awful lot of pain, it might be necessary to sedate him to allow a full examination to take place.

Treatment

If the glands are simply full or impacted and need emptying, your vet can do this manually. This procedure although not the most pleasant thing in the world for the dog, will bring instant relief as the glands are emptied of the foul smelling substance they carry (it often comes out at quite a spurt so remember to keep your mouth shut!)

If the glands are infected or have abscesses, they will usually require treatment under anaesthetic to express the glands as it would be too painful for the dog if it were to be done awake. Once the glands are emptied, treatment for the abscess and/or infection would need to be given which might include irrigation of the gland itself as well as a course of antibiotics and painkillers.

Outlook

Simple full or impacted anal glands tend to be a recurring problem for a lot of dogs and if this is the case, it is likely to require periodic trips to the vet to have these glands emptied. Some owners are able to do this for their dog themselves, once shown how by their vet, so if this is something you feel you could do, then ask your vet to show you how.

Dogs with softer stools or frequent diarrhoea such as is seen in colitis for example may be more prone to full anal glands. Increasing the amount of fibre in the diet (eg by adding some unrefined bran or giving the dog raw vegetables) may help the glands to empty by themselves as the poo is passed – although this is by no means a fail-safe answer in all dogs.

DIGESTIVE TRACT - CONSTIPATION

Constipation and straining can have many different causes but some of the more usual reasons for it are:-

* Change of diet or normal toileting routine
* Obesity or general lack of exercise
* Spinal, joint or mobility problems making a squatting position painful
* Impacted dry faeces
* Impacted bony material
* High percentage bone -v- meat in the diet
* Anal gland irritation, impaction or swelling
* Enlarged prostate glands in male dogs (see other blog)
* Perineal hernia
* Dehydration

The dog may attempt to strain over and over which is exhausting if it continues for too long. If the constipation is due to impacted bony material, he may yelp out as he tries to pass the hard stool. The stomach may feel hard or uncomfortable to the touch and the dog may tense his muscles to guard against your touch. The discomfort may lead to the dog pacing and an inability to settle comfortably in one place. He may also begin to pant and appear anxious.

If the constipation continues for quite a length of time, it can cause the dog to be extremely miserable, depressed and often lethargic too. If left for a long time, constipation can also cause toxaemia and other symptoms such as vomiting.

Treatment:

1.) Try adding several tablespoons of liquid paraffin to the food daily, which may help to relieve the discomfort when passing the stools.

2.) Try adding bran to the food (1-2 heaped tablespoons daily). Increasing the roughage in the diet should (hopefully) produce a softer stool which is easier for the dog to excrete.

3.) If you are trying a new raw diet, it might be that the percentage of bone in the diet is too high. If you are feeding a ready-made raw diet, you may wish to try a different brand. If you are feeding a raw diet that you are making up at home, then simply adjusting the ratios of raw meat to bone will help. (Another sign that the bone quantity is too high is very crumbly, dry, white stools).

4.) You may try adding raw liver – for a small dog around 3-4 table spoons, for a mid-large breed then perhaps around 300 grams. It doesn't matter if it's a little more, as it's nutritious rather than dangerous.

5.) If none of these work, then your veterinary practice may be able to advise on other products which can be used in an effort to promote bowel function and a more normal stool.

DIGESTIVE TRACT - EATING GRASS – IS IT NORMAL?

Three times recently I have been directly asked or overheard a conversation about this issue and then, totally by chance, I read a really interesting little snippet which sums it up beautifully. This little chapter comes from Andrew Gardiner's First Aid for Dogs book – An Owner's Veterinary Guide which I found in a charity shop of all places! Anyway, I thought it was worthy of a mention purely from a point of interest. I'm sure many people may have varying opinions and views about this subject, but I did think this article was pretty good.

"Many dogs eat grass occasionally. It is not considered abnormal or signs of a major dietary deficiency, nor is it accurate to say that the dog is "trying to make himself sick". It's true that some dogs will retch after consuming grass or tough stems, but by no means all do.

Wild dog relatives also eat grass and other vegetation; they will frequently eat the vegetable material present in the stomachs of their prey animals as well as nibble at growing grass and plants. The reason is thought to be a natural desire to obtain indigestible fibre (which is required for normal bowel function) in animals which, like dogs, are mainly carnivorous.

Feeding raw vegetables (eg carrots) occasionally may reduce the frequency of grass eating in some dogs which seem particularly keen on it."

It is important also to consider HOW they are grazing. If it is the normal nibbling and munching, then it's simply down to the fact that they like and enjoy it. If it is a frantic grabbing of the blades and ripping mouthfuls out of the ground, this is usually more indicative of a stomach upset and should be watched accordingly. If the behaviour continues, then veterinary advice should be sought.

Often we see our dogs making a bee-line for fresh lush shoots and many owners report that their dogs have favourite patches of grass to graze on and I know my lot certainly do too, with all three of them munching for as long as they can before they have to run to catch me up on our walk.

Perhaps this goes some way to explaining their constant fascination with eating horse, cow and sheep poo (or is that just my three???) It is important to remember that while the eating of herbivorous animal poo in itself can be seen as quite normal, we do need to take care and discourage this if possible. Not just because, well, frankly it's all a bit bleughhhhhh, but also because of the dangers should the host animal have been wormed recently. Horses, cows, sheep etc all get wormed regularly and if this has been done just prior to your dog tucking in to a steaming pile of "Poo au vin" then your pet will be ingesting the chemicals and worm infestation excreted by that animal. Some dogs react very badly to certain types of pesticide and, in cases such as those dogs with the MDR1 genetic mutation, this can actually prove fatal.

Another consideration is a drug called Monensin. The MRCVS put out a new warning in 2015 stating that care should be taken "not allow dogs, horses, other equines or guinea fowl access to formulations containing Monensin. Due to the risk of bolus regurgitation, do not allow these species access to areas where treated cattle have been kept. Ingestion or oral exposure to Monensin can be fatal in these species."

Further information about the symptoms of the effects of this drug can be found at: http://mrcvs.co.uk/en/news/14578/Vets-warned-of-monensin-toxicity-in-dogs

DIGESTIVE TRACT - BLOAT AKA TORSION/GDV

A condition most frequent in, but not restricted to, large and giant breeds. The stomach fills with gas and rather than expelling it as normal, the gut twists and flips over on itself cutting off the blood supply and results in the tissue dying, often with fatal consequences for the host.

The following flow chart was not produced by Rhodes 2 Safety and I'm very sad to say that I do not know the exact source of the information or who to credit this fantastic chart to but if you do happen to spot it elsewhere and can let me know of its origins, I would love to be able to do so on this page.

Quick Reference Guide For GDV
BLOAT

Vet's Emergency Telephone Number...

	What Is Happening	What The Dog Does	What You Should Do	Treatment
Stress ►►► Excitement ►►►► Vigorous Exercise ►►►► Large Meals ►►►► Long Drink ►►►► Swallowed Air ►►►► Familial Tendency ►►►►	Stomach function is normal. Gas accumulates in the stomach but the stomach does not empty as it should.	Dog behaves as usual. Seems slightly uncomfortable.	Keep the dog quiet; Do not leave the dog alone; Give Antacid if your vet agrees. Be aware of Phase I symptoms.	During this period the dog may recover without going on to develop Gastric Volvulus.
PHASE I GDV	Stomach starts to dilate. (Gastric Dilatation) Stomach twists. (Gastric Volvulus)	Anxious, restless, pacing; Trying to vomit-may bring up stiff white foam but no food; Salivating; Abdomen may be swollen.	Call your vet, tell him what you suspect and why. Take the dog to the vet without further delay.	During this period the dog may recover if your vet releases the pressure with a stomach tube.
PHASE II GDV	Blood supply to part of stomach tissue is cut off. Stomach tissue is damaged. Portal vein, vena cava and splenic vein become compressed and twisted. Spleen becomes engorged. Shock begins to develop	Very restless; whining & panting; Salivating copiously; Tries to vomit every 2-3 min; Stands with legs apart & head hanging down; Abdomen swollen & sounds hollow if tapped; Gums dark red; Heart rate 80-100 beats/min; Temperature raised (104°f)	Get someone to tell your vet you are on your way and why. Take the dog to the vet as quickly as possible.	During this period the vet will need to relieve the stomach pressure, start an intravenous drip and perform surgery to untwist the stomach.
PHASE III GDV	Spleen and stomach tissue become Necrotic. Shock now very severe. Heart failure develops. Shock now irreversible. Death	Unable to stand or stands shakily with legs apart; Abdomen very swollen; Breathing shallow; Gums white or blue; Heart rate over 100 beats/minute; Pulse very weak; Temperature drops (98°f)	Death is imminent. Get someone to tell your vet you are your way and why. Take the dog to the vet as quickly as possible.	As well as doing everything above, the vet will need to remove part of the stomach and the spleen. He will also need to use powerful drugs to counteract shock. It is no longer possible to save the dog's life.

Shock is mentioned above as one of the serious signs that something is going badly wrong. With any condition, and particularly life-threatening ones, it is always advisable to keep up to date on the latest research and theories. Since writing this blog, breakthroughs have been made in research and studies suggesting a link between bloat and hereditary factors and also a possible link between bloat and IBS (Irritable Bowel Syndrome). This information is still quite new but if you are interested in reading up on this aspect, a good source can be found at: https://greatdanegnosis.wordpress.com/2016/03/19/bloat-a-major-breakthrough/

What to do?

Note the time
Note your dog's breathing rate, pulse rate and gum colour
Take a tape measure and note the size of his tummy & time of measuring
Administer Simethicone
Monitor the breathing, pulse and gums
Re-measure the tummy 3-5 minutes later
Phone the vet and tell him you are on your way as an emergency
Massage the acupressure point en route to the vet

Because this topic is such a serious one and one which many people do panic about, I've attached a link to an article I came across on the subject which is well worth a read and may clarify things for you. http://www.globalspan.net/bloat.htm

There is a medication referred to in the article which it suggests we have on hand to reduce gas should we notice the dog burping more than twice and we consider it may be bloating. They refer to Simethicone. Simethicone is an ingredient found in products taken to alleviate the symptoms of trapped wind, gas and bloating. There are many products which fulfil this role such as Rennie Deflatine and Wind-eze but Simethicone can also be purchased in tablet form under its own name.

Another good technique to consider if you think your dog has bloat is massaging an acupuncture pressure point that stimulates the release of gas. This technique is not "instead" of seeing your vet, but rather something you can do to try to help en route to your veterinary professional. You can read about this technique here: http://www.bluefrontiers.us/bloat_accupress.html

Rapid Bloat -v- Slow Bloat:
For the most part, symptoms are reported as coming on very quickly and deteriorating with alarming speed. However, in a few instances it has been a "slow bloat" rather than the usual rapid bloat. For this reason, if you feel that your dog is NOT HIMSELF or OUT OF SORTS for a couple of days, there is an outside chance that this could be the start of bloat. In all instances, keep your eye on his breathing rate, heart rate and gum colour and if you are unhappy that any of these three things is out of the ordinary, PLEASE SEE YOUR VET as a matter of urgency.

I've also included the following article, which was written by Elena Jeffery, all about **TORSION** – Although Elena has a strong Rhodesian Ridgeback interest as do I, it is nevertheless a very important thing for all dog owners to know about, be able to recognise and act on accordingly. Please spare a little time to read through this very well written and worthwhile article by Elena Jeffery.

"BLOAT and Other Emergencies – A Delegate's Eye View"

When I attended the Rhodesian Ridgeback Club of Great Britain seminar in March entitled Bloat and Other Emergencies I had some idea of what Bloat was as well as an understanding of the word Emergency. However, even having been around animals all my life and owning dogs as an adult for over 25 years (RR's wouldn't you guess!) I realised that, fortunately having never experienced Bloat first hand, I was amazingly ignorant. The following is a précis of what I feel to be the practical, salient points taken from the excellent presentation given by Mike Hewitt MA, VetMB, CertVR, MRCVS, Practice Director at Wendover Heights Veterinary Centre.

BLOAT – Gastric Dilation and Volvulus Syndrome is also known as Twisted Stomach, Gastric Torsion and GDV. This can be defined as a sudden and catastrophic Rotation of the Stomach, following AND resulting in gross enlargement of the stomach with gas. If untreated this will normally result in the death of the dog. Bloat is a true emergency where minutes do matter and even with prompt, competent intervention some dogs will be lost.

Although difficult to answer the common question of Why did it happen to my dog? there are a variety of risk factors:

Typically occurs in large chested breeds such as Great Danes, German Shepherds, Doberman Pinschers, Flat Coated Retrievers but Bloat can occur in any breed including Rhodesian Ridgebacks, as well as Dachshunds, Labrador Retrievers etc

Other causes are **activity in relation to meal times** which is why you should feed your dogs at least an hour before exercise and preferably the same on return.
Elevated food bowls (May need to change that one as opinions are now changing!)
Rapid Eating
Too much water directly before, or after, meals

The list is long! Some studies show a hereditary effect from a first degree relative and stress is also thought to be a factor. Certain medical conditions also increase the risk as well as the X-factor – the unknown or idiopathic.

<u>So what are the symptoms?</u>
Again the list is long but the most common and obvious signs to watch out for:
Quiet, unusual behaviour
Salivating
Restless and appears uncomfortable
Usually refuses food, not on the agenda for many RR's I suspect!
Abdomen appears full
May try to retch or vomit, typically unproductively
Shallow panting/rapid breathing
Abdomen becomes grossly enlarged and when tapped is like a drum
Ultimately the dog will collapse, feet and ears will feel cold (shock) and the gums may cease to be a healthy pink

Don't let it get this far... if you suspect Bloat, call your Vet immediately and be prepared to transport the patient to make sure help is at hand including a heavy blanket or something that can be used as a stretcher if required.

This is where every animal owner should be familiar with their veterinary practice's arrangements for emergencies, particularly for out of hours cover, although you should **await instructions before setting off**. In the meantime avoid unnecessary cooling and try to give the patient room to stretch out. If possible take someone to help and remain contactable.

Bloat often occurs within two hours of feeding, more at night than day, symptoms progress over 1-2 hours and early intervention improves prognosis so as a rule of thumb: veterinary attention within one hour of significant symptoms is suggested.

Once you reach the vet, as time is critical, it is important to assess the situation and plan. Diagnostic tests may be required: X-ray, blood tests and Ultra Sound Scanning.

One of the most important things, as an animal owner, is to choose a Vet that you like, respect and trust. One where you can ask questions (there's no such thing as a stupid question!!) and strive for a mutually respectful relationship where you can work together in the interests of your beloved pets. (Oh am I a lucky girl here!). This will help you make a decision, sometimes a difficult one, as treatment may not always be the best option but failure to treat or euthanize a true GDV is a serious welfare issue.

Having said this – if dealt with promptly the prognosis for GDV is generally fair to good.

Treatment Objectives should be:

Decompress the Stomach

Correct the Rotation

Maintain Circulation

Identify and remove necrotic (dead) tissue

Fix/staple stomach in correct location (gastropexy) to avoid recurrence

Provide Post-Operative care

The outcome is always uncertain but probabilities can be estimated depending on the duration of the symptoms and the severity of the clinical signs.

Blood Lactate levels <6 are better, Blood Lactate levels >6 are worse.

Plasma Lactate concentration as a predictor of gastric necrosis and survival among dogs with gastric dilatation – volvulus: 102 cases (1995-1998)

de Papp E, Drobatz KJ, Hughes D

J AM Vet Med Assoc 1999 July 1;215(1):49-52

From the above study, lactate can give some indication of whether gastric necrosis has occurred and gastric necrosis is a reasonable indicator of outcome. If NO gastric necrosis has occurred dogs had a greater than 90% survival rate. Even WITH some degree of gastric necrosis there was a 66% survival rate. In broad terms it would usually be appropriate to initiate treatment and make decisions when more information is available.

Behind the scenes you would expect:
Fluids – first and fast
Possibly X-ray
Sedate/anaesthetise
Decompress if possible (intubation)
Whether, or not, decompression is successful, often the best course of action is a Laparotomy (investigative abdominal surgery) followed by appropriate action.

All dogs treated surgically for GDV should have a gastropexy. Approximately 40% of dogs require partial or complete splenectomy (spleen removal) This and gastropexy are made easier by stapling (and you thought that was just for paper but please don't try the domestic variety!) Approximately 10% of dogs require partial gastrectomy (stomach removal)

Survival rates can be as high as 90% but may be, predictably, much lower. Fortunately Bloat is not all that common – Wendover Heights, with circa 10 small animal vets, state they may have approximately one case per month.

I sincerely hope that few of us will ever have the experience of Bloat but should it occur, or you suspect it at any time, I trust that this synopsis will have been helpful.

Thank you - Elena Jeffery

WHAT'S NORMAL AND HOW TO CLEAN

A healthy canine ear should not require any special treatment or care other than a regular check just to make sure all is well and that there is no irritation, wax, discharge, foul/sour smell, or excessive build-up of hair (which can affect certain breeds eg Poodles).

It is not recommended to use ear cleaners or medicated ear wipes on a regular basis unless this course of action is specifically recommended by your vet. Production of some wax is the normal process by which the canine ear self-cleanses but, if your dog does produce excessive accumulations of ear wax, then it may be useful to keep this under control.

Do a routine ear cleaning either with apple cider vinegar or with a mild white wine vinegar and water solution.

Use the vinegar and tepid water, mixed in equal parts.

Lift the dog's ear straight up without pulling and with a syringe or turkey baster; gently flush the mixture into the ear.

Your dog will reflexively shake her head. Before it does, massage the base of the ear with your fingers until you hear a squishy sound. Let it shake its head. This is best done outside because some of the gunk will be sent flying when it shakes.

For general maintenance, do this every three or four weeks. The vinegar provides a proper pH for the ear and helps dislodge dirt and wax.

Please make sure that when applying ear cleaners or drops, that you do not insert the nozzle too far.

Cleaning Your Dog's Ears: Inside the canine ear

Whenever you begin using a new product, use only a very small quantity to begin with. Some dogs react badly to even the most gentle of ear cleaners, so it is always best to check his level of sensitivity to the product.

Never use cotton buds (Q-tips), tweezers or other objects to clean your dog's ears. It is possible that the buds will nudge any waxy material deeper into the ear canal, making the problem worse. Tweezers can accidentally damage the internal ear so at any time that there is necessity to get right into the ear, this should always be done by a vet or qualified professional.

When using cotton wool, only swab from the top of the ear canal. Never push the cotton wool (or cotton buds) into the ear canal. In most cases, debris or wax will rise to the top naturally.

Prevention of Hair Build-Up
This is a common problem in Poodles, their crosses (such as Labradoodles) and many other breeds which contain excess hair in the ear canals. Often it causes the dog to shake their heads and scratch and rub at their ears.

Obviously, prevention of the build-up is preferable. Regular checking and control of the problem enables you to remove only a few hairs at a time. Do not persist for too long at each session if your dog finds the process extremely uncomfortable. This process is often best dealt with by a professional groomer as part of their regular grooming/clipping regime.

Most of the hair occurs near the opening of the ear canal and can usually be reached using fingertips alone. If this is the case, wipe your fingers with powder before you start to help you get a better grip on the fine hairs that line the ear canals.

It is best to avoid using tweezers, even in the most placid dogs, unless you are an experienced groomer and, if it is necessary to use tweezers, blunt plastic ones are preferable (and possibly a muzzle for your dog should he find the process very unpleasant indeed). Please remember that it is very easy to damage the ear if the dog moves suddenly.

If you suspect hair build-up, gently lift the ear flap and look into the external ear canal. You may be able to see a mass of matted hair and trapped wax. If so, the trapped hair and wax should be removed. This may prove rather difficult, however, as plucking out the hair may be painful. Struggling risks damaging the ears so if your dog won't tolerate plucking, a sedative or anaesthetic at the vets will be required.

EARS – CONSTANT SHAKING/SCRATCHING

* Examine the ear opening by lifting the ear flap and looking inside.

* Provided it is near the very top of the ear canal, if you are able to see an obvious foreign body, you can remove this yourself gently with your fingers. If you must use a pair of blunt tipped tweezers, be very careful not to push the object deeper into the ear canal.

* Never probe deeply into the ear and always be aware that the dog may shake his head or move suddenly while you are trying to help. Therefore, be mindful that the tweezers do not damage him further and also that you do not get yourself bitten (it's a good idea to use plastic tweezers rather than sharp metal ones).

* If you think your dog may have something like a grass seed in his ear, rather than trying to reach far down with tweezers in this risky fashion, trying filling up the affected ear with olive oil or mineral oil. Sometimes, this will float the seed up so that it can be easily removed. This technique can also be applied if the dog has managed to get an insect in his ear canal. In order that insects can actually fly and get off the ground, they weigh very little and so administering olive oil to the ear canal may well float these out too.

Remember that the seed can easily migrate further down the canal or even penetrate the ear drum or side walls due to the barb-like tip. If the dog shakes his head, this may mean the seed is lodged deeper in the ear canal. Deep seeds should always be removed by a vet and never left to work their way out by themselves.

To soothe the dog temporarily, simply use the olive/mineral oil but be ready for the imminent shake the minute to put it in. A pipette or small turkey baster is ideal for this job but please make sure the contents are dropped in carefully rather than squirted in under pressure.

N.B. It is worth remembering that if your dog shakes his head, it may be that he is suffering with ear mites rather than simply having a foreign body in the ear canal.

* Constant scratching risks damage to the ear, ear flap or side of the face. Fit a protective Elizabethan or Buster collar until the problem can be dealt with properly.

*If in any doubt, do nothing until veterinary advice has been taken.

EARS - FOREIGN BODIES

During dry weather, it is always a good idea to check a dog's body, between his toes and also in his ears for plant seeds after each walk.

Visible seeds can be removed with tweezers though it's important to stress that we should not try to grasp anything way down the ear canal. One twitch or shake from the dog as we are trying to help can very easily result in damage to the tympanic membrane (ear drum) or other delicate internal structures of the ear, particularly if you are using pointy tweezers.

Rather than trying to reach far down in this risky fashion, trying filling up the affected ear with olive oil or mineral oil. Sometimes, this will float the seed up so that it can be easily removed. This technique can also be applied if the dog has managed to get an insect in his ear canal. In order that insects can actually fly and get off the ground, they weigh very little and so administering olive oil to the ear canal may well float these out too.

Remember that the seed can easily migrate further down the canal or even penetrate the ear drum or side walls due to the barb like tip. If the dog shakes his head, this may mean the seed is lodged deeper in the ear canal. Deep seeds should always be removed by a vet and never left to work their way out by themselves.

To soothe the dog temporarily, simply use the olive/mineral oil but be ready for the imminent shake the minute you put it in! A pipette or small turkey baster is ideal for this job but please make sure the contents are dropped in carefully rather than squirted in under pressure.

N.B. It is worth remembering that if your dog shakes his head, it may be that he is suffering with ear mites rather than simply having a foreign body in the ear canal.

EARS - HEAD SHAKING & EAR MITES

Head shaking and ear mites can affect any dog or cat. You may notice that your dog is shaking his head or perhaps scratching a lot more than usual. This could indicate several things including:-

- ear mites,
- foreign body in the ear,
- an allergy,
- an infection.

Ear mites:
Ear mites are common in puppies and spread easily within a litter. They irritate the lining of the ear canal, stimulating wax production and are just visible to the naked eye.

It is important to consult a vet who can prescribe insecticidal ear drops to eliminate ear mites.

All dogs and cats that have come into contact with the affected dog should be treated, since these mites can be easily transmitted to other animals.

Because mites can live outside the ear, insecticidal shampoos are also beneficial.

EARS - INNER EAR INFECTIONS

To a dog, his sense of hearing is the second most important of his 5 senses (second only to his sense of smell). Your dog's ears are incredibly delicate and very important to him. Deafness, although something he can live with, will really affect the way he lives his life so if you ever suspect your dog may have an ear problem, please seek veterinary attention as soon as possible.

<u>Loss of Balance</u>
Unless your dog has sneakily been "down the pub", loss of balance can be the result of an inner ear infection.

Infection can reach the inner ear from the external ear, through the Eustachian tube which connects the ear to the throat, or via the bloodstream.

Since the semi-circular canals in the inner ear control balance, any infection here will make the dog unsteady on his feet.

This causes the dog to tilt his head **in the direction of the affected ear**.
The eyes often flick in the same direction.

Confine the dog to prevent him from injuring himself while his balance is impaired.
A vet can control possible nausea and treat the dog with high levels of antibiotics by mouth. Surgical drainage of the inner ear is sometimes necessary.

EARS - DEAFNESS

Deafness in our dogs can easily go unnoticed for quite a while. Sometimes, when we get older, we like to think that rules don't apply to us anymore and we like to do things our own way and the same is true of our dogs. I think it's because of that fact that deafness is so often overlooked in our furry senior citizens.

I video'd a blog all about deafness which you can find on the R2S website, and if the points raised in the Vlog resonated with you and you think yes, perhaps my dog is becoming a little hard of hearing, what should you do? Well, first I would suggest a few little tests to determine exactly what he can, and cannot, hear. I would perhaps start with something as straightforward as calling him to you from another room (in our case simply opening a bag of crisps would get our pack to come in double quick time!)

You could try waiting until he is looking away and call his name very quietly, then get louder and louder and see how loud you need to speak before he can actually hear you – he may be really quite profoundly deaf and unable to respond to you at all unless he physically SEES you gesturing to him.

Try a lady's voice, a child's voice and that of a man. You may find he is more readily able to hear the higher-pitched voices of females and children over and above the deeper base tones of a male. With this in mind, try using a whistle too. This may be something that he can still hear even if he is a little further away from you.

And that brings me to another point. You need to remember that if he is really quite deaf and can't SEE you, he may well have no clue that you are calling him. Add to that any possibility of him getting separated from you by a large distance or "spooked" so that he runs off, he will then be pretty much isolated and unable to find you again. (A great time to use your whistle if that is still working). If you do feel his hearing is very impaired, then it may be safer not to let him off the lead in areas where he could roam a long way from you or potentially be scared away, or chase wildlife taking him away from you. Perhaps using a long-line may give you more confidence that although he feels he is exploring "off lead", you still have the option of bringing him back to you on the line.

A good idea, particularly if he is not yet completely deaf, is to start introducing hand signals into your daily communication with him. It is fairly easy to assign visual cues to these behaviours such as a simple flat palm towards your dog for a STAY, both arms wide open for a COME, your arm straight out in front of you with your palm down and then pushed towards the ground for a DOWN etc. These very simple gestures mean that you can still communicate with your friend (provided he is facing you) and in fact it is often the reason we don't spot that the deafness is getting worse – dogs become very clever at reading us, our facial expressions, body language and hand signals so please don't beat yourself up too much if you haven't spotted the signs before now.

Remember, not all dogs that ignore a cue or command are naughty or disobedient .... some simply can't hear you (though others, of course, are simply monkey-trousers!!!)

As an aside, if you have noticed your dog breathing heavily/noisily and perhaps developed rear end weakness at about the same time as his deafness occurred, he could be suffering from something called Laryngeal Paralysis and that would be something worth looking into too.

CHAPTER 11 – EYES   PG

BASIC FIRST AID FOR EYE INJURIES

Object in the eye:

Our eyes are so important to us, whether we are humans, dogs or another species entirely. For this reason, any "messing about" with eyeballs causes extreme fear and wariness and so before you start trying to help, please think about your own physical safety and the possibility of getting bitten.

Have an assistant steady the dog's head firmly for you. Reassure the dog in a calm and sensible manner (remembering that they often take their cues with regards to their behaviour and emotional state from us) and use a muzzle if necessary for safety. If you have no muzzle to hand, follow this impromptu guide:

* Create a loop and pop it over the dog's nose, pulling the loop to close the mouth.
* Bring the long ends down and cross them over under the chin.
* Take the long ends around and fasten them at the back of the neck.

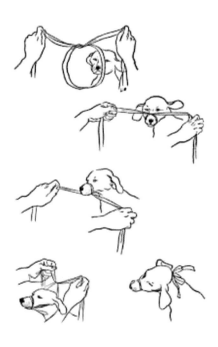

* For short-nosed breeds, do exactly as above but also connect the nose band to the strap at the back of the head to ensure the dog cannot get it off.

 Once the muzzle is safely in place, with one hand, part the eyelids and use the fingers of the other hand to remove the object, if this can be done easily and if it is **NOT** actually piercing the eyeball itself.

Objects in the corner of the eye may be easier to remove if wiped out using a moistened piece of cotton or gauze.

It may be possible to remove the object by irrigating the eye with tepid saline (salt water) solution. Tilt the dog's head towards the injured side and gently pour the water or saline into the eye at the corner of the bridge of the nose. Allow the water to wash across the front of the eye taking any dust or contaminants away so that it runs down the side of his face and not into his uninjured eye.

Liquid, dust or fine material in the eye needs to be flushed repeatedly with large amounts of saline (salt water) or water. Using a syringe or eye dropper will make this easier. If the eyelids are swollen, or there are bites or stings around the eye, bathe the eyelids in COOL saline or water.   Do not allow the dog to paw or rub the face.

If you cannot remove the object, ensure the dog doesn't rub its face or paw the eye while you seek veterinary help.

EYES - FOREIGN BODIES

If a dog has runny/watery eyes, is pawing at the eye or rubbing his head on the ground, it might be that there is something in the eye – be that dust, debris, a grass seed or some other type of foreign body. I have even seen a tick attached to the eyeball. The first thing to do is to have a good look and see if you can determine exactly what is going on and if there is anything in the eye that shouldn't be there.

Facing a window or good light source, stand behind the dog with him seated between your feet (we use the exact same position when we want to check inside the mouth, perhaps if the dog is choking for example or has something stuck in his back teeth). Put one hand under his muzzle/chin and tilt his head backwards so you can see clearly into his eyes.

If your dog is of a small breed, then simply do this kneeling down, again with your legs apart from behind him. Be it standing or kneeling, this position prevents him escaping backwards when you are examining him.

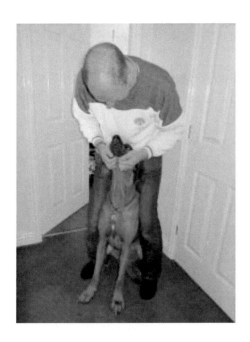

Remember, if your dog is frightened or in pain and you think there is any chance at all that he will snap at you, it may be safer all round to apply a muzzle before you start. In this position it is relatively easy to hold open the eyelid and look for grit or grass seeds, although you may require "another pair of hands" if you have a particularly wriggly customer!

Try floating out loose debris with eye drops, mild saline solution (salt water) or even olive oil as none of these fluids will irritate the eye ball.

If you can see the seed or foreign body lying towards the corner of the eye, you may be able to lift it off using the corner of a moistened tissue.

Do not attempt to remove foreign objects that have penetrated the eyeball, but seek veterinary assistance without delay. If for example there is a splinter sticking in the eye, or perhaps as mentioned above, a tick has managed to burrow its mouthparts into the eyeball itself or into the eyelid, please do not try to deal with this yourself. You MUST get professional help. We only get one pair of eyes so any injury of this nature should be treated as an emergency.

If the eye is damaged or you can see something in it, keep the dog's head as still as possible, preferably with the dog lying down. If he will let you, it's best to keep the eyes covered or at the very least in the dark as this will minimise the amount of movement the eyes make. Each time the eyeball moves, you run the risk of further damage from the foreign body so the more stable we can keep the head and the eye, the better it will be.

Remember, eyes work in pairs so if the undamaged eye moves, the poorly one will as well, so it's always best to try to cover both eyes so long as doing so doesn't cause the dog any further distress or discomfort.

N.B. ensure you DO NOT press on the eyes while covering them as we do not want to force any debris or foreign body further into the eye or make the situation worse.

EYES ARE PRECIOUS – PLEASE SEE A VET.

EYES - PROLAPSE OF THE EYEBALL

This can occur in breeds such as the Pekingese, the Pug and the Chihuahua with large protruding eyes. As a result of injury the eye may displace forward and the eyelids partly close behind it.

An injury of this nature usually occurs after a fight with a larger dog but it can occur if the dog is lifted by the scruff.

What should you do?

As soon as you possibly can, part the eyelids & gently push the eyeball back into its normal position using a moistened pad of gauze.

However, many owners would not feel confident enough to attempt this and if this is the case for you, please cover the eye with a moistened gauze as per our blog on treatment for severe eye injury and transport your dog to the vet immediately.

Please remember to 'phone ahead to the vet to let him know you are on your way. There is no point in turning up unannounced as you may find the vet out on his rounds or away on an emergency call if he does not know you are coming.

EYES - SEVERE INJURY TO THE EYE, EG BY STONE/BALL

Again, with such a serious eye injury, it is vitally important that we access professional veterinary help as soon as possible. Please be aware that the dog will be in severe discomfort so application of a muzzle may well be appropriate.

If the object that has hit the dog in the eye is dirty, say a stone or clod of mud, then rinse out the injured eye, ensuring there is nothing protruding or stuck in to the actual eyeball itself.

If possible, cover the injured eye with a sterile or clean pad, moistened with saline (salt water). We need to keep the injured eye as still as possible and, because eyes work in pairs, if the good eye moves, so will the injured one. Therefore, **IF** the dog will tolerate it, it is better to cover **BOTH** eyes even though only one is injured.

Gently hold the pad across the eye (covering it to block out any light but not actively pressing on the eye and causing further damage) while transporting the dog to the clinic or vets office. It's a good idea, if possible, to have somebody else do the driving while you sit with the dog in the back and have his head rested on your lap for comfort, support and reassurance. If you are alone and must drive the care yourself, then if you have your dog crated you can throw a blanket over the crate to keep it dark inside. This too will help the eyes stop moving around quite as much.

Remember, if possible, to monitor the dog closely en route to your vet, watching all the time for signs of shock. If, however, you are actually driving yourself, then simply getting to the vet as safely and quickly as possible will be your goal.

N.B. Remember to ring your vet BEFORE you set off so he knows you are coming and there is a qualified veterinary professional waiting for you as you travel in.

EYES - WEEPY/WATERY EYES

Weepy/Watery Eyes: Sometimes, particularly with dogs who have paler coloured fur, you might notice that their eyes are weeping or watery. Some breeds are more prone to this condition than others for example the Poodle, the Shih Tzu, the Bichon Frise and the Maltese, but any breed can suffer with it. Breeds with larger eyes, such as the Chihuahua produce lots of tears to help keep the surface of the eye moist and debris-free. This level of tear production can cause the appearance of "weeping".

The watery discharge or mucus overflows the tear ducts and runs down the face, often staining the fur towards the corner of the eye with a kind of "rust" colour. This is a condition called Epiphora. Epiphora may come and go or be a permanent condition dependent upon the cause and, depending on just how severe the condition is, it can even cause the skin to become infected and inflamed.

Temporary causes of Epiphora are things like allergies or irritants. Even things such as food colourings in their diets can be enough to cause a mild allergic reaction resulting in a weepy eye and dust in the air on a windy day can easily cause enough irritation to do the job.

Permanent causes are usually more structural in origin such as entropion where the eye lashes rub on the eye and cause irritation, corneal ulcers, glaucoma etc. All dogs have tear ducts, like we do, just at the corner of the eye to allow the nasal passages to remain clear. If these ducts become blocked, either partially or completely, the eyes may weep as a result. It's not uncommon for the tear duct on one side to be blocked and hence you end up with just the one watery eye.

Because there are various possible causes for watery eyes and because eyes are so important, it's always advisable to seek a professional veterinary opinion as to what is going on with your dog. However, on first noticing the problem, simply bathing with tepid salt water two or three times a day may be enough to ease the problem if it is merely being caused by dust, debris or an irritant. Your dog may need eye drops, a change of diet, diagnosis of an allergy, flushing of blocked tear ducts or even surgery if the cause is felt to be structural so please do check things out further with your vet.

EYES – CONJUNCTIVITS

Conjunctivitis can be caused by several different things
including:-

* allergies,
* irritation (dust or smoke),
* foreign bodies like grass seeds,
* hairs or eyelashes facing the wrong way and poking inwards,
* infections
* poor tear production.

Symptoms
* the most common symptom is redness of the eye
* may also be discharge weeping from the eye
* one or both eyes may be affected
* signs of pain/irritation
* the dog my rub his eyes
* even the slightest tinge of green denotes infection and
SHOULD NOT be ignored

You may be able to make your dog a little more comfortable by
bathing the eye using warm/tepid dilute salt water or, if you have
a good first aid kit, by soothing it with the saline solution in your
kit. There are also times when simply using cooled boiled
teabags may soothe and this route is often preferred by people
who like to employ natural methods.

N.B. If you are bathing your dog's eyes, use a fresh cotton wool ball each time you dip into the salt/saline water AND for each eye. It is important not to risk contaminating either the salt water bath or to transfer any bacteria into the other eye and cross contaminate.

Because the eyes are so important, please don't take any chances. Examination of the eye by a vet will help to establish the cause of the conjunctivitis. It may be necessary to send off swabs from the eye to determine exactly what the cause of the problem is. Different bacteria will require different antibiotics to treat them and your vet may wish to find out exactly what the problem is before giving any drops or ointments - the precise ingredients depend on the cause (which is why you should never use drops that have been prescribed for a previous disease or for another dog).

The good news is that most cases of conjunctivitis respond well to treatment. However, those cases which are caused by allergies may require a much more lengthy course of treatment or, in a few cases, it might be necessary to use drops or ointments permanently.

EYES - DOES MY DOG HAVE CATERACTS?

Many dog owners of older dogs think their pet has developed cataracts because they notice that the lens of the eye has taken on a greyish bluish colour at its centre. Any such changes in the eye should **ALWAYS** be checked out by the Vet but, in fact, in the vast majority of cases the condition is not a cataract – it is a much less serious condition called nuclear sclerosis, which is a normal ageing process in dogs.

A simple test at the vets can confirm this. No treatment is needed for nuclear sclerosis and vision is not significantly impaired.

CHAPTER 12 – FEET

FOOT ISSUES

With dogs, problems affecting the feet and nails are pretty common and can range from something as simple as a torn nail or be a symptom of a more general skin disease.

Common causes of foot problems are:-

1. **Parasitic Problems**:
Harvest Mite, Demodectic Mange, Hookworms

2. **Allergic or Irritant Dermatitis**:
Dogs who suffer with allergies often have symptoms of their feet and ears as well as skin problems throughout their body generally. Any chemical that is accidentally walked through may also trigger a pad irritation or dermatitis reaction.

3. **Interdigital Cysts**:
These swellings appear between the toes of certain breeds and can rupture, becoming infected.

4. **Infections**:
The skin between the toes may become infected, causing redness, itchy discomfort and pain. It might be that these infections are associated with foreign bodies such as grass seeds, glass or other objects lodged in the pads or skin. Small wounds can also become infected.

5. **Corns**:
As bizarre as it sounds, dogs can also get corns on their feet. These pads of very hard skin can be very painful to walk on and cause lameness. However, they are easily removed by your vet and should be treated as soon as possible.

6. **Nail Problems**:
Sometimes a bacterial or fungal invasion can cause problems to

flare up and these can often take some time to clear. A lengthy course of treatment is frequently required.

7. **Immune and Autoimmune System Diseases**:
Some immune system problems may initially show themselves as disease of the pads. The may look like weeping ulcers around the end of the pads themselves and can be due to something called Pemphigus which is associated with conditions such as Hypothyroidism. If not the pads, then perhaps the nails or the skin can be affected (this picture was taken from a dog with SLO) where the nails bleed and actually fall off.

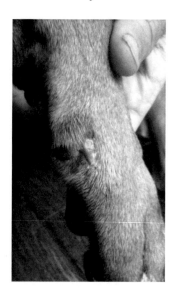

7. **Overgrown or Broken Nails**:
Nails that are left to overgrow, curl into the foot pad or break off are often the source of many a foot problem for our dogs.

8. **Tumours**:

Growths and tumours may appear on the feet. If the tumours are highly malignant, they may spread to underlying bone and possibly elsewhere on the body too.

SYPMPTOMS:

Lameness
Licking/Biting affected foot
Heat
Hair-loss
Weeping/Discharge

DIAGNOSIS:

It is important to examine not only the foot, but also the leg and shoulder, or the rest of the dog's skin if the problem appears to be more generalised.

It may be necessary for the dog to undergo skin scrapings, or biopsies for diagnosis, should a parasitic cause be suspected.

X-Rays may be needed for suspected tumours, foreign bodies, fractures and problems with bone growth/maturity with puppies and adolescent dogs.

The more simple wounds and nail injuries are usually more apparent and easy to spot.

TREATMENT:

It is preferable to be able to treat the specific cause of a foot problem with shampoos and washes applied locally to the affected foot, or with tablets.

Tumours and cysts may require surgery. Foreign bodies which have managed to lodge themselves deep within tissues may also require surgical detection and removal. Some foreign bodies, particularly grass seeds, are prone to migration and may travel quite a distance from their original entry point.

N.B. Always keep foot bandages completely dry. In wet weather, covering the dressing with a plastic bag while the dog goes out to toilet may be necessary. To keep the bag in place, it's handy to fashion some kind of makeshift toggle to wrap around the dog's leg/bag.

This is a version I created myself when Axl had an operation on his stopper pad. It worked a treat. Because of the elastic band, it gripped allowing the tab to be passed through the elastic and could be taken off and re-applied each time he needed to go out in wet conditions, hence keeping the dressing dry.

If shampoos/washes are prescribed, make sure they are used thoroughly. Ensure that the product reaches all the affected areas between the toes and that the contact time is followed as per the instructions.

Excessive licking and chewing should be avoided and it may be necessary for the dog to wear a Buster/Elizabethan collar to keep him from the problem area. Remember, some foot problems can require lengthy courses of treatment and may need to be continued for quite some time, even after the problem appears to have cleared up.

FEET - KEEPING A PAW DRESSING DRY

Why is it, whenever your dog damages his or her paw, the weather always seems to be wet, snowy or muddy? In England, we call this Sod's law! If your dog has a dressing on his paw, it is very important that we can keep a paw dressing dry and clean at all times. If the weather is dry, this is not so much of a problem but if it's not, well, you'll have the devil's own job getting them outside to toilet without them stepping in a puddle, a muddy bit or even just on damp ground.

You can, of course, purchase a medical boot specifically for such occasions. There are various types on the market:

Protective Buster Dog Sock

Buster Dog Socks have a waterproof sole used as a cover for paw bandages. It is made of rib knitted cotton enabling the bandage to breathe and has been reinforced with a hard wearing and waterproof sole. The sock is pulled firmly upwards and fastened with two pieces of plaster tape which are not included.

Healers also do a version of the Dog Sock, again with the non-slip sole. These are easy to slip on and off as they fasten with a Velcro top.

Mikki's version of the boot is for protection only and not for sustained use over long periods. They are used for foot protection whilst out and about or for sole use to cover a foot dressing or wound protection. They have a bonded Vinyl upper with a non-slip PVC sole. Sizing of the product allows for your dog to wear a dressing. Reduce size if not wearing a dressing.

And the final type of protection you might consider is what I can only describe as like a stretchy latex balloon! PAWZ Dog Boots are made of natural rubber and are comfortable for your dog to wear. Unlike other dog boots these stretchy, waterproof dog boots have no padding so your dog can feel the ground beneath him giving him more confidence and ease of movement. The natural rubber is strong and stretchy making them easy to put on and once they are secured on your dog's paws they stay put. Perfect for protecting tender paws at the beach, river, on hot or cold pavements and in rain and snow. Reusable, disposable and waterproof makes these dog boots an economical, convenient and versatile choice. (Remember to order a big enough size to cover the paw AND the dressing, if this is what you intend to use them for).

If you have a small breed dog and are not intending to walk on very rough ground, a condom makes a good waterproof cover or failing that, the finger of a pair of latex gloves or washing up gloves.

You could, of course, simply use a sturdy plastic bag (or if your vet is feeling kind, he may let you have some saline bags) and tape around the top of the leg to hold it in place although you will be going through quite a bit of tape through the course of a day – not to mention the adhesive causing sticky patches on the fur AND the possibility of your dog getting an unintentional leg wax each time you try to remove it!

A good way around this problem is simply to fashion yourself a kind of toggle. A rubber band with a piece of plastic or a bar of some kind attached to it makes an ideal fastening mechanism, as I found when Axl nearly amputated his stopper pad and needed to wear a bandage and dressings for a full 8 weeks during snowy weather.

After a couple of days fighting to keep the bag on his leg, I decided I needed a better solution, and this was it:

Toggle to hold bag in place

Pop the dogs paw into a bag and wrap the band around the top. Next, slot the plastic through the loop in the band and this will secure it without the need for a knot or tape.

Toggle in situ to fasten

This handy little device won't cost you a penny and means you can take the bag on and off as often as you'd like, quick as a flash.

Bag protecting foot dressing

Just as an aside (and probably because I have a sick sense of humour) if your dog has a poorly paw that he cannot put his weight on it properly, ensure he approaches the lamppost from the correct side when he cocks his legs to pee – dogs do tend to fall over if asked to stand on only 2 legs on the same side

FEET - INTERDIGITAL CYSTS

OK, that sounds like a scary medical term, so what exactly are interdigital cysts?

In actual fact, the correct term for this problem is *Interdigital Furunculosis* and you may hear it referred to that way but generally speaking, the word cyst is used instead.

If we break the term down into its component parts, we have *inter* (meaning between), *digital* (meaning toes or fingers) and *cysts* being a closed, bladder-like sac formed in animal tissues, containing fluid or semifluid matter.

Therefore, we are simply talking about a fluid-filled lump between the toes, usually found on the webbing part. These cysts can be incredibly painful for your dog causing discomfort, irritation and limping as the cyst increases in size and occasionally, rupture or discharge their fluid.

Causes:
There are many possible causes for this problem and if it's the first time it has happened, have a look around to see if there is anything different in your dog's surroundings starting with allergies to anything from carpet freshener to even the friction of walking on a new crate tray. Other triggers include excess weight, poor foot conformation, mites, foreign objects, in-growing hairs and yeast infections. Some vets even think that a cyst could really be a fungus that forms between the toes.

Although they are hard to prevent, proper treatment and a good paw exam after each walk should help keep cysts in check. You are looking for any puncture marks that could have arisen on their walk indicating a foreign body or cut, or any unusual substance on their pads. Clean the area thoroughly and watch for any signs of allergies or paw nibbling.

While any breed of dog can experience interdigital cysts, Labradors, Bulldogs, allergy-prone and short-haired varieties are more susceptible, along with overweight/obese dogs.

Treatment:
To start with, if you know that this is definitely the condition you are dealing with, fill the bath with a couple of inches of warm water and Epsom Salts to soak the paw (for about 10 minutes 3-4 times per day). Hopefully, after a couple of days you <u>should</u> start to see some improvement in the severity of the cyst.

If not, then your first port of call should really be your vet for a medicated cream such as a combination of antipruritic, antimicrobial, antifungal, and corticosteroid to treat infections and skin disorders caused by bacterial or candida infections. It is necessary, as a rule, to use a systemic medication, ie treating the whole of the body, and this can be with either oral or injectable medications. If your vet thinks there could be an allergic trigger to the cyst, he may decide to prescribe an antihistamine for your dog too.

Usually, the infection will respond really well to the medication but it <u>can</u> recur very quickly. It's a good idea to treat these infections with an extended course of antibiotics, perhaps for as long as 6-8 weeks, to really get to the bottom of it. Even then, in some cases it may be necessary to return to the treatment every so often and more infrequently still, it may be used continually to control some stubborn conditions.

On top of the medication your vet will prescribe for you, and as suggested above, it can be very beneficial to soak your dog's paws in warm Epsom Salts for around 10 minutes, 3-4 times per day. Remember to pat the area dry when you have finished soaking and don't let Rover drink any while he's marinating!!!

If after several weeks of treatment you are getting to the end of your tether with the constant pills, bathing, buster collars and general unpleasantness of the whole thing, it is tempting to try to look for a "quick fix" such as simply removing the whole cyst and the webbing itself between the toes. Tempting as this is, this will not address the underlying problem. It is important to remember before going down such an invasive route that removal of the webbing between the toes will degrade the integrity of the entire foot forever. A strategy of perhaps going for a biopsy or needle aspirate of the cyst itself will allow your vet to send the sample off to pathology and determine the cause. Once you have the cause, you can hopefully avoid this condition recurring in the future.

Natural Remedies to Help:
It is important that we try to get to the underlying trigger of the cyst as without this knowledge, there is a high likelihood that the cyst will return or may reappear on another toe. However, in the meantime, you can also try the following remedies:

Apple Cider Vinegar is amazing stuff in all kinds of health ways and you can try rinsing the paws with a dilute solution of apple cider vinegar. Please remember that this does sting so if the sores are oozing or open, then it is essential to make the solution VERY dilute indeed – I'm sure you know how it feels if you are eating salt and vinegar crisps and you get a little seasoning on a cut on your finger!

Still sticking with the apple cider vinegar and thinking from a systemic approach, it is also something you could try adding to their food or water (not all dog's like the taste however!!)

You could try applying Manuka honey to the sore (should you be able to police the wound and stop your furry friend from simply licking it off!) or you might try Colloidal Silver, adding a few drops to the sores a couple of times a day.

Please remember that interdigital cysts can be quite stubborn and a professional opinion from your vet should be sought rather than allowing such a painful condition to continue for any length of time.

FEET - POPCORN PAWS!

Does your dog have Popcorn Paws? or Frito Feet? or Dorito Digits???? If you're a dog owner, you'll instinctively know that smell of corn chips or cheesy Doritos, and for a lot of people it's actually quite a comforting smell of just "being home with your dog".

However, you may not be so keen to sniff Fido's feet if you know what the smell actually is.

In a nutshell, that aroma is a combination of yeast, fungus and bacterial microbes (pseudomonas and proteus) that thrive in the cracks of the pads, the nail beds and between the toes. As I'm sure you know, dogs sweat through their feet. If you get sweaty and don't bathe, I'm guessing you don't exactly smell as sweet as a rose either. Add to that the fact that dogs are walking "barefoot" through all types of substances, not all of them clean, and you start to see why their paws are so pungent.

It's also thought to be contributed to by diet. As many people will tell you, you are what you eat, and this plays a part in the smells that emanate from his feet too. As a lot of the smell is due to yeast growth, if you feed your dog with a diet rich in carbohydrates, you are also actually feeding the yeast and therefore encouraging it to thrive. The more the yeast grows, the smellier the paws.

All of this is, of course, a natural process and as such dogs have developed a natural immunity to the build-up of yeast and mites and other occupants of their paws, which shouldn't really cause them any trouble at all. But in some circumstances, it can get out of hand and become more than the dog can naturally deal with by a process of ordinary immunity and his daily cleaning regime. Often, in the summer when temperatures rise or in winter when you have the central heating on, we see an increase in sweaty paws and if this is for any length of time, the smell of Frito feet will get stronger. Added to this, the yeast/bacterial load can cause irritation and could be the root of the problem if your dog is frequently licking and nibbling his paws.

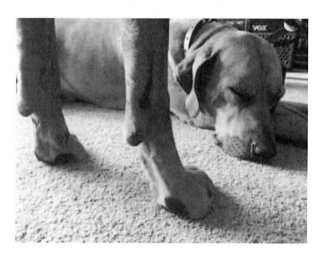

What to do?

Well, we can start with the obvious things such as general grooming. Dogs with longer coats and fur between the toes will generally hang on to the odour more, so the first thing to do is to trim away any fur between the pads as much as possible. If you don't feel confident enough to do this yourself, then have a word with your local groomer who will, I'm sure, be happy to help you with it.

Next, think about cleaning the feet. When you come in the house you either take off your shoes or usually at the very least wipe your feet to save bringing the bacteria on the soles of your feet indoors. A simple wash of the feet when they come in should cut down the build-up of yeast but to start with, washing the paws a couple of times a day for a week or so should break down the smell for you so you can then just keep on top of it.

There are several methods you can use to wash the paws including Apple Cider Vinegar, Hydrogen Peroxide, Epsom Salts, Hibiscrub and of course regular veterinary shampoos. Things like Epsom salts are great as a foot soak after a long walk or hard sporting activities such as agility and flyball (and not just for the dogs I might add)

The important thing is to soak the paws in the solution rather than merely clean off the paw with a wet cloth. The paws come into contact with all sorts of things including pesticides, bacteria, mites, toxins and as the feet sweat, this chemical load can be absorbed into the skin so a good soak of say 2-5 minutes is best to really get in there.

Once you have soaked the feet, dry them thoroughly, particularly between the toes and around the pads themselves so as not to leave a warm, moist environment for any beasties to grow. Remember if you are soaking each paw one at a time in the solution, do all four and then dry them in the order in which they were bathed so that the paw is in contact with the cleaning solution for the longest time possible before drying.

As a quick soothe or spruce up, I find using something like an Aloe Vera spray is great to have on hand – especially if you are away from home say travelling in a motorhome or camping environment. The one I use is this one by Forever Living which I'm sure you'd be able to find easy enough.

And there you have it, nice clean "popcorn-free" feet that even a hound's nose is happy to sleep by.

FEET - NAILS (TRIMMING)

Firstly, if you are on Facebook, check out the group Nail Maintenance for Dogs for some brilliant advice.

Have you ever looked closely at a dog's toe nail? It's got the shiny outer shell bit and running along the inside cavity of the nail is the blood supply called the quick. The ideal length for canine nails is just hovering above the ground when they stand. If the nails touch the floor, they are too long and will push the toes up and make it uncomfortable for them to walk and stand. It's important not to cut too much length off the nail all in one go or you will cut into the quick and it will bleed – a lot!

In order to get the nails nice and short you need to take only a little bit off every couple of days. As you do this, the quick inside the nail will recede a little each time and eventually the dog will end up with comfortable short nails. It's easier if the dog has pale coloured nails so that you can actually SEE the quick running along inside it, but if you just have the black or dark ones to work with, better to do it over time than get it wrong – something which will a) never be forgotten and b) never be forgiven.

A good tip given to me by a groomer was that when you clip the nails and take a sliver of nail off, have a look at that disc of nail and you will notice that there is a white coloured circle in the middle. While the colour of the circle remains white, you know it is safe to take a little more off. Should the colour change, get darker and become black, it is most certainly time to stop as you are right at the very edge of the quick and the next "snip" will cause pain and bleeding.

Occasionally, your dog may wriggle or get distracted while having his nails trimmed and even with the best will in the world, accidents can and do happen, leaving the tip of the nail bleeding. It's best if you have a styptic pencil or some styptic powder in your K9 kit. The styptic products help the bleed to clot very quickly and stop the bleeding.

If you don't have any styptic, there are a couple of other sneaky little alternatives that you can use. One is to dip the end of the bleeding nail in to some ordinary corn starch flour which will quickly seal the bleed. Another trick is to scrape the nail itself down a bar of soap which will plug the bleed and keep the wound clean too – bingo!

If the nail is cracked and keeps getting caught, you can of course opt for a veterinary glue to "stick" the wound together. There are several on the market that are recommended for veterinary use only. The monomeric formulation forms a thin, waterproof adhesion to bond/seal tissue in a variety of injuries. This type of glue is ideal for skin closure, sealing broken nails and generally used as a "quick fix".

Another way, and actually my more favoured way of tackling a nail trim, is to use what is known as the Alternate Cut Line. This essentially is where you clip on a diagonal to remove as much of the overlying pulp as you can from the top of the nail rather than just snipping off the very tip.

Another really good article I've found is by Dogs Naturally Magazine and it's well worth a read too. This one has some good pictures in and also angles to trim the nails at.

http://www.dogsnaturallymagazine.com/trimming-your-dogs-toenails/

One final tip. If you have a long-coated breed, please be careful when clipping (particularly if using a Dremel) not to catch the fur in the rotary stone. A great way around this is to slip a net over the paw first so something like fishnet tights, a hairnet or even the bag that tangerines come in works wonders in keeping the hair under control while allowing the claws to poke through to be trimmed

FEET - NAILS & THE DREMEL

OK, so it seems that Nails are as big a deal to you guys as they are to me, but lots of you are a bit frightened as to how to address using a Dremel to grind back the nails. This is how I do my boys as I find that big, tough claws like that of a Ridgeback can be tricky to clip and often causes the dog discomfort as the clippers squeeze the nail when they cut through.

There are lots of grinders and Dremels on the market. I would recommend a cordless one as this will make your life a lot easier when you don't have to wrestle with a dog AND a cable! The one I have is the Dremel 2800 cordless (this came in at about £90 on Amazon). It is rechargeable and I can usually get all 3 sets of claws done in one charge provided they aren't too long. They also do a Dremel Mini, which I hear good things about, but I've never used this one myself so can't comment on that any further.

Always introduce the dog to the Dremel (or the clippers) over time using positive force-free methods and stacks of treats. You want the dog to see the appearance of the Dremel as a prelude to good things ... not torture. If you are in a bad mood, short of time or suffering with PMT, do the nails another day

Remember that the spinning head of the Dremel should not remain in the same place for longer than 3 seconds as this will heat up and be incredibly uncomfortable for your dog.

I do my dogs standing up with their paws folded under (a little like a Farrier would do when shoeing a horse) so that I can see the pad and entire underside of the paw (I do very little work on them at all from the top or the front – just a tiny bit at the end of the trim).

When you look at the underside of the nail (as per the picture I've attached) you will see there is the hard shell of the nail wall around the outside, then a round part in the middle – just like that of the underside of a horse's hoof really. If you pop your finger on the underside of the nail, you will feel that the centre part is indented. This is the sole of the horn of the nail and I would start by grinding the underside of the claw until the sides of the nail are flat and level with the delve in the middle. It should now feel absolutely flat with no physical indented hole as such in the centre, although you will now be able to make out:

1) a darker shaded circle in the centre (the sole of the horn),
2) a chalky softer bit around that (the outgrown nail bed) and
3) the hard nail on the exterior.

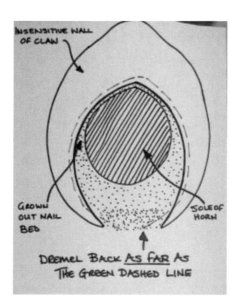

Next, you are going to grind down all around the sides of the nail (as per the dashed green line on the picture). You want to grind back to just before where the grown out nail bed starts. This will mean that you are not grinding into the quick if you:

a) stop at the grown out nail bed and
b) don't grind down further than level with the dip in the middle of the nail as we discussed at the beginning.

Finally, with the dog standing, replace the foot back on the floor to take his weight. You can now simply smooth around the front edge of the very tip of what is left of the nail, giving you a rounded, "stubby" type appearance instead. I am sure many people will have different ways of going about it, but this is the technique that works for me and my lot. I hope it has helped make things a little less scary but do of course let me know if I can help.

If your dog has long fur, try popping his foot in a fishnet stocking so that his nails will poke through the holes, but his feathers will be safely kept within the tights

I would recommend trimming every 10/14 days for maintenance or every 4-7 days for shortening. Each time you trim, they will come back a little shorter and it is better to do the nails regularly in short sessions than to torture your dog and risk over doing it and hurting him.

Please also check out our other blog which addresses the use of clippers

FEET - SNAGGED BROKEN NAILS

Because dogs like to tear around when they play, they do sometimes catch the odd claw on the ground or on loose surfaces – particularly their dew claws. This can be really very painful indeed and even though you may THINK you're helping, if ever there was a time you are likely to be bitten for interfering, this is it. For this reason I would strongly advise that unless you wish to lose a finger, muzzle your furry friend before you inspect the damage.

If you don't have a muzzle, you can always use a length of bandage to wrap around the snout and secure behind your dog's head so he can't remove it. I've already covered "impromptu muzzles" in a past blog.

If there is only a little section of nail hanging off, then as a rule your dog will prefer to nibble and lick at it to deal with it personally.

If, however, it's a bit more serious than that, then really human assistance is going to be vital. If we leave the dog to deal with it for himself, it tends to end in the nail ripping backwards, even further into the quick and boy does that hurt.

Please don't try to use your clippers to sort out the problem. Imagine if you had bent your fingernail back or ripped it a long way down the nail bed. You certainly wouldn't want someone to come along and just cut it off now would you? So I'm afraid it's definitely a case for the vet as if it is very severe, this is something that can only be dealt with under sedation.

If possible, soak the paw in saline (salt water) to get the nail as clean as possible (if the split in the nail goes right down to the quick or the quick is exposed at all, it could very easily become infected and if the infection travels up the nailbed, you will at best be left with a deformed nail and at worse a serious infection which could even travel up the entire leg). For this reason, wound hygiene is paramount and a professional opinion from your Vet should ideally be sought

What you can do is protect them from doing further damage to the injured nail as you take them to the vet. The damaged nail or claw really does need covering up to prevent them nibbling at it in the car. The best tool for the job is nothing more specialised than a sock. Carefully wrap the injured paw in a loose wound dressing and pop a sock over it. Secure the sock in place with some vet wrap high up the leg, and whisk them off to the vet as soon as possible before the situation becomes any worse.

FEET - FOREIGN BODIES

As spring takes hold and moves towards the summer, the plants start to grow again and belting through long grasses and shrubbery can pose an occupational hazard for a dog where foreign bodies (FBs) are concerned.

FB's such as grass seeds can often be found having entered the ears, nose, eyes, vulva or skin and especially the area between the toes. The dog then shakes its head, sneezes, paws at the wound or licks it vigorously due to the discomfort and possible infection it can cause.

The body tries to eliminate the object by creating a local bursting abscess. If this is the case, keep the wound clean until it heals by bathing in salt water (a simple dilution of one tea spoon of salt dissolved in a large cup of warm water will suffice) or with something like Hibiscrub which is an anti-microbial skin cleanser (remember if you are using Hibiscrub, this must be diluted until it only has a very slight tinge of pink colouration to it (a ratio of no more than 1:10). If left too concentrated, it will sting the wound and be very uncomfortable for your dog). Do not allow your dog to lick or nibble the area (if you have problems keeping his lordship off the wound, check out our blog on preventing licking).

Please remember that foreign bodies such as a grass seed (and even a microchip) can migrate throughout the body so the FB itself may not actually have come to rest at the place where it entered in the first place. For this reason, if you can see an entry wound but cannot detect the foreign body, please do check above and around the wound site in case it has migrated elsewhere. You are looking for swelling or hardness of an area, redness, warmth or oozing of any wet or pus-like material. If the seed has infected the tissues, don't be surprised if the foot itself swells up – this can be quite alarming as the paw and leg can swell to sometimes 3 or 4 times the normal size when infection sets in. Obviously, should you see any swelling or detect any warmth, please see your vet urgently. Do not leave a FB in your dog's skin.

If the dog is limping and you cannot see the object or any sign of where it may be, bathe the foot several times daily in tepid salt water (a teaspoon to a cup as mentioned above) or Epsom Salts, until the object comes to the surface of the skin and can be easily removed.

Application of a dab of Manuka honey will keep the wound clean and also help the skin to heal naturally (provided your dog doesn't decide to lick it off) in which case, simple cleansing until it is fully healed should be just fine – again salt water or Hibiscrub is great for this.

Keep a close eye on your dog from the point of view of the abscess or swelling itself, but also watch out for any changes in his behaviour which may alert you to infection spreading within his system.

N.B. Grass seeds have barbed tips so may be difficult to remove, in which case always take your dog to your vet for professional attention if you cannot get it out simply by yourself. Excessive picking and poking can make the situation worse.

FEET - STOPPER PAD INJURIES

Stopper Pad Injuries (or more technically, injuries to the carpal pad) can occur in various ways.

We often see friction burns to the stopper pad in dogs who compete high speed sports such as Flyball. When the dog stops swiftly, bounces and turns himself off the box for the second leg of his run, it's not unusual for them to damage the pad and/or strain the ankle joint if they don't get it quite right. The same injury can happen during enthusiastic play or chasing a ball on hard surfaces.

Another injury to the stopper pad can be received when dogs are tearing through undergrowth in the woodland. Often when chasing each other (or an unsuspecting rabbit), leaping over trees and shrubs with little or no regard for their footing, sharp edges and thorns can easily catch the flesh of the pad or dewclaw itself and lacerate it.

This injury happened to Axl many years ago now while chasing a squirrel through a wood. It ran up a tree and when he got to the bottom, he put his paw down right on top of a broken bottle and virtually severed his stopper pad entirely from his leg, necessitating emergency surgery and 8 weeks of dressings and treatment.

Once the pad dressings came off, I was very cautious for quite some time while out in the woods in case he caught it again. Stopper pad protectors were our lifeline.

So what can we do to protect our dogs if these are the kind of activities they love to do? Well, there are some brilliant little protector pads you can get which the dogs can wear for doing things like flyball or woodland walks. These same nifty covers are also great if your dog has already injured his stopper pad or dew claw area as they will protect the pad after the dressings are removed and until you are confident that the wound has fully healed.

These ones are available through www.CanineCavern.co.uk

Arthritis joints, strains and sprains can be supported and prevented by such covers.

FEET - CUT PAW PAD

It's not always obvious <u>when</u> a dog cut's his paw and often you might not notice unless you actually see him limping or spot blood on the ground. Sometimes, it's not until he comes home or you give his muddy paws a rub over that you notice the problem. The important thing is to start your treatment of it as soon as you do actually notice.

When dealing with a bleed, we always go through the **SEEP** checklist as follows:-

Firstly, if you are in any doubt as to whether you may get bitten as you try to help your dog, muzzle him first or take him directly to the vet. We certainly don't want another injury.

S = Sit or Lie the dog down so that the injured area can be raised.

E = Elevate the injured limb above the level of the heart to slow down the blood loss. Fluids do not like to go uphill, so if you can raise injured area so that the exit wound is above, the bleeding will slow down. In the case of an injured paw for example, the dog will need to lie down so that he can take the weight off the limb and you can raise it for him. If the injury was a cut to the head, then we would wish to place the dog in a sitting position so that his head becomes the highest part of his anatomy.

E = Examine the paw thoroughly. The cut may be a simple surface wound or it may be a deeper slice. There may be debris or even a thorn or piece of glass still left in the wound.

P = Pressure is necessary if the paw is bleeding. If it is not bleeding, then do not apply pressure to the wounded limb.

Treatment

Check the wound for any thorns or glass or splinters and gently remove them – you may need to use tweezers, a torch and a magnifying glass. Once you have removed any larger bits, you can carefully wash the area with mild antibacterial soap and water or a dilute solution of salt water. If the area is simply scuffed with no actual bleed present, then Hibiscrub antibacterial solution can be used to clean the surface of the skin. If you are going to use Hibiscrub, please ensure that you dilute it down thoroughly until it is only just a faint pink colour. If you do not dilute it sufficiently, it will sting and be very painful.

Next, if possible, bathe the foot in just warm Epsom salts for ten minutes, swilling the water across the wound as you go in an effort to remove any remaining smaller bits of debris.

Once you have soothed the pad in the tepid water and you are confident you have removed any bits of dirt or grit, dry the foot completely. It is advisable not to use a fabric cloth or cotton wool to dry the limb as this may leave fibres in the wound – always use a paper towel and try not to press on the wound itself. The bathing routine should be repeated twice a day until the wound has healed.

If you have any an antibiotic, such as Neosporin with pain relief, or failing that antibacterial cream, Aloe Vera balm or Manuka honey, this can be gently dabbed onto the wound itself. Each time you bathe the pad, be sure to dry it completely and reapply the ointment.

If the wound is deep or severe, you will need to protect the wound further by wrapping it in gauze to prevent further contamination. It is important to make sure that you do not wrap the gauze or dressing too tightly. There should be no flesh bulging at the top of the dressing and the limb should not feel too "firm" when you gently squeeze it. If there is no "give" in your hand, you have done it too tightly and may be cutting off the blood supply to the paw.

Remember to try to keep your dog from paying too much interest to the injury. If you are unable to stop him licking and worrying the wound, it might be necessary to use a Buster/Elizabethan collar.

It is important to keep a close eye on just how well the pad is healing and, as you will be bathing and treating the wound twice a day, you may need to take a picture of it so you can be sure if there has been improvement or not (often if we look at things too regularly it is difficult to tell if there have been any changes).

If you think the wound is not healing, is worsening, is causing the dog to limp or be in more pain, or is showing any signs of heat or infection, do not delay in seeking a professional opinion from the vet. It might be that a foreign body has been missed and is still in the wound and, if left, this could cause further and more serious problems.

FEET - BANDAGING A PAW

Bandaging a leg is pretty easy, but bandaging a paw is a little more tricky. Not only do you have a wriggly dog in discomfort to deal with, but you also have the difficulty of holding the paw with one hand, bandaging with the other, tucking the edges in, keeping it on, making sure it's not too tight and restricting blood flow and not so loose it falls off – as I said, TRICKY!

I was asked today how to do it by one of our followers while she waited for her vet appointment (as per our instructions, Rhodes 2 Safety training is not INSTEAD of seeing a vet – it is to keep the situation under good control UNTIL your vet can see you)

So, when I tried to tell her in a message, it soon became clear that describing it isn't easy so, instead, we've done a few photographs so you can follow the process. The dressing I have used to do it is vet wrap but this was only so that the lines of the bandage would show up clearly. If you are actually doing it for real, please first use an ordinary fabric wound dressing or bandage so as to prevent you pulling it too tightly around the paw and restricting blood flow.

HERE'S HOW:

*Clean the wound thoroughly
(ideally with saline solution – salt water).

*Pat the wound dry

*Apply Manuka honey or antibacterial cream to a square of gauze and place directly on top of the wound (the antibacterial cream/Manuka will prevent the gauze from sticking to the wound)

*Place some cotton wool between the toes of the paw to prevent sweating/rubbing

*Hold the bandage at the ankle, roll down the front of the paw and back under again.

Tuck in one side corner edge and come back down the front on a diagonal.

Come under the paw at the ankle, tuck in the second edge, then back up on a diagonal on the other side

repeat coming under the paw to the ankle, down the front on a diagonal

behind the ankle, down the front again on a diagonal in a figure of 8 action so you get the criss-cross lines on the front

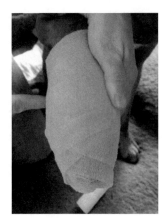

Once you have the paw bandaged securely, finish the dressing behind the leg and secure with a tape or, if you have had to use vet wrap, it should stick to itself in place. (We finish at the back of the leg to stop the dog finding a corner to be able to pick and pull at)

It might be necessary to then pop a child's sock over the top and secure above the ankle bone to make sure the dog cannot get the dressing off (though I'll bet they will try!)

It is important to remember that this dressing is a temporary measure only to protect the paw and save your home from being covered in blood. You MUST see a vet as soon as possible to have the wound checked as it may need further irrigation, removal of debris or dirt and perhaps a stitch or too as well. He may need pain killers and antibiotics too.

Check the dressing REGULARLY to ensure that the paw is not swelling. If the paw does swell, the dressing which may have seemed perfect in tension to begin with, may become too tight and this is incredibly dangerous for your dog. If you are in any doubt at all, please release the pressure a little and re-do the dressing.

FEET - LICKING THE PAWS .... *Why?*

This is one of the most common questions I get asked and, in all honesty, there is no simple straight-forward answer. First we need to establish whether the dog is licking his paws because there is a medical condition causing his discomfort or whether it is simply a behaviour he's got himself into a habit of doing.

So, first things first – we need to try to rule out an underlying medical reason for the licking and to do that, we'll need to employ a little detection and diagnosis session:

* Which paw is being licked – is it one in particular, just the front ones, or all four?

* Is the dog limping?

* Is there any redness, hair-loss, swelling, flaky skin, weeping or bleeding to be seen?

* Are there any lumps, tumours or cysts between the pads or around the toes?

* Are the toe nails too long or splintered? (even a tiny hairline crack can cause trouble)

* Have they walked through a corrosive substance or irritant causing a burn to the skin?

* Have they perhaps twisted an ankle and the pain is radiating causing them to lick?

* Could your dog have arthritis which, though not visible, can cause pain/irritation to him?

* Could there be a fungal or parasitic cause such as Harvest Mites/Mange?

* Could your dog be experiencing an allergy either topically or in his diet?

* Does your dog have ear problems? Often dogs with allergies suffer ear problems too.

* Is there a foreign body in the pad or between the toes such as a grass seed or a thorn?

(if so, bathe the foot several times daily in tepid salt water – a teaspoon to a cup – or Epsom Salts, until the object comes to the surface of the skin and can be easily removed.) A dab of Manuka honey will keep the wound clean and also help the skin to heal naturally. Remember, grass seeds have barbed tips so may be difficult to remove in which case, always take your dog to your vet for professional attention.)

Often the cycle of itching and licking can be self-propagating; the dog has itchy feet so he licks, the licking causes trauma to the skin surface making it sore, the soreness becomes itchy causing the dog to lick and so on.

Have a think back. It may be that none of the problems above are present, but have they happened in the past? Remember that a foot-licking problem can originally stem from a medical one and later become a habit or a compulsive behaviour.

So, if the dog is licking and you cannot see any specific cause or foreign object, it may simply be a habit that he has got into. Some dogs when relaxing, bored or stressed lick their paws or even chew their nails. When there is no apparent cause for the behaviour, it really is time to see your vet as he will likely be the only one to fully determine what is going on with your dog's feet.

Depending on the diagnosis your vet makes, there are various treatments which may be employed to resolve the licking:

For infections and some cases of allergies, medication or dietary changes may be made although allergy testing may be necessary to get to the bottom of this cause. It could be as simple as changing your food to raw if the maize or grain is causing an allergic reaction as it does in so many dogs. Perhaps, if you already feed raw, the chickens in your dog's diet may be maize fed and THIS could be the allergic connection? Perhaps it could be a yeast problem that your dog is experiencing

Where pain (be it strains, sprains or arthritis) are the cause, analgesia will be given which should reduce the licking markedly in a very short time.

Problems with the nails may require a professional trim if they've been allowed to get too long and are either curling round and ingrowing or simply pushing the dog's toes up into an unnatural and painful position. If the nails are fractured or splintered, it may be necessary to remove the nail completely, under sedation.

Growths, tumours or abscesses are usually treated surgically. It is likely that a biopsy may be taken and sent off for histological review so that the type of tumour can be diagnosed. Not all tumours are dangerous and some may simply be removed and never cause another moment's problem.

If the foot-licking starts in summer, it could be due to burns from walking on hot pavements in the summer heat.

If the behaviour starts in winter, it could be due either to cold burns from walking on ice or even coming into contact with anti-freeze or de-icer which may have been spilled on the pavement/road by a clumsy motorist.

Where the licking is a habitual activity, behavioural modification will need to be undertaken but this takes time and dedication to alter. Often the use of distraction techniques and games alongside the modification can help, but always seek a professional opinion to guide you through this type of resolution.

HEAD - FACIAL PARALYSIS

Droopy face on one side? Scary right? Sometimes, you may notice that your dog's face is droopy on one side – perhaps he can't blink properly or maybe one of his lips is saggy. There may be excess drooling from that side and possibly the dog finds it difficult to eat his food without it falling out of the side of his mouth.

In humans, this kind of paralysis or drooping may well indicate a stroke but in dogs, that's not really the case. It is an ailment more commonly experienced by dogs than cats, and usually occurs in middle aged dogs of say 5 years or older.

Some breeds are more susceptible than other breeds and these include Cocker Spaniels, Pembroke Welsh Corgis, Boxers and English Setters but again, any dog can be affected. Facial nerve paresis typically only affects one side of the face, although cases of bilateral paralysis have occurred which make it difficult to detect unless it is really pronounced as you have no "good side" to compare with.

Possible Causes:

Ear Infection – a middle or inner ear infection (also known as an otitis media-interna), is the most common known cause of drooping of a dog's facial expression. If an ear infection is confirmed by your vet, it is likely that he will be prescribed a course of antibiotics which may be for as long as 6 weeks or more. This course of treatment should, hopefully, resolve the droopy appearance but it is very important that you clean your dog's ears frequently from then on once he is healed, and talk to your vet at the very first sign of any ear problems in the future.

Thyroid or Nervous System Disorders – A thyroid problem such as hypothyroidism (see Hypothyroidism blog) includes symptoms such as facial paralysis. However, if your dog is suffering with this condition, it will likely be experiencing many of the other signs and symptoms too such as lethargy, decreased appetite, increased weight gain and a significant change in the quality of his coat such as dulling or even balding.

There are also a number of nervous system disorders which could possibly be responsible for drooping of the face. Your vet may decide to test for a brain stem disorder, just in case.

Idiopathic – When a condition is given the tag "idiopathic" it merely means that the cause is uncertain and unfortunately, many cases of canine facial paralysis fall into this category. A similar condition exists in humans called Bell's Palsy (something I myself have experienced and lasted for a good 4 weeks or more before things began to return to normal).

Sometimes it clears up on its own. Sometimes it may return. Sometimes the droopy appearance may stay with the dog permanently and require eye drops to lubricate the eye if the dog is unable to blink satisfactorily for himself.

If you notice that your dog's face is not quite right, please have him checked over by your vet so that appropriate treatment can be given.

HEAD - STROKE

When we refer to a Stroke in dogs, this is not actually the same as what we understand as a stroke in humans – it's just a kind of shorthand that vets sometimes use to help us understand. In actual fact, it is Vestibular Syndrome, which is caused by damage to the inner ear or the brain which leads to very characteristic symptoms, especially in older dogs (known as Geriatric Vestibular Syndrome). The symptoms do, however, usually begin to ease over a couple of days.

Diagnosis:
To diagnose the problem in dogs over 10 years of age, the vet will usually check your dog's ears to make sure there is no obvious disease which could account for the problem. He may run some blood tests, a urine analysis or perhaps even a CT scan if your surgery is hi-tech enough to offer such investigations.

Symptoms to look for:
Head tilt
Lack of co-ordination
Rapid eye movements
Vomiting

In more severe cases, vestibular syndrome can also cause the dog to fall over, roll or even circle continuously. Because each side of the brain controls the opposite side of the body, the circling and falling over will always occur in the same direction and will mirror the side of the brain which has been damaged.

Treatment:

In the initial days of the "stroke", care and patience will be needed to keep the dog from bumping into things or hurting himself if he falls or rolls over – confining him to a single room or crate with no obstacles in is often the kindest action until his condition improves. It might be necessary to feed by hand and also to support his weight as he goes out to toilet – often the use of a blanket as a sling to help him stand is all that is required, and of course the opportunity to go out with your help, say 4 or 5 times a day.

Improvement can be expected in pretty much all cases but occasionally, the head tilt may remain permanently. Other than drugs to ease the initial nausea, no treatment really seems to be particularly effective and the condition usually improves by itself in 2-4 weeks.

HEAD - HEAD PRESSING

Have you ever noticed your dog (or cat) sitting or standing with his head pressed against the wall? Perhaps he presses it against the floor or other solid object and stands/sits still in this very odd position? Don't confuse the normal "head-butting" that they often do to your shins, that's just dog stuff; we mean the full on standing with their head down, and the top of their skull pressed hard against a surface. This compulsive behaviour over extended periods of time should never be ignored.

If you EVER notice your dog doing this, please take him to your vet immediately to be checked out. This could be a very serious problem, be it neurological, infection, tumour, viral, trauma, toxic poisoning, metabolic problem or many other things.

HEAD INJURIES

Head injuries in dogs can be caused in a number of ways; from road traffic accidents, falls from a height say from a cliff top, collisions perhaps during normal play or Flyball activities or even infections which cause the brain to swell up.

As you'd imagine, any head injury should be treated very carefully and promptly so our aim is to get the dog to the vet as quickly as possible – remembering to ring first to let them know you are coming.

There are several different types of head injury which I'll list for you below, but really the advice would be that any time you think there has been contact with the head, take no chances.

Contusion (Bruising)
* No loss of consciousness
* Dog remains dazed, wobbly and disorientated
* The condition clears gradually

Concussion (shaking of the brain)
* Loss of consciousness
  (With mild concussion there is only a brief loss of consciousness)
* When consciousness is regained the dog exhibits signs as for a contusion.
* With a severe concussion the dog may be unconscious for hours or even days.
* Full recovery may take weeks or months.

Seizures
* Seizures can occur at the time of the injury or any time after.
* Seizures at the time of injury increase pressure in the skull & make the injury worse.

Compression (Brain swelling & bleeding)
* The increased pressure on the brain is accompanied by low levels of consciousness.
* Coma is common with compression injuries.
* Death may likely occur due to cardiac arrest and poor respiratory effort.
* One pupil may be dilated and unresponsive to light.
* There may be weakness involving one or more limbs

What you should do

* If it is safe, do not move him – keep him calm/warm/still and call the vet **URGENTLY**.
* Apply a clean dressing to any injury
  (do NOT plug a leaking ear, but cover it to prevent infection getting in).
* If it is NOT safe, move him limiting movement as much as possible
  (flat lift/log roll).
* Ideally, use a board, keeping him as still and straight as you can.
* Use a flat lift or log roll to put him on the board.
* Keep him warm & prevent rolling: wrap a blanket/towel around him AND the board.
* If you have no board, 2 people can hold the 4 corners of a blanket or jacket.

* If unconscious, gently extend his neck and pull his tongue forward.
* Monitor his breathing/heart rate throughout.
* Perform artificial respiration or CPR as appropriate.
* Phone ahead and take the animal to the **vet ASAP**.

INFECTIONS - PARVOVIRUS

Parvovirus is a word that strikes fear into the heart of every dog owner, but many people don't actually know how to recognise the signs, how it is spread or what to do if you think your dog may have contracted it. So, here's a brief overview to help make sense of what is a very serious disease for our furry friends.

Canine Parvovirus is an incredibly contagious disease. Some cells in the body reproduce rapidly and it is these types of cells that the virus tends to attack – cells such as those lining the gastrointestinal tract.

Once the dog is infected, the virus is deposited in the stool for up to several weeks.

The disease is transmitted by oral contact with infected faeces but it can be carried on the dog's hair and feet, as well as on contaminated crates, shoes, and other objects.

When the dog licks the faecal material off hair, feet, or anything that came in contact with infected faeces, he acquires the disease.

Although puppies 6 to 20 weeks of age are most at risk, Parvo can affect dogs of all ages. (It is said that "black and tan" dogs such as Doberman Pinschers and Rottweilers appear more at risk than most breeds, although the reason for this is unknown)

The illness usually starts to show itself some 4-5 days after contamination.

Signs of Parvovirus include:-
Depression
Vomiting
Diarrhoea (which is profuse and contains blood/mucus)
Dehydration
There is sometimes, but not always, a high fever
Puppies with severe abdominal pain exhibit a "tucked-up" abdomen

Dog owners should suspect Parvovirus in all pups if they develop sudden vomiting and diarrhoea and contact their emergency vet straight away.

Treatment:-
Hospitalisation for intensive veterinary management.
Correction of dehydration and electrolyte imbalance (may take 3-5 days).
Intravenous fluids/medication to control vomiting and diarrhoea.
More severe cases may require blood plasma transfusions and other intensive care.
Antibiotics will be given to prevent septicaemia and other bacterial complications.

Puppies and dogs should not eat or drink until the vomiting has stopped. They do, however, still need fluid support during that time and this is one of the main reasons for the need to hospitalise the animal.

Outcome:
Many factors play a role in the final outcome such as which strain of Parvo has been contracted, the age of the dog, its immune status and how quickly diagnosis and treatment was administered.

With good veterinary care, most puppies will recover without complications.

Prevention:
Because Parvovirus is extremely resistant to most cleaning products and can in fact survive for months on crates, floors and other surfaces in general, it is advised to thoroughly clean and disinfect the quarters of infected animals with household bleach in a 1:32 dilution. The bleach must be left on the contaminated surface for 20 minutes before being rinsed.

N.B. Jeyes Fluid is often what people think of when cleaning contaminated areas. Please be aware that if the dog walks on it before it is dry, it is very dangerous as it absorbs through the surface of the pads and can actually poison your dog. Please always ensure you rinse the area and dry it thoroughly before any animal is allowed to walk on the surface, whatever you choose to use.

INFECTIONS - KENNEL COUGH

This is a highly infectious disease. It is caused by a mixture of bacteria/viruses all at the same time. It can be picked up from anywhere that dogs congregate such as dog shows, training classes, grooming parlours and even vet surgeries and not merely in boarding/rescue kennels as the name would imply. The disease is transmitted in infected coughed breath and via feeding utensils. If you have more than one dog in your "pack", remember to ensure the unaffected dogs have a different water bowl to drink from, just in case.

About 3-4 days after exposure, the dog will develop a cough. It is usually a dry, loud cough which is worse on excitement. The bouts of coughing may be quite extensive and occasionally cause the dog to retch clear fluid or foam and can make owners think the dog has something stuck in his throat. There may also be a mild nasal discharge but other than this, in MOST cases, the dog is well in himself otherwise – usually serious cases are restricted to very old, young or sick animals, or animals who suffer with respiratory or heart problems.

Generally diagnosis is fairly easy as, provided there is no reason to suspect Distemper, most dogs will have been in contact with a coughing dog within the previous week or so. **Gently touching the windpipe usually produces a bout of coughing**.

It is unusual for the dog to require medication for this condition although it may take a few weeks for it to resolve. You can use cough syrup such as Benylin (check with your vet regarding the dosage as this will vary from breed to breed and the age/weight of the dog) or you could even try applying some Vicks Vapo Rub to a bandana for your dog to wear to help ease his chest. If coughing is severe and frequent, drugs to suppress the cough can be administered to make the dog more comfortable. As pressure on the windpipe can trigger a bout of coughing, it is often a good idea to switch to a harness or head collar for walks until the dog has recovered.

Another more natural aid to consider is Coltsfoot which I am reliably informed works well for kennel cough. Simply use the tincture and put a few drops in the dogs' water bowls.

NB Please remember that this is a highly contagious disease and the animal should be kept away from other dogs until he is completely well.

INFECTIONS - YEAST IRRITATIONS

Yeast Infection in Dogs can cause them to be very uncomfortable indeed. It can strike in various places including within the ear itself or anywhere on the skin of the dog. Wherever it appears, it will make your dog miserable.

SKIN:

If the infection is affecting the skin, it may appear reddened or have areas where the skin itself seems thickened or have scabby or balding areas. These infections are usually very itchy for your dog and if the dog scratches a lot to try to relieve himself, it may well bleed too.

EARS:

So, what kind of things can cause an ear infection – is it always down to yeast? Well, in a word no. Although yeast infections are often brought about by allergies to food, feathers, cleaning products, medication or intolerances of things like cereal etc, there are lots of triggers that can be responsible for ear problems with your dog, not just overproduction of yeast. These include such causes as bacteria, something lodged within the ear canal such as debris, water or a grass seed for instance. It could even be caused by a ruptured eardrum.

The ear is split into two parts; the inner ear is, as you would expect, within the head of the dog and comprises of the tube that runs all the way down (the Eustachian tube) and the eardrum itself. The outer ear is the part you can see inside the flap of the ear. If the infection has taken hold in the outer ear you will usually be able to see a black, tarry, wax-type substance forming and gunking up within all the little folds of the outer ear. Often you will be able to smell a strong "sour" smell from the ear itself, which is a sure sign.

An inner ear infection is by far the most dangerous as this can, in extreme cases, lead to deafness in your dog. Because it is usual for an inner ear infection to occur and be triggered when there is an outer ear problem too, it is important to treat any outer ear problems as soon as possible to prevent escalation into the inner ear too.

If your dog has an overgrowth in the amount of yeast in his ear, there are several tell-tale signs you can look out for:-

* Shaking his head
* Flapping his ears
* Rubbing his head on the carpet or furniture
* Scratching his ears with his paws
* Tilting his head
* Sour smell from the ear

WHICH DOG SUFFERS?

Because yeast thrives in warm, damp or moist environments, dogs with long, floppy ears often suffer the most with this problem. Breeds like the Spaniel, Basset Hound, Beagle or Rhodesian Ridgeback for example have the perfect ear to create yeast-heaven. Some breeds, for instance the Schnauzer, grow hair inside their ears and this can become matted and also act as a good breeding ground for yeast and bacteria. (If you have a breed which grows hair in his ears, then remember to have your groomer pluck this regularly for him). Add in to the mix a dog who likes to go into the water such as a Cocker or Springer Spaniel, and it's not surprising that these breeds need constant vigilance to prevent a yeast infection taking hold.

HOW DO WE TREAT IT?

Your vet will need to examine the ear of your dog to determine if there is anything in there that shouldn't be such as a foreign body, mites, water or some other irregular finding. He will also be checking to see that the eardrum is neither perforated nor inflamed. He will take a sample from the ear and likely both look under the microscope and send the swab away for culture to see what grows from it. Taking a swab is very important because if it is decided that antibiotics are required, it will be essential to give the right antibiotic to deal with the specific infection – not all antibiotics are suitable for every different strain of 'nasty'.

Once the vet has determined which part of the ear is infected, he will usually prescribe a course of antifungal cream to rub on the skin of the ear. If the infection is within the ear itself, then it is more likely to require a course of antibiotic tablets to treat it. Please be sure to administer the medication exactly as prescribed by your vet. Failure to complete the course of medication may result in the infection coming back.

REMEDIES:

Zymox Otic Enzymatic Solution with Hydrocortisone is a really good product for yeast of the ears and one which I personally wouldn't be without. After suffering for 18 months on and off and spending £££ on vets and tests and swabs and antibiotic drops, this stuff cleared up the problem within a week and with only 1 recurrence the following year, we've now been free of any problems for 7 years straight! This product is applied daily for a week (or two at most) WITHOUT cleaning the ears. It works through the action of antifungal enzymes that literally break up wax and discharge.

For dogs with skin yeast infections you can try products such as topical sprays that go directly on the skin itself or a shampoo that uses antifungal medication in their approach. In severe cases however, oral medications such as Ketaconazole or Fluconazole are recommended to help alleviate the infection.

To instantly soothe the itchy feeling and dryness, a good product to try is Aveeno – either as a colloidal oatmeal shampoo, or a moisturizing cream. This range of products is kind and gentle to the skin but still has the soothing relief you would hope for. Great for both yourself or your dog and available readily in pharmacies and supermarkets.

PREVENTION:

Prevention is usually better than the cure and there are many specifically designed cleaning products on the market for your dog. Some are to be used just when you see any residue appearing while others are to be used as part of your regular hygiene routine. You may prefer to go down the more natural route and seek out remedies such as those that use Apple Cider Vinegar in their make-up. Check out our blog on ear cleaning for further information.

CHAPTER 15:   MISCELLANEOUS   PG

MISCELLANEOUS - STORING MEDICATION SAFELY

Today I received a message from one of our followers asking me to do a blog as a reminder about safely storing medication. She wrote that "one of my clients this week had to take their puppy to the vets because she got hold of a packet of Ibuprofen. She spent the night at the vets & came home with meds, but the long term damage is unknown as yet."

How could I say no?

When we have a baby or young child, it's drummed in to us that we should always do a mini risk assessment in every room that child may go in to. You wouldn't leave a bottle of bleach or detergent where a toddler could get it, nor a bottle of alcohol that could be mistaken for pop or juice and we definitely know anything that looks like sweeties may as well have a flashing neon sign saying "eat me" on it! For this reason, the message about safe storage of medicines has filtered through to us as parents.

But it's not only children who fall into the category of needing to be protected from their own inquisitive nature. The same is true for dogs and puppies. Often, our babies and children may have long since grown up and our children moved out . As such, all those safeguards about medications and dangerous substances may have slipped our minds too.

It's important to remember that dogs, as well as young children, learn by touch, smell and taste so invariably a new thing is shoved in the mouth and chewed, licked or swallowed as one of their best testing methods and what might be safe for us is very often anything but for our dogs.

Please consider the kind of things you regularly leave lying about the home or in your garden. The oddest of things can be a hazard:-

Medication
Contraceptive Pills
Hair Straighteners
Perfume
Shampoo/Soap
Cleaning Products
Toilet Cleaning Brush
ANYTHING in a squeezable tube
Alcohol
Weed Killer
Pesticides
Lawn Feed
Slug Pellets
Dog Food in sacks
Matches/Lighters
Plugs/Cables

Food from the cupboards/fridge need a lock if you live with a safe-cracker!

All these things should be safely out of the reach of little fingers, tongues, muzzles, paws, claws and fur-coated Houdinis! If things cannot be put up high (perhaps if you have a counter-surfer who explores all surfaces) then pop them in a cupboard and apply a cupboard lock to the outside – these are readily available on the internet or in mother and baby shops. There are many types including a multi lock that fixes to everything including cupboards and fridges to stop your furry thief helping himself to the contents of your fridge! I do know of a friend who had to buy one of these after her Jack Russell broke into a cupboard and licked clean the entire contents of a deep fat fryer!

Above all, please don't stop thinking about what you have around just because the kids are grown or because your dog is no longer a puppy. Dogs do the strangest things out of the blue when the fancy takes them and as this lady found out, even a packet of Ibuprofen can seem mighty attractive if they are left unsupervised.

If they do manage to come across something they shouldn't, check out our poisoning blog with the actions you need to take IMMEDIATELY.

MISCELLANEOUS –

WHY IS MEDICATING YOUR DOG A BATTLE?

Giving a Pill or bandaging a wriggly furball can be tricky!

This weekend we were training in Horsham. A beautiful day meant as we set up, we had the doors open so the dogs could trot in and out and enjoy the garden. True to form, when Chi came back in, I noticed that he had been bitten 5-6 times on his side and these bites had swelled up making his fur stick up, forming little raised blotches. Typical!

As I know that Piriton antihistamine has been OK'd for Chi to use by our vet, it was a simple enough case just to nip to the first aid kit in the car and administer a tablet to counteract the reaction. By this time, our class had already arrived and so we used the situation as a teaching session.

I popped my finger behind his canine fang which encouraged him to open his mouth. Using the cue "open" as I did so, Chi obliged without any trouble and allowed me to insert the antihistamine into his mouth and place it on the hump at the very back of his tongue. I then quickly withdrew my hand, closed his mouth and gently massaged his throat and gave him a love ...... simple!

Once I had finished, I looked up and saw a sea of big-eyed, impressed faces looking on, all of which were remarking how good he was to allow me to do this, and how their dogs would have put up one hell of a fight if they had to do the same thing.

Later in the course, we came to the part on demonstrating how to apply a wound dressing to an injury. This time my "patient" was Axl who lay very still while I applied the wound bandage and then the pressure dressing over the top. Again, when I looked up, the faces were all saying how easy I made it look and how they were sure that doing such a thing on their own dog would be much, MUCH harder because they were unlikely to be quite so amenable to this kind of treatment .... and that got me thinking.

"WHY is it such a battle to medicate or treat your dog?"

I guess the reason is purely down to how often you've practiced or carried out the procedure and how comfortable your dog is with what you are doing to him. So why wait until he is ill? Why wait until he is stressed and anxious and the treatment you are giving is very important to his wellbeing, before you embark on applying these techniques for the first time?

I would suggest using times when you are already going to be rewarding your dog with any old titbit as an easy way to introduce them to taking a pill. If you have a tasty morsel you are going to break in to bits to give him, why not give one treat normally, the next as if it's a pill, then another normally again so he gets used to the procedure in a positive way. Done like this, when you actually NEED to give a tablet, he'll be more than willing to participate with you.

Remember to assign a cue to the behaviour too so he associates that word with the behaviour you are doing, and then he knows what's coming.

I would also suggest practicing things like bandaging every now and then on an evening when you are just sitting together in a relaxed atmosphere. Doing it when there is no pressure at all to get it right means you will both be more chilled.

Remember to practice on different legs and different paws, so no matter which limb is injured in the future, he'll be happy to let you do what you need to. There's a reason I "make it look easy" and it's not because I'm any better at it than you are (I just get a whole lot more practice!)

Check out our other blogs on taking tablets and liquid medication too.

MISCELLANEOUS - GIVING LIQUID MEDICATION

Liquid Medication – Some dogs, no matter how hard you try, just refuse to take their medication in tablet form. If this is the case, you may be able to crush up the pill, mix it with sugar water and syringe it sideways into the mouth. Melted ice-cream and sugar water to help raise blood sugar levels in a dog with hypoglycaemia, and also cough syrups can be given in this way too but you should always check with your vet before using any medication which has not been specifically prescribed for your animal.

NB Not all tablets can be crushed and administered as above. Some tablets have a specific "enteric" coating on them which is designed to keep the tablet intact until it reaches the stomach. Often these types of medication may irritate the digestive tract if they start to disperse too early and so crushing these pills would be inadvisable. If you are unsure as to whether the medication you have been given is enteric coated, please check with your vet.

1) Ensure you have a syringe with the right measurements printed on it so that the dose you administer is correct for your dog. It is VERY easy to mistake 0.1 for 1 and vice versa and when giving medication, that decimal point is incredibly important so please check that you are giving the right amount and not 10 times as much in error.

2) Gently pop the syringe in the side of the mouth into the pocket of the cheek and squirt the fluid in slowly, in a controlled

manner. You may need to do this in several stages so as not to put too much in all in one go.

3) DO NOT squirt the fluid quickly

4) DO NOT aim to the back of the throat as this may choke the dog

5) if the dog is lying down, always pop the syringe of liquid in the cheek nearest the ground, so the liquid does not go across the airway as explained below.

N.B. It is important that the medication **does not** go down the airway rather than the throat as this can be incredibly dangerous. If the fluid goes into the lungs it can cause what is known as aspiration pneumonia or secondary drowning where the lining of the lungs react and swell and in severe cases can even "drown" the dog.

MISCELLANEOUS - GIVING A TABLET

Dogs are not keen on taking their medication and can be very good at hiding pills in their mouths and spitting them out when you are not looking. Rather than calling a dog to you for his medication, have it ready and wait for him to come of his own accord. You won't want him to associate you calling his name with the rather unceremonious act of stuffing a tablet down his neck! Perhaps you could disguise the pill in his dinner? Or maybe if he's too savvy for that, you could try hiding it in a piece of ham, moulding it inside a bit of bread or smearing it with a good glob of peanut butter or cream cheese. If he's a dog who likes to catch his treats, perhaps throwing one treat, then another, then his "spiked" titbit could be successful.

You can try breaking or grinding the tablet up into a powder a hiding it in their food. Please remember that if the tablet is to be given on an empty stomach, this method cannot be used. Similarly, if the tablet is "enteric coated" i.e. it has a shiny smooth coating on it, this should not be ground up either as the coating on it has been designed to ensure the tablet does not disperse until it is in the correct section of the digestive tract. Often, these tablets will cause acid or nausea if they do not go down far enough before they begin to disperse.

If none of these methods of subterfuge works for you, it might just be easier to actually administer a tablet manually. There are pill poppers you can buy to help you with this task. To use one, simply put the tablet in the soft rubber end and you can safely and harmlessly insert the tablet onto the back of your pets tongue by pressing the button on the end. Easy to use with a little practice, and saves getting your fingers bitten! It is a good idea to get your dog used to taking a tablet by practicing the procedure using something like a tiny bit of cheese or ham (any soft titbit will do that your dog likes). If he regularly gets given a bit of roast chicken or something nice in this way, he will be more than happy when its "medication time".

If you don't have a pill popper, this is how I would go about administering a tablet in the usual way:-

1) Ask him to sit and hold him firmly between your legs, using your knees just behind his shoulders to prevent him from escaping. You are going to be using one hand to open his mouth and the other to drop the tablet as far to the back of his throat as you can, if possible beyond the hump of his tongue.
2) Open his mouth by holding his muzzle with one hand and using your other hand to take hold of the lower jaw, slotting a finger just behind his large canine "fangs". Be very careful not to get bitten, as a fearful dog may nip out of fear rather than aggression.
3) Drop the tablet as far to the back of his throat as you can, if possible beyond the hump of his tongue, hold his muzzle and begin to stroke his throat with your other hand, around the region of his Adam's Apple, all the while reassuring him.
4) Continue holding his muzzle and stroking his throat until he swallows and licks his lips which indicates that the pill has been swallowed   successfully.
5) Praise the dog enthusiastically for being such a good boy and make the experience more palatable to him.

Another option (and a much sneakier way for those cunning canines who always know what you're up to) is to hide the tablet in a small piece of food and leave it where they can "find" it, say just by the back door before you let them out. It will be down the bone-shoot quick smart if they think it's a bonus find rather than a suspicious offering!

N.B. this is only possible if you are sure that the dog you intend to find it, does! If you have more than one dog then perhaps this is not the method for you unless you can ensure the other dogs are kept right out of the picture at the time.

Administering Tablet Medication - Felines

The following was sent to me by one of our Rhodes 2 Safety Facebook followers – I'm sorry I have no idea who the author is but did think it worthy of a share, particularly for our cat lovers – JUST BRILLIANT AND A MUST READ!

How to give a cat a pill...

1. Pick cat up and cradle it in the crook of your left arm as if holding a baby. Position right forefinger and thumb on either side of cat's mouth and gently apply pressure to cheeks while holding pill in right hand. As cat opens mouth, pop pill into mouth. Allow cat to close mouth and swallow.

2. Retrieve pill from floor and cat from behind sofa. Cradle cat in left arm and repeat process.

3. Retrieve cat from bedroom, and throw soggy pill away.

4. Take new pill from foil wrap, cradle cat in left arm holding rear paws tightly with left hand. Force jaws open and push pill to back of mouth with right forefinger. Hold mouth shut for a count of ten.

5. Retrieve pill from goldfish bowl and cat from top of wardrobe. Call spouse from yard.

6. Kneel on floor with cat wedged firmly between knees, hold front and rear paws. Ignore low growls emitted by cat. Get spouse to hold head firmly with one hand while forcing wooden

ruler into mouth. Drop pill down ruler and rub cat's throat vigorously.

7. Retrieve cat from curtain rail, get another pill from foil wrap. Make note to buy new ruler and repair curtains. Carefully sweep shattered figurines and vases from hearth and set to one side for gluing later.

8. Wrap cat in large towel and get spouse to lie on cat with head just visible from below armpit. Put pill in end of drinking straw, force mouth open with pencil and blow down drinking straw.

9. Check label to make sure pill not harmful to humans, drink one beer to take taste away. Apply Band-Aid to spouse's forearm and remove blood from carpet with cold water and soap.

10. Retrieve cat from neighbour's shed. Get another pill. Open another beer. Place cat in cupboard and close door onto neck to leave head showing. Force mouth open with dessert spoon. Flick pill down throat with rubber band.

11. Fetch screwdriver from garage and put cupboard door back on hinges. Drink beer. Fetch bottle of Scotch. Pour shot, drink. Apply cold compress to cheek and check records for date of last tetanus shot. Apply whiskey compress to cheek to disinfect. Toss back another shot. Throw tee-shirt away and fetch new one from bedroom.

12. Call Fire Department to retrieve the bloomin' cat from tree across the road. Apologize to neighbour who crashed into fence while swerving to avoid cat. Take last pill from foil-wrap.

13. Tie the dang thing's front paws to rear paws with twine and bind tightly to leg of dining room table, find heavy duty pruning gloves from shed. Push pill into mouth followed by large piece of steak. Be rough about it. Hold head vertically and pour two pints of water down throat to wash pill down.

14. Consume remainder of Scotch. Get spouse to drive you to emergency room, sit quietly while doctor stitches fingers and forearm and removes pill remnants from right eye. Call furniture shop on way home to order new table.

15. Arrange for Humane Society to collect mutant cat from home address and call local pet shop to see if they have any hamsters.

How to Give a Dog a Pill: 1. Wrap it in bacon

MISCELLANEOUS – PAIN KILLERS

I often get asked if there are any pain killers we can give to dogs if they injure themselves - for example if they suffer a sprain or strain. Many people get confused about what we can and cannot give to dogs - and rightly so. There are many drugs that are perfectly fine for humans to take but would have serious and sometimes catastrophic effects on our furry friends such as Ibuprofen. It is important to ascertain which drugs are OK for canine use and never just guess.

While the odd pain-reliever in a first aid capacity for those times when your vet's office is closed is one thing, veterinary advice should always be sought for on-going problems such as arthritis, lameness or if you are unsure as to why your dog appears to be in pain. Many a mistake has been made when a lay person has self-medicated their dog in the mistaken belief that they know what their dog needs, when in fact there has been something much more serious going on. Please ALWAYS seek your vet's advice when giving your dog medication - there is a reason why it takes them so long to get through vet school you know!

So, it's Saturday evening and your dog has had a minor accident of some type. He's not seriously injured enough for you to call out the emergency vet, but neither do you want to leave him in any discomfort over the next 36 hours while you wait for the vet's office to open on Monday morning. What do you do? Is there anything you can give your dog to safely alleviate his pain?

In these particular "ONE-OFF" type situations, you can give your dog a type of canine Paracetamol. There is one prescribed and licensed specifically for canine use and this drug is called Pardale.

Pardale-V prescription-only canine Paracetamol comes in 400 mg tablets and the recommended dose is no more than 10mg to every kilo of body weight. Therefore, for a Ridgeback such as my adult males (40 kg), we'd be looking at a whole tablet and for smaller breeds such as Labradors or Collies, for example, half a tablet would be more reasonable.

Because the weight to medication ratio is so important **PLEASE CHECK WITH YOUR VET** as to how much would be safe and suitable for your dog. <u>You may not want to pay for an emergency consultation, but there's nothing stopping you telephoning the on-call vet for some advice rather than guessing and giving your dog an inappropriate dose or medication.</u>

It is also worth remembering that Paracetamol may not be safe for ALL dogs - ie those with certain pre-existing medical conditions or those who are already taking some other forms of medication. I cannot stress enough how important it is to check with your vet before giving ANY tablet or medication to your dog.

Another pain-killer we've been familiar with for years is Aspirin. It's a good pain reliever and can also be used to bring temperatures down and to help with conditions where there is swelling, such as in a sprain or in arthritic conditions. Buffered Aspirin is something which can be given safely to your dog and is known as an NSAID (non steroidal anti-inflammatory drug).

So, everybody has heard of an Aspirin - but what does "buffered" mean? Well, buffered Aspirins are Aspirin tablets which are coated with a substance such as calcium carbonate. It is common for Aspirin to cause an uncomfortable acidic reaction of the stomach lining and so the "buffered" coating helps to neutralise acid and reduce the incidence of your dog getting an upset stomach. (N.B. It is different from the enteric coated varieties).

Brands of Buffered Aspirin

The generic name for Buffered Aspirin is acetylsalicylic acid. It is not licenced by the FDA for canine use and is actually intended only for human consumption, although it is commonly prescribed for dogs. There are several different brand names of Buffered Aspirin including Aftercare, Ascription, Arthricare, Bufferin and Palaprin. There is, however, a Buffered Aspirin specifically intended for use in dogs and that is Drs. Foster and Smith Buffered Canine Aspirin.

Although I understand it can be readily purchased in the USA, **Buffered Aspirin is NOT AVAILABLE in the UK.**

If you intend to source this drug over the internet, please be very careful indeed as you have no real way of knowing what's in the product you receive. There are many unscrupulous "dealers" on the net and goodness only knows what you could be giving your dog, just one of the many reasons why your medication should always be prescribed by your vet.

Administration of Buffered Aspirin

The recommended dose for Buffered Aspirin in tablet form is 5 to 15 mg per pound of the dog's weight, given every 8 to 12 hours. It is important to remember that while it is fine to give smaller doses than as stated above, you should certainly never go over this dosage unless your vet directs you to do so. Also, if you have a giant breed, please ascertain what the highest dose of buffered aspirin is, as there are always maximum amounts with any drug. Please take the time to ask your vet in advance just what would be a safe dose for your dog - and make sure you know how much he weighs!

Tell-tale signs to look out for that your dog has been overdosed are:
* vomiting
* blood in the stool or vomit
* depression
* loss of appetite
* high temperature
* fits

* coma
* death

Because the acidic nature of the Aspirin can cause an upset stomach and, over time and long-term use there may be ulceration of the stomach lining, it is advisable for the tablet to be given orally with food.

It is important to remember that it should never be given to any dog who has stomach ulcers, asthma or kidney disease and should certainly never be used for any dog who is due to undergo surgery within a week of taking it. Aspirin thins the blood and could cause serious complications when the animal goes to theatre. Always make sure you tell your vet if you have given your dog any medication not prescribed directly by him for your dog.

Side-Effects:

The side effects of long-term use of Aspirin are well documented and for this reason it is always best to use it only in a first aid capacity, for short spells, unless directed otherwise by your vet. Continued use can cause:

* Allergic reactions
* Kidney damage - (indicated by lower levels of water intake)
* Vomiting
* Loss of appetite
* Stomach ulcers - (indicated by vomiting, lack of appetite, blood

in the stool)
* Blood loss
* Anaemia

Please remember that any emergency medication or pain-relief you give to your dog should be appropriate to his weight, his unique medical history and to work in accordance with any drug he is already taking. Seek professional advice from your vet at your earliest convenience rather than guessing or administering the medication over any length of time.

MISCELLANEOUS – DIATOMACEOUS EARTH

I've been asked on a number of occasions about Diatomaceous Earth. As people get more and more keen to avoid pumping chemicals and drugs into themselves or their dogs, alternatives such as DE are coming more the fore. DE is suitable not just for dogs but for humans, horses, chickens .... you get the drift.

It has lots of uses and applications and can be taken internally or even applied directly to a wound or to prevent ticks and mites taking hold in everything from dogs to chicken coops.

Here's a list of just SOME of the things DE can be used for:-

- replenishing cells with depleted silica (essential for bones, tendons, skin, cartilage and blood vessels)
- regulating bowel movements
- cleansing the colon
- improving urinary health (diuretic and cures infections of the urinary tract)
- improving joint mobility
- reducing arthritis pain
- improving the respiratory tract
- strengthening teeth, gums, hair and nails
- reducing blood pressure and cholesterol levels
- increasing energy levels
- helps keep the immune system stronger and healthier

Sue Craigie of Imbali Rigebacks is to my mind, one of the most well informed people on this subject so rather than me trying to re-invent the wheel, I asked Sue for a little breakdown on what DE is and how it can be used. Here's what she had to say:-

"DE is one of nature's wonders, it is eco-friendly and a naturally organic material comprising of algae-like fossilized water plants called diatoms. These deposits have been around since prehistoric times and are mined and finely ground.

DE has been used for many years as a natural eliminator of internal and external parasites as well as a mineral supplement (besides silica, it also contains approximately 14 trace minerals essential to our well-being).

There are numerous benefits from taking DE on a daily basis and it can be used by humans, dogs, cats, poultry and farm animals. I take it for relief from osteoarthritis in my knee and would not be without my daily dose. I give it to my dogs as a worm control and have recently had two worm counts done on their stools. One was for usual internal parasites and the second was a specific one for lungworm/French heartworm, both counts came back completely clear.

For those people wanting to use DE as a worming regime, it is recommended that DE is given daily for 60 days and for lungworm/French heart worm it should be given daily for 90 days.

The reason it is done this way is that DE is not retained in the gut but by giving it daily it cleanses the gut, clears out worms and then is present when the next batch of eggs and larvae migrate to the stomach and gut. These are then dealt with by the DE and it breaks the life cycle.

I always recommend that people then have a worm count carried out and I would have these done every 6 months.

Once people know their dogs are worm-free there are two options, the first is that the owners stop giving DE for 3 months then repeat the worming regime again (ie wormed every 6 mths), the second option is one I take and that is to continue giving DE daily but to give a reduced "maintenance" dose.

There are a couple of reasons why I do this, firstly DE contains about 14 trace minerals which are essential to our well-being and secondly, dogs can pick up worms from just about anywhere and an adult roundworm can lay something like 200,000 eggs a DAY!!!! By giving DE daily it is present in the gut should a dog become reinvested and the ova/larvae/worms are dealt with immediately. As it is so cheap to use and has so many benefits I continue to give daily.

The more I read up on DE, the more fascinated I became. It is a wonderful, natural product with many uses.

There is lots of information available all about DE on my Imbali Ridgebacks Facebook

To give you an idea of the benefits of DE in a real life scenario, a lady locally to me has a litter of German Shepherd pups. It would be usual to use Panacur from day 40 for her bitch but instead, she had her on DE. The puppies are now just 6 weeks of age and have been having DE mixed into their food since she started weaning them (raw fed).

She has had two worm counts carried out on their faeces and both tests have come back showing the puppies are completely clear of worms, she is delighted. The puppies will have another worm count done just before they leave her and each puppy will have a bag of DE as part of their puppy packs. It is great to know that they have not had to be chemically wormed, most pups would have had 4 lots of wormer plus a cocktail of vaccinations by the time they were 12 wks of age, on top of that the Vet would probably have had the owners use Advocate monthly. No wonder so many dogs have severe reactions to the over-use of these products."

Thank you very much to Sue for taking the time to pass on so much wonderful information and if this has tweaked your interest, please visit Sue's website at:-
www.imbaliridgebacks.co.uk

MISCELLANEOUS - TEA TREE OIL

There have been a number of occasions where I've read on various forums of people (and in some cases as advised by their vets) advocating the use of Tea Tree oil when treating conditions like skin irritation or hot spots for dogs. Tea Tree oil is indeed wonderful stuff but it can, in fact, be quite toxic for dogs. It's not unusual for humans to use it at 100% strength, totally undiluted and while it is no doubt very good for us, I'm not sure that people realise that there are any toxicity-related problems when using it with our dogs and cats.

Should it be used on our pets without diluting it?
Are the dangers of using Tea Tree possibly worse than what we are using it for?
Could it cause adverse reactions and if so, what should we be looking out for?

Reactions that have been commonly documented *include* depression, lethargy, weakness, incoordination, muscle tremors and excessive drooling/salivation so we really ought to know what we are doing BEFORE we do it.

We really should be better informed when choosing remedies and treatments for our animals and this includes if and when we opt for using things like Tea Tree Oil. I'm not saying don't use it, but I am suggesting caution, dilution and a better understanding of the effect it has on our animals – in fact, is there a better option out there?

I myself always prefer to go down the herbal route rather than the pharmaceutical one whenever that direction is available so please don't think I'm poo-pooing the more natural remedies – I simply want us all to THINK more and stay safe.

MISCELLANEOUS - MEDIC ALERT TAGS

I'm sure you've seen medic alert tag for humans, right? When you have a history or illness that requires medication such as epilepsy or diabetes for example, the patient will often wear a bracelet or necklace with information on it about their condition so that if they are taken ill, a first aider or medic will know they require immediate attention and medication.

With that in mind, does your pet have an illness like this? Perhaps he needs medication every day to "stay well" and without it, they'd be very poorly indeed. Now imagine that your beloved dog (or cat) has gone missing – if found, it may take a while to get them back to you and all the while they'd be missing their vital medication.

It's a good idea to order an extra tag for your dog's collar which simply states something like "I need daily medication" and the telephone number of your vet. Obviously, it goes without saying that your dog should be microchipped and that number along with your own contact details should already be attached to your dog's collar, but having the extra security of your vet's phone number and the need for daily medication on a separate tag can really make all the difference.

There are lots of different types of tags you can get, from the flat metal ones that simply slide onto a flat collar so there are no "dangly bits" to get snagged:-

To the ordinary circular disks or even shaped ones that hang from the D ring on their collar.

You can also get ones that are like tiny barrels that screw together encasing a role of paper with the information written on by hand.

Whatever you choose, be sure you do choose something and clip it to your dog to keep him safe, even if he does manage to Houdini himself off into the ether!

MISCELLANEOUS - ACTIVATED CHARCOAL

Charcoal is amazing stuff with many uses. I've always used it with my dogs in the form of charcoal biscuits, as it's great for stopping unwanted odours when your furry friend passes wind – and we all know how pungent that can be! Simply giving a couple of biscuits in the morning and before bed has made such a difference and I can say hand on heart that it's very rare we EVER smell anything unpleasant of that nature now.

There are, however, many other uses for activated charcoal too and many of them fall into the first aid category (not just for our dogs, but for humans too).

Common charcoal is made from peat, coal, wood, coconut shell, or petroleum. "Activated charcoal" is similar to common charcoal, but is made especially for use as a medicine. To make activated charcoal, manufacturers heat common charcoal in the presence of a gas that causes the charcoal to develop lots of internal spaces or "pores." These pores help activated charcoal "trap" chemicals.

Activated charcoal is not expensive and is certainly something I always have on hand for the dogs and the family too.

There are many uses for Activated Charcoal including treating digestive problems, poisoning, teeth cleaning and even snake bites.

MISCELLANEOUS - CBD (CANNABIS) OIL

Cannabis has long since been known to have health properties but its use in the wider population has been frowned up. Now it seems there is a wave of evidence supporting its use, particularly in the form of CBD oil. CBD or Cannabidoil is said to be helpful for a huge raft of problems and uses, but many people are frightened of it thinking they would be "taking drugs". CBD oil is legal. It has had the THCs removed (in essence, the bits that make you high) so you get all of the positive, medicinal properties but without the experience of tripping out or feeling stoned. (Yes, I know that's not a particularly scientific explanation but you get my drift).

So what kind of claims are being made for its uses? Well, they are many and these range from analgesic properties, treatment of anxiety and digestive disorders, anti-psychotic uses, reduction of fits, seizures, tremors and neurological disorders, reduction of nausea, travel sickness due to stress, lower incidence of diabetes and even claims that it can help with the treatment of cancer.

Certainly you won't have to look very hard to find many advocates of its effects and, since there appears to be little down-sides in terms of side effects, many people are giving it a go, me included. I use it for two of my dogs, with very good results:

Rain has epilepsy and also canine autism (see our Canine Autism blog for more information on that topic). Since beginning the CBD oil he has become what I can only describe as a really good version of himself ... like "him", but on a very good day. He certainly isn't stoned or changed other than to say he appears to be in a good mood and up for anything without any side of stress or reactivity. He used to find a lot of situations overwhelming and very stressful indeed and while I won't go as far as to say it has cured his canine autism (that would be ridiculous), it has certainly smoothed out the edges and given him the coping mechanisms to get through situations that would once have triggered a seizure, and we've seen both a reduction in frequency, length of seizure and violence of the fit itself.

Axl always used to be great travelling in the car but, as he has aged, he has become more and more stressed by it until we got to a stage where he refused to jump in to go out for a drive, even if he knew there was a lovely walk at the end of it. He would slobber and pant in the car and need a window to be opened no matter the weather. We started him on CBD oil and literally the following day he ran out the door and was the first one in the back of the car. His stress levels have come down when travelling by about 75% – and a happy Axl makes for a very happy Kerry!

So, where do you get this amazing stuff? Who should you trust? How much should you give? How much does it cost???? There are lots of places on the internet that will sell it and lots of places now springing up on the high street too. I would always advise doing your research personally to make sure it is right for your dog. Ensure that the place you buy it from is reputable and with a person you can physically speak to, to ask questions and guide you to enable you to use it in the right way and in the right quantities. Different suppliers sell in different purities which will have an impact on both price and amount you need to use, so it is important before you give anything to your dog, that you are giving the correct dose – so please do speak to people who really know their onions and check out their reviews and reputation fully.

Speak to your vet, particularly if your vet is on medication, just in case it has any effect on the way the drug acts or on the therapy he needs. As with anything you may want to try with your dog, your vet's opinion is always your first port of call.

If you would like to read more on this fascinating subject (and there is stacks and stacks of literature to read and research), then I would direct you to a company called Canine Health Concern (known as CHC) who have lots of literature, help, background and information. If having read and spoken to them, or another reputable company, you feel it is right for your dog, then you can purchase from their company too.

MISCELLANEOUS – POSITIONS TO PRACTICE

I was asked on one of our canine courses recently about the best position to be in when you check inside your dog's mouth. One of my main suggestions is that you should practice the various positions you intend to use to examine your dog to get him used to it and thus preventing him "freaking out" if you need to do it in an emergency situation, say if he is choking for example.

On the back of that question, one of our Rhodes 2 Safety Facebook followers contacted me to ask if there were any other positions or examination techniques she should be practicing with her dog so, here is a rundown of the sort of positions that would be great for you to get Fido used to "just in case".

Examining the Mouth

Your position when checking a dog's mouth should be with him facing away from you and you standing astride him (or kneeling for a small breed) behind him.

Get him comfortable with being in this position first, and then move on to having him tolerate you looking inside his mouth …. only for very short seconds to start with. Being careful not to get yourself bitten, place your fingers in the gap behind his fangs and gently open up his mouth so you can see right to the back of his throat and also the roof of his mouth. I usually say something like "mummy's looking" before I do it so he knows what's coming next.

Choking

Once you have checked to see if there is anything visibly blocking the throat when your dog is choking, you will need to administer "back blows" between the dog's shoulder blades. This is easy with a small breed as one would merely hold them just above the hocks (DON'T PRACTICE THIS POSITION ... ONLY TO BE USED IN EMERGENCY SITUATIONS)

Hold small breeds just above the hocks

For medium and largish breeds we need to lift the dog with one arm under the hips so that he is tilted, head down, so that gravity is helping (the wheelbarrow position). Allow him to take his own weight on his front paws while the back end is elevated. This is a very odd position for the dog and a good one for you to practice and get him used to:

For very large breeds, then reversing the dog onto a chair or some kind of platform with his back legs means you do not need to try to hold him, lift him and administer the back blows all yourself, which is very difficult with a large breed.

The next position to practice for the treatment of choking is the one we need to use to administer abdominal thrusts. If the dog is small breed, you'd simply hold him with his back against you, head up. If, however, your dog is medium sized or slightly larger, have him sitting, facing away from you. Kneel up behind him and tilt him backwards against you. It will take some time for him to be comfortable in this position and to trust you .... it took Rain about 10 minutes to become happy with being placed in this position. If your dog is very large, long bodied or "top heavy" such as a Greyhound, GSD or a Mastiff for example, this position may simply not be possible, in which case you will need to administer the abdominal thrusts with him standing as you come from behind and under his diaphragm.

Muzzle Acceptance

You should try to make sure that if you need your dog to wear a muzzle, say if he has been hurt and your vet needs to examine him, that he is used to the feeling of wearing one. Far better to teach him muzzle acceptance in a kind, gentle, force-free manner well in advance of ever needing it. Here is a video by Claire Staines of Lothlorien Dog Services to explain how to introduced a muzzle the RIGHT way

http://www.rhodes2safety.co.uk/canine-tip-of-the-day-teaching-a-dog-to-accept-a-muzzle/

Temporary Treatment for Shock

As a temporary treatment for shock, we need nothing more specialised than having your dog lying on his back and you holding his back legs up to encourage as much of the blood in the thighs as possible to return to the body core

Stabilisation Treatment for Shock

For the stabilisation position you need to find a board strong enough to take your dog's weight. The lid from an old toy box is perfect, the tray in the bottom of your dog's crate, a parcel shelf from your car or if you have a small breed you could use a chopping board or the tray you have your supper on.

Take your board and position a cushion or perhaps your jacket at the very end of it. Lay your dog on the board, on his right side, with his bottom elevated by the cushion under the board.

CPR & Artificial Respiration Position

The final position doesn't really need practicing, but I thought I'd put it in as a memory jog – for CPR and Artificial Respiration, your dog should ideally be on his right hand side so that his heart is uppermost (if you are worried that your dog may have a spinal injury, please don't try to turn him over if you find him on the other side as we can administer CPR on either side if absolutely necessary) – you will find his heart roughly where the elbow would touch the ribs if you bent his front leg back.

NEVER EVER PERFORM CPR ON ANY ANIMAL WITH A HEARTBEAT.

Of course, aside from all of these specific positions, it's great to get your dog used to being handled and examined regularly by checking his paws, nails, ears and eyes for example once a week while you groom him.

Another great thing to practice is a straight forward bandage. I would suggest that you practice on a human a couple of times just to make sure that your dressing is not too tight (your human "dog" will soon tell you if it's uncomfortable). Once you are confident that your dressing won't hurt your dog, you can practice on him regularly, say to the leg or the paw, just so that your dog gets used to you faffing about with him. Once you have applied a bandage, leave it on for a few minutes or so to get him used to having to tolerate it – use a different leg each time so he's not bothered which one you practice on. Remember not to apply the dressing too tightly as we do not want to cause any problems with the blood flow.

MISCELLANEOUS - LICKING WOUNDS OR STITCHES

Licking wounds/stitches: When a dog has an injury, be that an irritation, a wound or stitches after surgery, the natural thing is for him to try to lick the area to clean it, reduce irritation or soothe himself. Unfortunately, licking can do more harm than good as the saliva may cause bacterial infection. He may nibble and pull at stitches with catastrophic results and sometimes may simply lick and lick and lick to excess making the irritation worse.

So, what do you do to stop it? Well, there are several ways you can come at this problem and some can be used simultaneously. Of course you could simply use a basket muzzle but this is neither very good as a longer term solution or one that I would wish to use when the dog was unsupervised. Other, more preferable alternatives are:

The Elizabethan collar (or "Cone of Shame" as it's come to be known): a cone-shaped piece of plastic that fastens to the dog's collar and prevents him from reaching back to nibble or lick any part of his body. There is no doubt that this device works but a lot of dogs find it very uncomfortable, it restricts their peripheral vision and also takes chunks out of your shins, skirting boards and woodwork!

This Elizabethan style collar also comes in softer fabrics now – still in the same design but with much less damage to your woodwork and less obtrusive for your dog.

Other alternatives to the Elizabethan style is a soft neck brace type of collar which is similar to those you might wear if you had a whiplash injury to your neck or an inflatable version like those used by travellers on long-haul flights.

You can also make a DIY version of this device by simply stuffing the leg of a pair of tights with soft fabric and then tying it around the dog's neck. These versions of the collar will again prevent the dog from turning his head back on himself, but as this collar simply goes around the neck rather than all the way over his head, it does mean that longer-bodied dogs may still be able to reach various parts of their anatomy such as the feet and lower legs.

There is also the alternative of a harder "Neck Brace" type of collar. It is a little more heavy duty than those mentioned above – the one I found was called Stop Bite and does not restrict peripheral vision at all.

If none of these collars appeal to you, you can of course cover the wound with a barrier dressing of some sort:

Paw/Leg: a bandage or child's sock for a lower leg or paw injury (simply slip it over the paw and secure with Micropor tape or vet wrap ensuring that you do not do so too tightly to restrict blood flow).

Upper Body/Shoulder/Torso: a child's t-shirt is excellent for this (put it onto your dog and then tie a knot in the top to prevent it rolling up.

Lower Body/Abdomen: take a length of material and stitch it into a tube that you can have the dog wear as a body stocking. Attach ties to the top of the stocking and loop his collar through them to prevent the stocking rolling down.

Nipples: a friend and follower of Rhodes 2 Safety, Elizabeth Halliday sent me these fantastic pictures. During the very hot summer of 2013, her bitch was nursing a litter and developed severe mastitis. The mastitis required surgery in the end and obviously this meant that the pups could no longer suckle from the affected teat. To protect the operation site and prevent the pups suckling, the very talented Carol Ann Carlton fashioned an apron specifically for Chana. You will see that it not only covers the teats, but also is open at the back. This apron was much better than a full shirt as it also prevented her from overheating. Great idea and not too difficult to make.

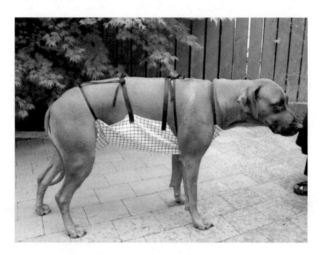

Lower Body/Upper Thighs: a child's pair of shorts provides an excellent cover for this part of the body – stretchy ones in particular like cycling shorts or long-legged trunk style underpants work a treat. If the waist band is not tight enough to stay up on its own, simply apply a couple of loops to the waist band and slot the collar through the loops a little like braces.

There are also various medical shirts that look a little like leotards, specifically designed for dogs following medical procedures.

Of course you may just decide to apply something that the dog does not like the taste of in the general vicinity of the wound to put him off licking. Please be sure that you do not get it on the wound itself as this may cause further irritation and hinder the healing process.

Another option is to apply an anti-lick stip. These are applied over the top of the usual dressing and have an unpleasant taste. The intention is to stop the dog removing his dressings to deter licking and nibbling.

In many cases, if we can stop the wound itching as it heals, we can stop the dog taking so much interest in it too so it's worth considering potions and lotions that will help reduce the discomfort and itching to use alongside a collar or dressing. Applying something like Aloe Vera or Calendula can really help and there are many other products which can be purchased over the counter, but please ensure that they are suitable for use with dogs.

MISCELLANEOUS - DIAGNOSTIC TESTS

Often when our dogs are ill, we trundle off to see the vet and he recommends various diagnostic tests to try to shed a bit of light on exactly what is wrong with them. In the absence of their being able to talk to us to tell us exactly how they are feeling, these tests are even more important when dealing with animals.

I thought today we'd have a look at the various tests available and what they are used for. The most common diagnostic tests used by vets are:-

X-Rays – X-Rays provide pictures of the inside of your dog's body. The pictures are in different shades of grey rather than in colour and to try to help avoid any confusion, several pictures are often taken from differing angles. Sometimes, the vet may use the X-Ray to look at bones and joints, such as when your dog is hip-scored to check for things like hip dysplasia

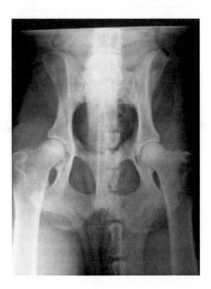

In some cases, your vet may need to see structures like the gut or intestines and for that it may be necessary for your dog to be given a substance called barium which will highlight the area much better on the X-Ray. Although X-Rays are painless, it is usual for the dog to be sedated or under anaesthetic so that he stays nice and still.

Blood Tests – Blood tests are used to measure the levels of chemicals in the blood. Every animal's blood (yours and mine included) has naturally occurring chemicals in it and these give what is known as a "baseline" level that we would expect to see in a healthy sample. By checking for certain chemicals in the blood, if the levels come back higher or lower than expected, it can give a good indication of whether a particular organ is not working so well and may help the vet diagnose a problem. Blood tests can reveal all manner of problems from immune disorders, failing organs, infections and even cancer. It might be that he has to do a whole battery of blood tests to get to the bottom of the problem as each test reveals a different result and in order to build up a complete picture, it may be necessary to check for a lot of different things.

Ultrasound Examinations – Ultrasound is also used to look inside the body. It's the same technique we would use to see a baby in a pregnant lady's uterus but instead of using X-rays which can be harmful in high doses, it uses sound waves which are very safe. It is not so important to be extremely still and so there is not usually any need to sedate the dog before the ultrasound is performed.

Endoscopy – Endoscopy is the technique that allows the vet to see inside the dog's body directly, by inserting a long flexible camera inside. This method of investigation can be used to check the respiratory tract (for breathing difficulties) or the digestive system. Unlike ultrasound, it would be necessary to anaesthetise the dog when performing an endoscopy because the equipment is very fragile and could easily be damaged if it were bitten! Apart from allowing the vet to see the organs, it also allows him to take a biopsy from inside the tract or, in a case such as a dog who has swallowed a foreign body, removal of that object with some grasping forceps. Removing the object this way prevents the need for major surgery.

There are many other tests available too, although they may be a little more specialised and used at more hi-tech clinics and surgeries. More advanced computer-controlled scanning techniques are now also being used for our animals such as:-

MRI scans – An MRI (magnetic resonance imaging) scan creates detailed pictures of the inside of the body. The test is painless. It is, however, necessary to be still for several minutes at a time so the pictures come out clear, so sedation or anaesthesia is usually required.

CT (or CAT) scans – Actually, CT scans have nothing to do with cats, except that when people talk about them, they usually say "CAT scan" instead of "CT scan." CT stands for computed tomography, so you can see why people prefer to say "CT." CT scans are a kind of X-Ray that gives the vet a much better picture of what's going on inside the body. CT scans show much more detail than X-Rays and don't hurt.

Laparoscopic surgery – Often referred to as "key-hole" surgery, this method of investigation uses a small whole through which a camera is inserted so that the vet can see what he is doing, and another small whole through which he can pass tiny operating equipment rather than having to make a large incision to open up the body to get a good look inside.

MISCELLANEOUS - FIREWORKS!

Tonight and throughout this weekend we are more than likely going to contend with fireworks going off. There are steps you can take to try to make the evening all round a safer and less stressful event for your pets.

1) Ensure your pets are walked throughout the daylight hours, so they're more tired & relaxed.

2) Take them into the garden for a pee/poop BEFORE the festivities start.

3) Make sure they are microchipped/tattooed AND wearing their collar.

4) Have them on a long lead so that if a firework DOES take you by surprise, they cannot bolt from you.

5) Leave the door open while you are in the garden so that if they need to get in quickly, they can.

6) Ensure your garden is escape-proof. Even if they've never tried to jump a fence or gate before, a terrified dog is an irrational dog and they can easily tear off in a blind panic (hence the lead).

7) Turn up the TV or radio to muffle the sounds (serious Rock Music does the trick beautifully – as a rock chick myself, I can promise you that a bit of AC/DC or Guns n Roses never comes in wrong).

8) Close the curtains and keep the lights on full – this will disguise any bright flashes from outside. Sitting in the dark will only intensify how bright the explosions appear and will be counter-productive.

9) Provide a safe area where they can retreat to hide if necessary, but stay with them.

10) Comfort them if they appear afraid and reassure them that all is well – your comfort will NOT reinforce their belief that something is wrong.

11) Use calming scents and smells such as Lavender and the DAP machines and perhaps consider using a collar with such fragrances embedded in it.

12) Use calming herbal remedies such as Serene-um which do not "drug" your dog, but will hopefully take the edge off the level of anxiety or perhaps look at CBD oil.

13) Thundershirts – specially designed dog vests that wrap them up tightly, giving a sense of security to help them cope with various things including, as the name implies, thunder and many other stressful situations.

13) Perhaps try something like a dog buff or the "Mutt Muffs" to keep the noise down and protect those precious ears. (I would suggest getting these well in advance if you intend to use something like this as they will need to be introduced gently so that your dog doesn't mind wearing them).

There is also a company called HappyHoodies.com who make soft expandable, fabric bands with gentle compression that relieve anxiety and calm dogs during stressful situations such as force drying, thunderstorms, fireworks, toenail clipping etc. You could, of course, fashion something similar with a scarf or snood but please be careful NOT to restrict the windpipe.

Another thing to look into is an app called "The Soundproof Puppy" training app. It comes very highly recommended by force free trainers who use positive techniques in their training methods

All the advice above applies for then and there. If left this late, then so far as helping your dog to cope with the stresses, this year is a lost cause.

But, WHAT ABOUT NEXT YEAR OR THE YEAR AFTER?

Getting to the week before November 5th and then complaining about fireworks and demanding a petition to ban their sale to members of the public is not going to help – you're just too late!

You need to work on desensitizing them gently, ALL YEAR, so that when the time comes, they are able to cope with it. There are some great techniques you can use right down to watching the History channel so they get used to hearing cannon and gun fire – you have to think outside the box. Initially, we would be talking about exposure to low level noises with a "prize" for every time the noise happens so they get used to hearing the noise, looking at you for reassurance and getting a reward for checking in with you. Eventually, the noise can be increased and varied until it becomes "oh great, there's a loud noise, that means treat time". It's a long, LONG process that needs to be conditioned throughout the year so it can be used at any time in the future be that thunder, lightning, gunshots on a hunting shoot or the dreaded fireworks themselves.

You need to be shown correctly, from the start, how best to introduce the noises in a positive way, without making the situation and their phobia worse. "Flooding" the dog with bangs and crashes and whooshes is not the way to go and will have a completely negative effect. I would seriously consider having a consultation with a good FORCE FREE behavioural trainer as soon as you can so that next year, your dog has a less stressful time.

It's very tough, and I think it's fair to say there are very few dogs who actively "like" fireworks, but with the guidance of a good trainer and positive techniques, I'm sure you'd both be much happier. The main thing is, there is NO instant fix unfortunately, so put in the work NOW, for a better result next year.

MISCELLANEOUS - ZOOPHARMACOGNOSY

Zoopharmacognosy – wow, that's a big word but what the heck does it mean? Well, in simple terms, Zoopharmacognosy is a behaviour in which non-human animals self-medicate by selecting, inhaling, eating or topically applying plants, soils, insects, and psychoactive drugs to treat or prevent disease.

So what, if anything, does that mean for us? We have vets who can minister to all their needs right? Well yes, we do, but many people are opting for a more holistic and natural way of looking after our furry friends, often seeking out treatments of an altogether more natural route.

In the wild, it's long been known that animals will forage and hunt for specific plants or minerals to help them "feel better". Whereas, when we feel under the weather, we simply nip down to the local pharmacy to pick up a tonic or treatment, a wild animal would do much the same in sourcing just what he needs from Mother Nature's drug store.

For our domesticated or captive animals, such foraging is simply not an option so considering the practice of applied Zoopharmacognosy would enable our pets to display this self-medicating behaviour for themselves. By offering various plant extracts, oils, minerals, seaweeds or clays for example, the animal would then have the opportunity to select its own remedy. Once chosen, it could then self-medicate either by inhaling the vapours in pungent oils, or perhaps by chewing on a plant which might aid in digestion, or by rubbing a part of its body into it.

Oils such as such as Eucalyptus, for example, could be placed on a cloth and placed in your dog's crate for them to use and inhale when they choose. Eucalyptus is known to be effective in respiratory and sinus problems along with the sort of chesty coughs that accompany such conditions as Kennel Cough. Perhaps you might consider Lavender for your pet. Lavender is well known to have relaxing and calming properties which could be useful for treating things like separation anxiety and even as an aid to get through Firework Night should your pet be fearful of loud bangs and noises.

The opportunities and applications with Zoopharmacognosy are really wide spread and as more and more people are beginning to seek the natural alternatives to main-stream medicines; it's certainly something worth considering.

If you are interested in using such methods, please speak with your veterinarian to ensure that any pre-existing medical conditions or medications they are currently taking will not be affected by the introduction of such therapies, and speak to a professional Zoopharmacognosy specialist to get the full "inside track" on this exciting approach.

MISCELLANEOUS - COAT CONTAMINATION

Coat contamination with whatever chemical or substance should always be taken very seriously. Any product on the coat can easily work its way onto the skin and then absorb through the layers of the dermis and into the blood stream. If this happens, there is the potential for your dog to be poisoned. This is the first danger associated with it.

The other problem with coat contamination is that the substance is also likely to be licked off by the dog and then swallowed too. If it is toxic, it could well seriously harm your dog.

What should you do?

If possible, clean the substance from the coat as soon as you notice it to avoid any chance of poisoning. N.B. If the substance is a paint – never use solvent, paint stripper, concentrated detergent or fabric softener on a dog's coat. These substances are all highly toxic if swallowed.

To remove paint or tar, soften it with petroleum jelly, or products safe for human skin.

To remove creosote/oil, try soaking for 20 minutes in baby oil and then combing out.

Cut off any heavily contaminated, matted fur, then wash the area with canine or baby shampoo, and rinse thoroughly. Check the skin beneath the substance to ensure there is no evidence of redness, irritation or a burn to the skin. If there is evidence of burning, treat as per our Burns blog.

To remove a chemical type substance from the paws, please only ever use fresh running water to clean the area – NEVER STAND A PAW IN A BOWL – If you try to wash the substance from the paw while in a bowl, all you will do is dilute the chemical throughout the entire contents of the bowl and then be soaking your dog's foot in a chemical solution.

If you have noticed your dog licking the area, remember to wash out the mouth thoroughly from the side and across the tongue. You may need to use a wet wash cloth to wash the tongue and rinse frequently throughout. If possible, do not allow the dog to swallow any of the water. Monitor him closely and seek veterinary advice immediately should you think there is any possibility that he has swallowed the substance.

MISCELLANEOUS - TRAVEL SAFETY

These days, most of us travel about by car quite a bit and as such, we need to know that our furry friends are safe too. Long gone are the days when we used to drive our cars without wearing seatbelts now that our awareness of health and safety has grown.

The same should now be true for our dogs – for our benefit as much as for theirs. If you have an accident in your car, and your dog is not safely secured, he will to all intents and purposes become a "missile" in the cabin with you. As you stop or impact, the inertia will be transferred to him. He may, be flung against the side or the roof. Worse still, he may be flung forward at the windscreen and possibly through it. There is, of course, always the chance that he will connect with you or your passengers during the course of the accident – and a dog colliding with your head at speed is not good for either of you.

There are options to keep everybody safe and these range from the very cheap and basic, all the way through to the bespoke and pricey. Whichever you choose, please do choose SOMETHING.

Dog Guards fit behind the rear seats of your car to ensure your dog is stowed safely in the compartment behind you. The guard separates the dog from you so that should you have an accident, he is not rolling around inside the cabin where you are and therefore cannot collide with you. There are lots of adjustable ones on the market and also ones designed specifically for the model of your car.

Seatbelts for dogs work just as ours do. They clip into the seatbelt mechanism in your car in exactly the same way and place as you would put a seatbelt for a human. The belt is then attached to the dog, ideally by a harness (a harness is accepted to be safer and healthier for your dog than attaching the belt to a collar which, in an accident, could choke or hang your dog or damage his spine/neck)

Harnesses work in conjunction with the belt so that the dog can sit in the rear or front seat of your car. The travel harness made by Bergan is the only one at time of writing available in the UK that has been safety tested to UK standards. Others are available which may also be equally as good, but the Bergan one has the testing and documentation to support it.

Tailgate Guards fits at the rear of the boot/trunk of your car. It is a single panel that means you can open up your rear door without the dogs being able to jump out. It also means that on a hot day, perhaps if you have to wait in your car for any length of time while stationary, the rear door can be opened allowing good circulation of air but can still be locked and secured. As always, we strongly recommend that dogs are NEVER left unattended in a vehicle.

Bespoke Fitted Car Cages/Crates can be purchased specifically for your make and model of car. They are designed to fit exactly to the shape of your boot to maximise the space available but also to create a secure and stable compartment for Rover. There are several companies you can contact with your measurements who will make exactly what you want, to your own personal requirements. The ones I use are by Barjo.

Another great crate for your car is by a company called Safedog. Safedog crash tested car cages, TransK9 and 4Pets ProLine cages are, as far as I've been able to ascertain, the best and most well tested car cage for dogs available in the UK right now. The ProLine products are of European manufacture and have not been available in the UK for very long. Safedog have a policy that they won't sell to you if you are going to position the cage in an unsuitable place in your car/vehicle (they are designed with their own crumple zone which depends on being backed against the rear seats).

Window Vents are a good way of allowing the windows to be open to get good ventilation while still preventing your canine companion from poking his head out! It's an image everybody has seen, the crazy dog with his head out of the window, ears and chops flobbling about in the wind as they drive. While admittedly very comical to see, this is in fact a very dangerous thing for your dog to do on a number of levels including possible damage to their eyes from the wind and particles on the air and also the possibility of them colliding with on-coming traffic or leaping from the vehicle.

Window Sunshades When you travel for any distance, the sun moves around. As it moves, it invariably at one point or another ends up shining through onto your dog. This can be very uncomfortable and even dangerous for dogs as they may over heat and/or dehydrate as a result of the sun beating down on them. A simple and temporary solution is the application of sunshade panels. They fold up fairly small, then "ping" open when you need them. They have suction pads that you simply stick to your window to fix them in place so installation literally takes seconds.

Non Spill Travel Bowl Obviously, we recommend that your dog has access to clean, cool water at all times – even while travelling. Depending on the road surface, your suspension and the way you drive, keeping water in a bowl can be quite a tricky undertaking. It is now possible to get non spill bowls designed specifically for travelling. There are lots of different makes and types on the market. A full size drinking bowl has a special rim to prevent water from spilling over. The external rim helps to stop water from escaping and to catch those dribbles that fall from their mouths. Non-slip, non-tip and lightweight plastic, great for use in cars, caravans, camping and holidays with your pet.

MISCELLANEOUS – TRAVEL SICKNESS

Vomiting, shaking, anxiety and drooling can be as a result of car travel or nervousness, and this is very common indeed in puppies – with my boy Axl having just sired a litter, I'm in constant contact with our new puppy owners and this is something that all of them, my puppy Chi included, have suffered with. Simple vomiting is common and not usually associated with discomfort.

Sometimes, these symptoms can be reduced and eventually removed by careful, gentle, acclimatisation of the dog to travelling in the car. If you know you are going to make a journey, ensure your puppy does not have a full tummy before you begin. Start with a very short journey of only a couple of minutes' duration, giving copious reassurance throughout, and making sure that your final destination is one that the puppy will really enjoy.

Use a crate not only for safety purposes, but also because you can pop in a blanket with familiar smells on it (perhaps from his litter) to make it easier for him to settle. Dogs enjoy a den type environment too so once in the crate, pop a blanket over the top to make it a little darker and feel safer on his journey.

As with humans, ginger can be really good for settling the stomach. It can often be very successful simply to give your dog a ginger biscuit some 20 minutes or so before travelling (2 for a larger dog) and if nothing else, they'll be pleased with the treat!

If you have other dogs in your home, often having the dogs travel together for moral support can take some of the fear out of the journey for your puppy.

If even this is too stressful to begin with, there are some very good techniques to help your puppy overcome their fears. It might be best to start with something as gentle as simply opening up the car doors so there is a clear entrance and exit and take the dog right through the car and out the other side without even stopping. Gradually, increasing the length of time between entering and exiting, all the while offering reassurance and rewarding with his favourite treats may get your puppy over the hurdle. However, if you feel that your dog is so frightened of the car as to need this kind of intervention, then speak to a registered canine behaviourist to help you accomplish a stress-free outcome for your puppy, using positive force-free learning techniques.

You may also consider giving an anti-sickness tablet to help make the experience a little less unpleasant. Tablets can be obtained from your vet but please remember that with some anti-emetics there may be a mild sedative effect which, if you are wishing your dog to "perform" at the other end of your journey say as a show dog, agility/flyball competitor or shooting companion etc, this might not be a viable option.

If you are looking for a homoeopathic first aid remedy, Petroleum is the remedy of choice. Petroleum is liquid crude oil that comes from beneath the earth's surface. The remedy is made from purified commercial petroleum. Borax (boric acid) can also be tried. If there is an actual fear of the car itself, then Gelsemium should be given. For longer journeys, start treatment around an hour before the journey commences and repeat at hourly intervals during travel.

Another option, and one that has worked for us, is CBD (cannabis) oil. Axl used to be fine travelling but, as he got older, he found it more and more stressful and began drooling and panting. We introduced CBD oil, a few drops to start with and finally around 15 drops (he is a big dog) into his breakfast and literally within a couple of days he went from sitting at the back of the hall refusing to come out if he thought he was going to go in the car, to being the first out the door and jumping straight in the back, so maybe this could work for you too

Check out the CBD oil blog for more information on that.

MISCELLANEOUS - FIRST AID KITS

List of essential items to include in First Aid Kits for dogs, & the uses of each item.

Essential Items	Use of the item
Bandage (small)	* To hold a gauze and/or sterile dressing in place while covering a small injury. The bandage should be applied and secured with tape* A small bandage can also be used to muzzle a frightened animal prior to treatment to ensure the first aider does not get bitten.* Another use might be as a tourniquet in the event of severe blood loss, but only as a last resort. It is however, important to remember that this should only be applied for a maximum of 15 minutes and should never be covered with a bandage. If a tourniquet has been applied, the dog should never be left unattended.
Bandage (medium)	* To hold a gauze and/or sterile dressing in place while covering a medium sized injury, to keep it free of bacteria and or control blood loss. The bandage may be applied and secured with tape or used in conjunction with an adhesive bandage.
Bandage (large)	* To hold a gauze and/or sterile dressing in place while covering a large injury.* Large bandages can also be useful when treating sprains or strains requiring stabilisation prior to veterinary attention. The bandage should

	be applied and secured with tape, while ensuring adequate blood flow to the extremities throughout. Application of a bandage with too much tension can result in the same effect as a tourniquet so care must be taken to ascertain the presence of capillary refill on a regular basis.
Bandage (vet wrap)	* For use in the treatment of strains and sprains as a stabilisation medium.* For application on top of a gauze or dressing to create a pressure bandage for the purposes of controlling blood loss.
Cotton Wool	* Cotton wool should never be applied directly to a wound because of the risk of fibres becoming embedded. It can be used to help soak up bleeding if applied on top of gauze.* Can be used as a pad to protect a wound prior to bandaging to ensure that a sensitive part is not knocked or banged. It will increase the comfort of the dog if the limb is wrapped with a cotton wool dressing such as Softban, prior to application of the bandage. This should NOT be used on a wound as the fibres will stick to the injury.
Adhesive Tape	* Used to secure gauze pads if no bandage is to be applied. * Used to tape down a bandage at the end of its application rather than using safety pins or tying knots.* If a pad or nail is injured and you need to stop the dog licking it, you may wish to apply something

	like a sock over the injury and secure this to the upper part of the limb with the tape.* To hold together a gaping wound which may require stitching by the vet.
Antiseptic Cream	* Once a bleed has been controlled and a wound has been cleaned, it is a good idea to apply antiseptic cream prior to dressing the injury. The antiseptic cream will help to prevent infection in the wound. Creams such as Manuka Honey, Aloe Vera, Sudocrem and Savlon are excellent
Sterile Dressings	* To apply directly to a wound to cover the injury and keep it clean. Skin is the body's barrier to infection and if that barrier is broken, there is opportunity for bacteria to enter and cause infection.
Gauze	* Gauze is often used to cover an injury that is bleeding, prior to the application of cotton wool or bandages. The gauze will prevent the cotton wool fibres from sticking to the wound and becoming embedded in it.
Thermometer	* A dog's normal temperature is between 100.5°F to 102.5°F (about 38°C to 39.2°C). A temperature over 104°F or under 99°F indicates an emergency situation. An elevated temperature is often a sign of infection, pain or stress (or just excitement). A temperature below normal usually indicates a debilitating disease or disorder. Thermometers are

	considered most reliable if used rectally, although thermometers specifically designed for use in the ear of a dog are also available.
Tweezers	* Used for the extraction of small foreign bodies in wounds such as glass, splinters, ticks or grit. Although objects such as grass seeds can be removed with tweezers, it is advisable NOT to try to remove anything from the ear canal including seeds or ticks as your attempt could make the situation worse. Please do not try to remove BEE STINGS with tweezers as this will merely inject the poison deeper into the dog – something like a credit card that can "scrape" the stinger out is always preferable.* Useful in ensuring a wound dressing remains sterile when applying it to the injury. If the first aider already has blood, dirt and debris on her hands, being able to open a dressing and apply it without actually touching the sterile area is very important.
Scissors	* For cutting away fur surrounding an injury prior to cleaning and dressing the wound. * For cutting any unwanted length of bandage when the dressing has been applied.* For cutting free long fur, a collar or lead should the dog have become entangled in something such as barbed wire, a fence or branches in the under growth.
Gloves	* A first aider's priority is always to ensure their own safety. Before treating any animal

Windeze/Gas Relief Imodium Rehydration Sachet	(or human for that matter) it is essential to wear gloves which will act as a barrier to cross infection and assist with general wound hygiene.* Gloves can also be applied should a wound on a paw need to remain water-tight. The paw can be slipped into the glove and then be secured with adhesive tape.* Because a glove is waterproof, it can also be used in the temporary treatment of such injuries as sucking chest wounds. If applied and stuck down across 3 sides (the top, left and right sides allowing the bottom side unstuck), a very successful draining dressing can be fashioned, which will prevent the chest cavity filling with blood en route to the vet. It's a good idea to carry a gas relieving product such as Windeze or something with Simethicone in it for occasions when your dog may develop bloat. Bloat is a life threatening condition and your fast action can make all the difference to the outcome. Please check with your vet that he is happy for you to prescribe Imodium in cases of diarrhoea. Some breeds (usually listed as herding breeds such as Border Collies) may have a serious reaction to this type of medication which can be much worse than the diarrhoea so it is always best to check before administering any drug to your dog. That

Emetic (Salt, mustard, hydrogen peroxide or washing soda crystals)	said, it is widely recommended as a safe over the counter product for dogs. Always pays to be sure though Rehydration sachets are for use following an extreme bout of diarrhoea or any form of dehydration problem. Salt, mustard, hydrogen peroxide or washing soda crystals can all be used to induce vomiting in an emergency situation. Personally, I always use the washing soda crystals. If they are in crystal form, they can be swallowed as a tablet. If they are in granule form, mix with a tiny amount of water to meld into a lump and then this too can be administered to the dog as a tablet would be.

Other items (again, not an exhaustive list) that would be sensible to include as an addition in the kit:

Other items to include	Uses for the extra items
Saline Pods	* To wash away dirt and debris from the eyes and other areas. Wipe away the excess fluid with a gauze swab or paper handkerchief. * To moisten a dressing prior

	to application when covering a serious burn during transport to the vet.Hibiscrub can be used for humans or canines. Simply dilute to a pale pink colour and then use as a sterilising wash to wounds or bleeds. Not for use in the eye – for eye injuries, use saline wash.
Vinegar & Bicarbonate of Soda	* Vinegar will neutralise a **wasp** sting* Bicarbonate of soda will neutralise a **bee** sting
Cool (& heat) packs	Chemical cool packs (and heat packs) are fantastic. They lie dormant until you need them. There is a small device within the pack that you "snap" which causes a chemical reaction. This reaction causes the contents of the pack to freeze and become instantly cold (or hot in the case of heat packs)
Whistle	* Whistle to attract attention – especially in the dark
Foil Blanket	* To retain body warmth and help combat shock. * For use in cases of shock, hypothermia and when an animal is collapsed outdoors and needs sheltering from wind or rain. * To attract attention of rescuers as it affords a large silver target for view from air sea & mountain rescue helicopters etc.

Plastic Pouches	* To safely dispose of any used first aid products. Blood products need to be disposed of properly as they present a bio-hazard.
Alcohol-Free Cleansing Wipes	* To cleanse a wound prior to dressing it, particularly helpful when there is no access to clean running water
Torch	* Not all accidents happen during the day! * To check inside an ear canal.* To check dilation of pupils and reaction to light in the case of a collapsed animal which checking for response.
Emergency Number for the Vet	* Fast and direct communication with veterinary professionals in an emergency is a must.
Styptic Pencil	* For use with minor bleeds such as a snagged nail or dew claw, or a cut or graze.
Spare Lead	* Perhaps the injured animal is not your own, and another lead would help to calm and secure it while you tried to help or find its owner. * A lead can be used to loop around the top jaw and hold the mouth apart in the case of a choking incident allowing you access to the mouth and throat with less chance of being bitten while trying to help.
Antihistamine	* For use in cases of allergic reaction such as nettle sting, bee/wasp stings, various forms of bites and also incidents such as licking frogs/toads. N.B. Antihistamine should only be given

	having sought veterinary advice, to ensure that the right dosage and form of antihistamine is used. Antihistamines fall into the category of medications and should therefore generally only be prescribed by a vet.
Pencil/Paper	* Having the means to jot down information such as the heart rate/respiration rate of your dog means that you don't have to remember all the facts. * Being able to note down what time an incident occurred or the instructions a vet gives you when you phone will make it much easier for you to take all the facts on board.
Instructions/ First Aid Manual	* Often even the best first aider can go to pieces under the stress of an accident. A good memory aid can be of significant help in an emergency.
Tick Picker	* If you notice a tick on your dog, try to remove it as quickly as possible. It is important NOT to squeeze the tick so a purpose-designed instrument like a tick picker will prevent this from happening. If the tick's abdomen is squeezed it will inject contaminated blood from the tick into your dog.

We all know that oral hygiene and keeping our teeth clean is very important, but what about your dog's teeth? Some dog's suffer terribly with a build-up of tartar on their teeth, gum disease, tooth decay and bad breath – just as we would if our oral hygiene wasn't up to scratch. But how do you make sure your dog's gnashers are in tip top shape?

Firstly, look at what you feed your dog. Raw-feeders, who give their dogs a natural raw diet which includes meaty bones, swear by it as the gnawing and scraping on the bones cleans their teeth naturally – please be aware that feeding bones is a contentious subject with people for and against on both sides of the argument.

I personally do feed my guys a raw diet, but what I would say is that if you are going to feed bones, make sure they are RAW and never cooked. As soon as all the meat has been removed from the bone, throw it away and watch very carefully for any splinters of bone which could be dangerous for your dog.

Toothpaste for dogs also comes in canine-friendly flavours such as chicken or fish, to make the whole process less unpleasant for them. If you are looking to brush your dog's teeth, start very slowly by introducing them to a rubber thimble type toothbrush that fits on your finger as they will likely be more accepting of that than going straight for the bristles and the brush. It's a good idea to start when your dog is a puppy so this becomes the norm for him.

Please be aware that these pastes are designed to be abrasive and so shouldn't be used every day. Perhaps once a week would be enough and if you want to brush them more frequently, then simply taking a toothbrush and dipping it in water would be absolutely fine.

If you do notice a build-up of tartar on your dog's teeth, then it is possible to have them cleaned professionally by your vet. Your vet will give him an anaesthetic and have a thorough check of his teeth, extracting any he feels are diseased or decaying and cleaning up the remaining teeth to leave a Hollywood smile to be proud of.

Another thing you can try is a homeopathic treatment called Fragaria. Fragaria (strawberry) appears to soften tartar on teeth. Once softened, the normal action of brushing is more effective and can remove what would otherwise result in a heavy plaque build-up.

The suggested dosage on encrusted teeth is to take one of the tiny Fragaria pills per day for up to one month until tartar is significantly reduced. Simply hold the pill in the lid so you don't touch the surface of it with your fingers and pop it in the back of your dog's mouth. Once you have the tartar under control, it can be used as a preventative against new tartar build-up in the dosage of one pill, Fragaria 3c once weekly.

I admit that I was sceptical when I purchased this remedy but, after using this for 2 weeks, the difference was clear. After 3 weeks the teeth were perhaps 75% improved and by 4 weeks, they were virtually spotless.

MOUTH - LOSS OF AN INTACT TOOTH

On very rare occasions, say as the result of rough play, an accident, fight or even just getting caught up in something, complete loss of an intact tooth can occur – although it is fairly unusual in dogs.

Should you find yourself in this position and you are able to retrieve the tooth immediately, it should be placed in milk and the dog taken to the vet as soon as possible.

It **MAY SOMETIMES** be possible to replace the tooth. In most cases, however, the loss of the tooth will be accepted and will cause the dog no problems at all.

As in humans, dogs are born without any teeth.

By about the age of 7 months, most dogs should have their full set of permanent (adult) teeth. In some smaller breeds it is quite common for dogs to retain some of the primary (milk) teeth but, if this causes problems for the dog with overcrowding for example, these should be removed by your vet. A full set of adult teeth should total 42 as follows:

The Upper Jaw –
your dog should normally have:

3 incisors on each side
1 canine tooth on each side
4 premolars on each side
2 molars on each side

The Lower Jaw –
your dog should normally have:

3 incisors on each side
1 canine tooth on each side
4 premolars on each side
3 molars on each side

Incisors:
These teeth are designed for nibbling and grooming the dog's fur

Canines:
These teeth are designed for tearing flesh from bone

Premolars & Molars:
These teeth are designed to shear the food into swallowable portions

It is important to pay attention to your dog's dental hygiene and ensure that there is no build-up of tartar on the tooth which may lead to gum disease (bad breath is often a sign of poor oral hygiene). Often the diet you choose to feed your dog can play a big part in the health of their teeth – brushing your dog's teeth is a great way of ensuring these problems do not develop. If you do notice that your dog has developed tartar build-up on his teeth, a visit to your vet can determine whether he may need to have this removed with a "scale and polish".

MOUTH – EXCESSIVE DROOLING

As the owner of a very "slobbery" dog, I can tell you for sure that ALL dogs drool (it's just that some do it a hell of a lot more than others and some take it to a whole new level). Usually, with the prospect of food, the flood gates open and before you know it, you find yourself with a small pond at your feet. Dogs with heavy lips such as Mastiffs, St. Bernards and my own very beautiful Rhodesian Ridgebacks collect the saliva in their chops until it overflows!

Those of us who are owned by such animals just accept it as part of the package and invest in a good slobber towel!

Sudden, excessive drooling usually means that the dog is feeling off-colour so it's important to get to the bottom of the cause quickly, and certainly before it causes dehydration. As with most things, the time to sit up and take notice is when there is a change from the norm so, if a normally drool-free dog suddenly starts slobbering excessively, it's time to have a look in his mouth to see if you can identify the problem.

The most likely culprits for excessive drooling are:

Foreign Objects: Because of the way that our furry friends gulp down everything and anything, it's very common for them to get a foreign body lodged rather uncomfortably. Maybe he has a fragment of bone, fish scale or stick embedded in his gum, or something like a hide chew-stick wedged between his back teeth? Perhaps he's cut his tongue or managed to get a bit of bone jammed at the roof of his mouth? Check inside to see what you can find and if possible remove the offending article. If you cannot do it safely and without causing further harm to your dog, please see your vet for professional help immediately. Remember, the best way to check in your dog's mouth is by sitting him down between your legs, facing away from you as you tilt his head **backwards.** This position allows you to see right to the back of the throat and across the roof of his mouth.

Tooth Decay or Gum Disease: As mentioned in our blog on bad breath, poor dental care can result in a build-up of tartar, gum disease, tooth decay, wobbly and fractured teeth. A broken or decaying tooth could certainly be a cause of excessive drooling, so remember to take a sniff of Rover's breath just in case it gives you a clue.

Remember also while checking that you'll need to open up your dog's mouth – and not just so you can see the teeth at the back. When closed, a dog's fangs will overlap one another and it is possible to get a fragment of bone or wood lodged painfully against the gum line where these teeth overlap. If this happens, the fragment can penetrate the gum and cause an ulcer and decaying flesh which will smell badly as well as be painful. With the mouth closed, this fragment can be hidden from your view and easily missed.

Teething: When puppies grow, they begin to lose their baby teeth as their new adult teeth push through. Just as with humans, this phase can be quite painful and drooling is very likely at this stage in a puppy's development. Giving plenty of good chew toys for your pup to "cut his teeth" on is a good idea and using things like sticks of frozen vegetables such as carrots can really help as the cold soothes the discomfort on the gums.

Tumours:

There are tumours that, just as in humans, can arise in your dog's mouth. Tumours such as these can also be a cause of excessive drooling and they often go hand in hand with some other problems too such as bleeding from the mouth, depression, shying away from your hand as you stroke the head, difficulty in eating and, once again, the dreaded bad breath.

Other Causes:

If, having looked in your dog's mouth you cannot find anything out of the ordinary, it might be that your dog is feeling a little nauseous. It is very common to see dogs who are not keen on car-travel for example, drooling excessively on the journey. If this is the case for you and your dog, check out our blog all about travel sickness.

Pain:

Is there any chance that your dog is in pain for some reason? Has he hurt himself, pulled a muscle or could he be suffering with arthritis perhaps? Could he be starting with bloat or been poisoned by something he's picked up on a walk? Could he have an infection such as a poorly ear for example. Remember to check your dog all over and consider the day's events in case you are able to pinpoint any possible pain he could be in.

Liver Disease:

Dogs suffering from disease of the liver may also drool excessively. It is important that if you suspect liver disease in any way you should see your vet as soon as possible.

MOUTH - BAD BREATH

There's not much of a worse insult than the term "dog breath", but your dog really shouldn't have bad breath just because he's a dog. Bad breath may be a sign of many different problems from tooth decay, gum disease, an upset stomach or perhaps it's just that he has consumed something far from palatable to humans (we all know that there appears to be nothing quite like a mouth-full of cowpat!)

Bad breath could, however, indicate a more serious condition and in some cases the type of odour may give you a good clue as to the cause:-

* General "dog breath" (bad or necrotic smell on the breath)
When the smell is generally <u>bad</u>, it suggests bacteria in the mouth. Does your dog have an upset stomach? Has he eaten something different of late that hasn't agreed with him or perhaps picked up a bug (it might be that one of your other dogs has been off-colour and passed it on to him).

Alternatively, it may well be that your dog needs to have his teeth cleaned professionally or perhaps even undergo some dental work such as the removal of a bad tooth. Check your dog's dental hygiene and if you see any decay, bleeding at the gums or even a wobbly tooth, an appointment with your vet is advisable.

If you think you may need to look at dental hygiene for your dog, check out our blog on Keeping Teeth Clean.

* A sweet smell like pear drops or alcohol
If you can smell a fragrance like pear drops or nail varnish remover, this could suggest a problem with your dog's blood sugar levels, perhaps indicating diabetes or an infection. A sweet smell is something you should address as a matter of some concern and should not be left un-investigated. Your dog may require medication for the rest of his life to control his sugar levels or simply addressing his diet may be enough.

* A smell of urine or ammonia
If you can smell an ammonia type odour on your dog's breath, this could indicate a problem with the kidneys and an appointment with your vet should be organised immediately.

Please do not just accept bad breath as "normal" for your dog. It certainly isn't and neither you nor he need put up with it

MOUTH - BLEEDING TONGUE

A dog's tongue is important for many things including eating, cleaning themselves, lapping up water, bonding with the pack and showing submission. Luckily, there aren't many issues or illnesses that effect dogs' tongues, however they are susceptible to injury perhaps during general investigation with their mouths by biting, chewing or picking up something which may be sharp or have rough edges. Injuries could also arise in many other innocent ways including chewing a bone, rough play or maybe even simply trapping their tongue between the teeth (hey, I'm sure we've done that ourselves!)

Although small cuts or abrasions on other body parts may not be deemed all that much of a concern, tongue injuries can lead to significant problems. When a dog's tongue is cut, it bleeds excessively and this bleeding can be difficult to stop.

When to See a Vet

See your vet immediately if the cut appears deep or the bleeding is difficult or impossible to stop.

An ice cube held directly on the wound will constrict the blood vessels, and help stop bleeding. If you are unable to hold an ice cube to the tongue, offering ice cold water to drink should have the same effect.

Applying direct pressure while holding the tongue with a gauze pad will also work, assuming you can hold the tongue of course.

Everyday all-purpose flour can be used for small cuts to stop the bleeding. Simply pack the wound with the flour and then hold a gauze pad tightly against the wound. The flour should help the blood to clot.

If it's a small nick, keep an eye on it for a day or two to make sure it isn't becoming infected. If you can't get the bleeding to stop, or if it stops and starts to bleed again, then don't delay in calling your vet as your dog may need a stitch or two. If you are in any doubt, then call your vet.

NOSEBLEEDS

When dogs have nosebleeds, they usually occur as a result of trauma while running/playing or can sometimes happen after violent sneezing or even if they have got something lodged up a nostril. Dogs can have nose bleeds just like we do.

The best action is to try to keep the dog as quiet as possible and have him lie next to you with his head on your lap horizontally. We **do not** want to tip his head back very far as this may cause a choking incident so merely a slight degree of incline is sufficient.

If possible, you can use cold packs over the top of his nose and also on top of the muzzle to help slow down the bleed. Please be careful that you do not obstruct the dog's airway by blocking the nostrils.

N.B. Ice packs and frozen peas for example are great for this but we need to remember that the hair covering the muzzle is more sparse than on the rest of the body so please lay a cloth or towel over the muzzle BEFORE the cold packs to ensure they do not come in direct contact with his skin.

If the nose is still bleeding with no signs of reduction in volume of blood after half an hour, a quick call to your vet should be made to clarify the situation and get some professional advice. While it is likely he will merely tell you to keep doing what you're doing for another hour or so, as a mere "first aider" treating a bleed, we really should be talking to the professionals if things do not look like they are resolving after 30 minutes.

Remember to keep one eye on your dog's breathing rate and heart rate at all times as any increase in either could indicate that he is going into shock, something that can happen if the cause of the bleed is serious or if the amount of blood he is losing is severe. If his breathing rate or heart beat increase, check his capillary refill by gently pressing your finger on his gum, just above his canine tooth. When you take your finger off, you should see a white finger mark which will turn straight back to pink again. If it takes LONGER than 2 seconds to return to pink where your finger had been pressing, your dog is very poorly and needs an emergency appointment with your vet NOW.

NOSE - NASAL DISCHARGE OR SNEEZING

There are many different causes for nasal discharge or sneezing in our furry friends and it seems that longer-nosed dogs are more likely to suffer than their shorter-nosed counterparts.

The more common ones would be foreign bodies, allergic reactions, kennel cough viruses, fungal infections and, sadly, nasal tumours. Occasionally, severe dental infections can cause a nasal discharge too. This discharge is usually of a cloudy appearance and may well come from just the one nostril.

If grass seeds become lodged in the nasal passages, they can cause infection and discharge so it's a good idea to let your vet know if the sneezing or discharge starts when you have been exercising your dog in tall grasses. If you do believe your dog has something up his nose, please don't try to remove it yourself as you will likely push it in and make it worse, injure the dog as you try to help or possibly even get yourself bitten.

Symptoms:
Discharge (varying from clear, cloudy or bloody depending on the cause)
One or both nostrils may show discharge
Sneezing
Snorting
Gagging

N.B. Remember that dogs do like to lick away the evidence of nasal discharge, so you may need to keep a close eye to determine if there are actually any visible signs.

Once the vet has examined your dog (probably with the use of x-rays and a tiny camera with a light at the end called an endoscope) he may be able to diagnose the problem and remove it if it is something like a seed. If not, it might be necessary to take blood samples and biopsies to reveal the cause of the discharge.

Outlook

If the problem is diagnosed as kennel cough, a fungal infection or a foreign body in the nasal passages, the outlook for a cure is very good. However, if the tests reveal a nasal tumour or chronic inflammatory disorder, the outlook is sadly much poorer.

Therefore, if you notice your dog sneezing or having problems with any kind of nasal discharge, please seek professional veterinary attention for him. The sooner a foreign body is removed, an allergy is treated or a tumour is detected, the better the chances of a happy resolution.

NOSE - CRACKED OR DRY NOSE

So far as your dog is concerned, his nose is his most important organ. When it is dry, cracked or damaged in any way, that's a big deal. We often use our dogs' noses as an indicator as to whether they are well or not. Many people go with the concept that a wet nose is good, and a dry nose is bad, when in actual fact the surface of the nose can change with many things including the humidity, time of day or what he was doing and it doesn't necessarily denote a problem. If you check your dog's nose when he wakes, you will probably find that it is dry. This is because he naturally licks his nose throughout the day to keep it moist but, while sleeping, this does not happen and so the nose dries out as you'd expect. This is not a cause for concern and as soon as his normal day begins, it will promptly return to its normal cold, wet state.

There are, however, some things that you should take notice of such as excessive dryness of the surface of the nose causing it to become cracked or bleeding. Some things do of course need a trip to the vet including things like bleeding or green discharge from the nostrils or the nose flesh itself, the dog rubbing his face or scratching at his nose, or if you see an actual change in texture of the surface of the nose, thickening of the skin or even growths.

The causes for such changes can be quite varied, from those which are easily fixable, to the more serious. Just as we have triggers than can "set us off" so to do our dogs and they can be very varied indeed including:

* a new type of food

This can be a problem not only from the point of view of ingesting something that doesn't quite agree with him on the inside, but also contact with the food on the surface of his nose as he pushes it around his dish can cause irritation.

* his food bowl

We sometimes see problems arising with metal or plastic food bowls. Sometimes it's a straight-forward reaction to the metal or plastic and sometimes it is down to bacteria on the bowl if it is not washed out regularly enough – you wouldn't want to eat off a dirty plate now would you? If you find this to be a problem for your dog, then often an old fashioned ceramic dog bowl will solve your problems.

* dehydration

In order to keep the mucus membranes in tip top shape, all animals need to keep a good level of hydration. It is essential to keep a source of clean, fresh water available for your dog at all times. Failure to do so will quickly cause dehydration and in turn, the nose will suffer.

* central heating

In the winter, we often resort to central heating or natural fires. Our dogs like to snuggle up next to the warmth as much as we do and often this can cause the membrane of the surface of the nose to dry out and crack. Going from hot to cold and vice versa can also play havoc with the nose so protection with something like petroleum jelly when going outside could really help. (similarly in the summer, you may need to protect your dog's delicate nose with a good sunscreen. Check out our blog on doggy suntan lotion and warm weather advice.

* autoimmune problems such as Pemphigus or Lupus
Some autoimmune problems can affect the nose in this way and these can also affect other parts of the body too, so you may notice hair loss in some areas, blistering, bleeding, blackened flesh or thickening of the skin. It is however, likely to take a battery of veterinary tests to pinpoint the exact type of autoimmune problem, but once this has been established, medication can be commenced and usually fixes the things swiftly.

* Infection
When you think of the surface of the nose it's easy to understand how such an organ can become infected. If you have a warm, moist surface that frequently comes into contact with food, genital organs, urine or faeces as a dog's nose does, then any wound or damage to the surface of the skin very quickly admits germs. This environment is perfect for bacteria to breed so if it takes hold, it often multiplies very quickly. If a wound or damaged area has become infected, treatment from your vet should be sought immediately.

* Cancer
Just like us, our dogs can, of course, develop skin cancer. Thickening of the skin, asymmetrical growths, bleeding or blisters can certainly be a sign to look out for. Your vet will need to take a biopsy to get a definitive diagnosis and rule out any other possibilities.

So what should you do?

Hopefully, the information above will give you a few ideas as to what MAY be the problem. If you think it could be an autoimmune problem or tumour, then obviously a visit to your vet is urgent. If you think it's down to a food allergy, change his diet or see your vet for further investigation to detect the food he is intolerant to. Do you clean his food and water dish regularly? If not, let's start TODAY

Things you can try to soothe the nose go from purpose made remedies such as NatPet Salve (my personal favourite) or Natural Dog Company's Snout Soother, through to the more everyday things such as Petroleum Jelly, Coconut Oil or even common-or-garden Chap-Stick (the Forever Living Aloe Vera range also do a super chap-stick which is a great addition to pop in your first aid kit for minor scrapes, abrasions and dry bits).

The key to the application of any of these topical products of course is that you MUST keep the mouth and muzzle tightly closed as you apply it. You need time to rub in the product so that at least some of it gets the chance to be absorbed before your dog is able to lick it straight off again. Good luck with that!

We recently suffered with this problem after our tour away in the motorhome for 2 weeks teaching in Scotland. Two out of three of my dogs got dry, cracked noses due to the cold nights and the heating coming through the vents as they slept. After 3 days of coconut oil application, Axl's nose went from cracked and actively bleeding, to soft and supple with just a silver line where the crack once was.

CHAPTER 18:   PARASITES   PG

WORM COUNT

The document below was created by a Facebook friend of mine, the lovely Jodi Davies. Many people are opting to try to reduce the amount of chemical medication, pesticides and wormers they use with their dogs and one way of checking to see if your dog actually needs to be wormed is by carrying out a *WORM COUNT*.

Although it is practice to worm every 4 months or so (as per manufacturers guidelines) oftentimes this is just not necessary. The level of worm infestation can rely heavily on various factors including the dog's life style, what animals he mixes with including cats etc and where you choose to walk. If you perform a **WORM COUNT** you may find that he doesn't actually have any in which case you are simply pumping him full of chemicals for no good reason.

So, here's Jodi's document which explains what **WORM COUNTS** are for those of you who've never heard of them but may just be interested.

WORM COUNTS –
By Jodi Davies for the Facebook Rhodesian Ridgebacks Show Page UK - http://www.wormcount.com/companion-animals/

Until Wormcount.com was created, routine worm counts for companion animals were expensive and time consuming, as they were carried out almost exclusively by a Vet. You took your pet to the Vet, and then had to return with a faecal sample, which was then sent off to the lab. Several days passed and you were presented with the results, and a big bill. Worming advice was given and generally chemical worming products were also sold to you. There is nothing wrong with this process, except that it is taking up a Vet's very valuable diagnostic surgery time on a routine process.

Now Wormcount.com offers a personal, fast, reliable, cost-effective alternative. This will save a visit to the Vet for you, and maximise the Vet's time for sick animals.

So what is a worm count?

■A Faecal Egg Count or FEC counts the number of worm eggs in your pet's faeces (poo).

■The results are presented as 'eggs per gram' (epg) of faeces. There is an easy to understand key on your Wormcount.com result sheet.

■The number of eggs is an indication of the number of adult worms in the gut of your dog or cat.

■Lungworm and heartworm tests are different as they test for live larvae in the faeces.

Why should I use a worm count?

■It will help you to decide whether you need to worm

■It can tell you if your worming regime is working

■It can give you information about the amount of contamination going into your environment.

PARASITES - FLY STRIKE

I always encourage our Rhodes 2 Safety followers to get in touch if they have any questions or any past experiences they'd like to share with us all. Yesterday, I received this one in relation to Fly Strike:-

"Years ago I had a dog suffer with fly strike. I never did find what caused it - is it preventable?"

What a great question, and one worth covering especially at this time of year when the temperatures are hot and humid and everybody is finding it just a little bit too warm and sticky.

Fly Strike is also known as Myiasis and leads to an infestation of maggots. When the maggots appear, we call it "fly blown" or "fly strike".

Fly strike can occur in all animal species, even humans, if the conditions are just right. Flies are attracted, basically, to anything "stinky", so we are talking infected skin, sweaty/dirty skin folds, matted fur, diarrhoea, vomit, blood and pus (as I said, basically anything stinky!).

The flies are attracted to the stench and lay their eggs which, in a matter of just 8-12 hours, will hatch out into maggots. The maggots will feed only on dead skin tissues and rotting wounds and as you can imagine, this is a very painful and irritating sensation for the animal playing host to the little wrigglers. As the eggs hatch out so quickly, fly strike is a condition that increases in severity at an alarming rate. If left untreated for any length of time, the maggots will begin to eat the healthy flesh as well which can actually prove fatal for your pet, particularly if they are old, young or frail due to a recent illness or poor condition.

Getting your dog, cat or rabbit to the vet as soon as possible cannot be stressed too highly. It is important for you to determine exactly what it was that attracted the flies to your dog in the first place – perhaps he has been ill recently with an upset tummy or "runny bum". Maybe he has been vomiting. Is his fur matted which could be disguising a wound or sore beneath? Is he overweight or "designed" to have skin folds which may have become sweaty and sore or infected without you realising? Is he incontinent and the smell of the urine is enticing the flies or perhaps he has weeping eyes and this is what the flies are homing in on? Any unpleasant odour if left without bathing could easily be the source of your problem.

As well as addressing the actual cause of the infestation (say an upset tummy in the case of diarrhoea or matted fur causing a sore beneath), your vet will need to remove all the maggots as soon as possible before doing anything else.

In order to get full access to the wound site to ensure the area can be flushed and cleaned thoroughly, the fur will likely need to be clipped away and any moist or weeping areas allowed to dry off.

Once the immediate "maggot-removal" treatment has been done, your dog will probably require a course of antibiotics and possibly painkillers to help make him more comfortable. If the area is one that he can reach, then please try to keep him from scratching or gnawing at the wound site – the application of a Buster or Elizabethan type collar to prevent this might help.

Obviously, prevention is better than the cure so taking care to bathe and groom your pet regularly will prevent problems such as dermatitis and wet eczema which will attract flies.

If your pet has been ill, please seek professional help quickly - it's a good idea to keep him indoors while he is ill to prevent flies landing on him while you are out.

If your dog is overweight or is supposed to have rolls of skin on his body, such as the Shar-Pei, the Basset Hound or the Dachshund for example, then please take extra care, particularly when the weather is warm, to keep the skin folds clean and fresh and free from sweat or "cheesy" exudate

PARASITES - WALKING DANDRUFF (CHEYLETIELLA MITE)

Cheyletiella Mites (or walking dandruff as they are often known) are Zoonoses.

Zoonoses are diseases that can be transmitted between vertebrate species, including man, which means they are not restricted just to our furry friends.

As with the Harvest Mite, "walking dandruff" lives on the surface of the skin and feeds on skin cell debris. It can cause a scaly coat and some, but not all, dogs find this condition itchy.

Diagnosis:
Detecting walking dandruff mites can be achieved by brushing the coat onto a dark surface and, as the mites themselves are pale in colour, they show up on the dark background and can be seen walking about – and thus the reason for their charming name! Alternatively, a visit to the vet can see the use of the sticky tape method of detection where the vet may simply use a clear sticky tape on the dog's coat to pick up any adults or eggs and then examine them under the microscope for confirmation.

Treatment:
Insecticidal preparations obtained from your vet, including sprays and shampoos, are an effective way to treat these mites. This parasite has a long life cycle and therefore it is important that all dogs which have been in contact with the affected animal should also be treated. Please take care to thoroughly clean any bedding and vacuum the house. It is often prudent to treat soft furnishings and carpets with treatments sold for flea prevention

due to the fact that these mites can continue to survive <u>off</u> their hosts for a short time.

If you would prefer NOT to go down the chemical route for treatment, Diatomaceous Earth is another good alternative – see blog on D.E. for further information.

PARASITES - HARVEST MITES

The most recent information suggests that there could possibly be a link between Harvest Mites and SCI (Seasonal Canine Illness) but as yet, more research is needed. With that in mind, I thought we'd take a look at what they are and what to do about them.

Harvest Mites (known as chiggers or berry bugs) appear, as the name suggests, around harvest time – ie late summer/early autumn. Harvest Mites usually infest field mice but can also live on the surface of the dog's skin, and feed on skin cell debris rather than burrowing under the surface.

The mites themselves are just visible to the naked eye and often appear as tiny red or orange dots and form clusters – hence their name "berry bugs".

Symptoms:
Severe itching which is usually found on the underside of the abdomen or on the feet/toes
Irritation causing the dog to lick his feet
Larval stage mites may be visible between the toes
Larval stage mites may be seen between the skin folds at the edge of the ear flaps

Treatment:
Various insecticidal preparations and shampoos can be used in the treatment of Harvest Mites, although some dogs may require treatment with anti-inflammatory medication as well. It is usual for this type of mite to just "disappear" following the first frost in September.

A great non-chemical treatment that has been suggested is something called Neem Oil. Neem oil on the coat can be an effective deterrent to various critters including ticks, fleas and mites as it has a very pungent, savoury odour. It is, however, worth noting that if you intend to use your dog for breeding any time soon, this treatment should be avoided as the smell can be very off-putting for any would-be suiter! Apparently in some parts of the world it is even used as a contraceptive.

Another great way of treating Harvest Mites, particularly if you favour non-chemical alternatives is Diatomaceous Earth (DE). We have done a blog all about DE and its many varied uses on another post, but one of our followers, Sue Craigie of Imbaliridgebacks.co.uk sent me this message about using it for Harvest Mites. Sue writes "One of my Ridgebacks had a Harvest Mite infestation and I cleared it up completely by rubbing DE (Diatomaceous Earth) into the affected areas. Within about a week the mites and sores had gone and her skin was back to normal."

PARASITES - DEMODECTIC MANGE

This is caused by the Demodex Mite that ALL dogs have, and lives in the hair follicles in the skin. These mites are transferred to them as puppies from their mother when suckling. Usually, because their numbers are small, they cause no problems but in some cases (possibly when associated with a hereditary or immune problem) they can increase and cause symptoms.

* Symptoms can be restricted to small areas or be widespread.

* The mites can cause hair loss and skin reddening on the face and front legs.

* Often there is evidence of crusty skin areas and severe dermatitis.

* Unlike Sarcoptic mange (scabies), it is not particularly itchy.

Most cases of localised infection clear up on their own after several weeks and treatment may only be required if it worsens into the generalised form. If it does, this may require clipping, medicated bathing and repeated injections to kill the mites.

Prevention: Dogs with severe Demodectic mange should not be used for breeding as there is some suggestion that the tendency to the disease may be inherited.

PARASITES - MANGE - Sarcoptic (Scabies)

As per a request, today's and tomorrow's info is about **mange** (and can I just say that typing this for you all is making me itch like a good 'un!!!)

Sarcoptic mange (**scabies**) is caused by a tiny, microscopic mite, which lives permanently within the top layers of the skin.

* It causes relentless scratching and rubbing.

* Initially, it is often the ear tips, elbows and hocks which are most affected but, if neglected, symptoms can spread over the entire body surface.

* It is highly contagious and easily transferred between dogs.

* It can be transferred to humans and appears as small, red, circular areas on the skin which are very itchy.

* Owners who develop any skin irritation while their dog is affected should seek medical advice for themselves also.

PARASITES - STAPH (STAPHYLOCOCCUS) SKIN INFECTIONS

Sometimes, dogs get itchy or you might notice that their coat is not quite as good as it might be and this could actually be something called Staphylococcus – also known as a "Staph" skin infection. Infection might be noticed in many locations including the eyes, feet, skin, ears and respiratory system.

Signs that might catch your eye may start with nothing more significant than a thinning of the coat or a flaky/dandruff or scurfy appearance of your dog's usually glossy coat.

This condition can affect both dogs and humans alike. The Staph bacteria are sometimes present in the upper respiratory tract and can generally be found living quite harmlessly on the skin of most animals. It lies dormant in healthy animals but if for any reason the skin is irritated, this can trigger a Staph infection within the pores.

Because it can be passed from animal to animal, or animal to human, care should be taken when treating this condition to ensure you do not infect yourself or other animals in your household in the process.

Signs & Symptoms:

You may also see:

Inflammation and balding patches of hair loss
Plaque-like lesions with crusty edges where the hair falls out

Pimples and scabs around the lesions
Abscesses and pustules, often around the foot pads
Itching
Lethargy
Fever
Loss of Appetite

Animals Most At Risk:
Young animals with an under developed immune system
Old animals with a "worn out" immune system
Compromised animals with autoimmune problems such as
hypothyroidism

Allergies to many things are the most likely triggers and these include:
New Diets
Fertilizers
Grass Seeds
Pollen
Insect Bites
Detergents

Diagnosis:
A visit to your vet is a must. She will need to take a complete
history and then likely run a full set of bloods, biochemical profile
and urinalysis. To try to find exactly which bacteria or fungus
they are dealing with, skin tests including skin scrapes for
microscopy will be taken and, if required, possibly even a skin

biopsy to get to the bottom of things.

Treatment:

A course of oral antibiotics will usually be prescribed and, with serious cases, it can be for as long as 3-6 weeks. This very long course is necessary to prevent recurrence of the infection and to keep the situation under control and, as this form of infection can be caused by **MRSP** (Methicillin Resistant Staphylococcus Pseudintermedius) it can be notoriously difficult to treat. MRSP is a superbug – I'm sure you will have heard of **MRSA** and know how difficult that can be to treat and the same is true of MRSP which is resistant to many, many different forms of antibiotic and it can be quite a task to find one that responds.

As well as the medication, it is important to ensure your dog is given a high quality, nutritious diet and that any autoimmune conditions are addressed. Regular bathing with an antimicrobial body wash to clean the skin and lesions will also help the healing process. Remember that this condition can be spread very easily so hygiene should be taken seriously when cleaning the wounds, bedding and grooming equipment. These should be regularly cleaned, and other animals within the home should be carefully monitored to ensure they do not contract the infection too.

PARASITES - LUNGWORMS

I was just sitting having my breakfast and saw an advert on the TV about treatment for lungworm and I wondered just how many "ordinary" pet owners actually know anything about it. So, here goes ...

Lungworm infestation can be acquired from slugs or snails as intermediate hosts, through sniffing or licking them, which causes the parasite egg to enter the dog's respiratory tract. It is frequently passed from mother to puppy when the young are suckling. Once the parasite takes hold, adult worms produce nodules which cause inflammation and swelling in the trachea (windpipe) and branches of the lungs. This inflammation causes wheezing and a harsh cough, similar to kennel cough. When infestation occurs, it is usually seen in younger dogs, housed together. Another sign you may also notice is that the dog may appear lethargic or depressed.

Because lungworms are not terribly common in dogs, and there are many other, much more frequent causes for these same symptoms, a process of elimination must take place to diagnose the cause and treat the underlying condition.

Diagnosis may require a faecal sample, the use of a stethoscope, x-rays and possibly endoscopy (endoscopy is using a camera to look inside – in this case down the throat and into the lungs), but it is usually sufficient to treat lung worms with prescription wormers. Severe reactions/infestations may require steroids for 3-10 days, although the outlook for complete cure is very good. If you have any other pets in the home, please make sure that you get them tested and treated too.

Please clean your dog's area thoroughly and wash all bedding regularly to prevent the condition recurring. Remember to monitor your dog closely while he is recovering as occasionally they may have a reaction to the deworming treatments. If you do notice any diarrhoea, vomiting or changes in his behaviour, please contact your vet for advice.

PARASITES - TICKS

Ticks come in lots of different colours and sizes; from grey, pink, red, brown and black, and right through from the size of a pin-head to a big fat juicy rice-crispy. They are carried on things like sheep and deer and drop off into the grass and undergrowth so that when an animal passes through; they grab onto it and thus have a new host. Dogs most often get them on their heads or necks because of the way they like to shove their faces into all sorts of places to sniff and explore, but also because the ticks like to latch on to parts of the body with a good blood supply near to the surface that's easy to get to.

The tick starts off small, with skinny little black legs and 2 pincer-type mouthparts at the front, and a round abdominal sac at the back. They burrow their mouthparts into their host's skin, administer saliva that turns to a concrete to lock them in position on the skin, and then suck the blood straight out.

But how do they do that? Do they screw themselves in clockwise? Anti-clockwise? Straight down???? Well in actual fact, their "style" is more likened to the breast stroke. Type the following link in to your search engine to see a video and brilliant demonstration of just how the tick burrows into the skin. http://www.smithsonianmag.com/science-nature/watch-a-tick-burrowing-into-skin-in-microscopic-detail-6649718/?no-ist

The abdominal sac then fills up with blood and swells to the size of a raisin.

They carry all sorts of nasty infections (including Lyme's Disease) which they can pass on to the dog (and to you if you are not careful when you are dealing with them) so it's really important to remove them as quickly and carefully as you can, and this is how you should do it.

First things first – get your gloves on. The infected blood and "juice" in a tick is dangerous stuff and you don't want to risk getting it on yourself as you try to help your dog. Even the tiniest cut or injury to your fingers gives an excellent entry route for the contaminated tick blood to enter YOUR body too.

There are lots of old wives tales written and passed on about how best to get a tick off and although a lot of them will work, they do have a lot of risks associated with them, so first how **NOT** do it.

Do Not Squeeze the tick between your thumb and finger – This will just inject the poisonous infected blood into your dog

Do Not Burn them off with a cigarette or match head –
The tick will regurgitate the poisonous infected blood into your dog as it tries to get away from the heat of the cigarette or match **(the same is true of using alcohol or liquid soap)**.

Do Not Cover the tick in Vaseline –
Although this WILL suffocate the tick eventually, the tick will die potentially leaving his head buried in your dog.

Do Not Throw the tick into the toilet to dispose of it –
Ticks are fantastic little swimmers and will merely live to bite another day

Do Not Throw the tick onto the fire –
The tick will "pop" as the contents of its abdomen heats up and the noxious vapours will be released into the air and is dangerous if breathed in (particularly by young children and pregnant ladies)

Do Not Pull the tick's body off the dog abruptly –
If the head is left in the dog it may become infected and cause an abscess

Removing ticks – what you SHOULD do:

Do Put on your gloves

Do Invest in a "tick-picker" which is a special tool just for the job. There are several versions of this instrument but the main two have either a loop at the end to hook around the tick's body or a 'V' shape at the end to wedge under the abdomen.

Either tool is fine but if you don't have one at all, provided you have your gloves on, you can use your nails to grip the tick, as close as possible to the dog's skin, and then firmly, but not too tightly, grasp the tick by the body and pull straight out in a constant movement, keeping the pressure on firmly but not "with a jerk". The tick will put up quite a bit of resistance due to the saliva it used to glue itself to the skink, and then will suddenly let go (often with a bit of a "snap" kind of noise and feeling).

Do check that the tick's head has not been left behind in the dog's skin. If you are unsure, run your finger across the front end of the tick. If the head is there, it will feel a hard, grainy bit at the front which is the tick's mouth parts. If it feels soft, then likely you have left the head in the dog's skin. If it has, keep an eye on it as usually the head will be ejected as a "foreign body" by the dog's skin on its own within a couple of days anyway.

Do clean the wound site with sterile wipes or soap and water.

Do dispose by killing it in some rubbing alcohol, putting it in a jar or popping it in a freezer bag, placing it in the freezer and keeping it for two or three days. If during this time your dog displays any behavioural changes or the wound appears infected, please take the dog AND THE TICK to the vet to be checked for infection. It is easier to test a tick for Lyme's Disease than the dog himself so having the critter with you to present to the vet is the best idea.

If you do not want to keep the tick, then please kill it by crushing in toilet tissue then place it in an outside bin.

For the most part, that will be that and a veterinary appointment is not usually necessary unless:

*   The head is still in the dog's skin after a couple of days.

*   The area looks red and/or inflamed after a couple of days.

*   The dog shows signs of behaviour change/discomfort.

*   The tick is in the ear canal, the genitalia, or very close to the eye lid, in which case you should not try to remove it yourself, but seek veterinary help.

As always, prevention is better than the cure. There are lots of pharmacological preparations you can use to try to prevent ticks with your dogs. Some of these drugs can be a little harsh or even contraindicated with some dogs so always check with your vet before starting on a new treatment regime, just to make sure he is happy with your choice of therapy (particularly if your dog is a herding breed as some have more problems than others – dogs with the MDR1 genetic fault in particular can struggle with pesticides so please do check first.)

I usually use grapefruit essential oil – a few drops in some almond oil – sprayed on to a grooming mit and then wiped on to my dog's coats weekly in "tick season" paying close attention to the head, ears and neck – as the ticks really don't like either the citrus smell or that of the almond and this seems to do the job for us with a short-coated breed

HEALTH TESTS

Many people seem to think that breeding a litter is a license to print money. Honestly? ... if it's done right, it really isn't at all. The costs involved in producing a healthy puppy are not insignificant and the work and time spent getting all your "ducks in a row" before mating even takes place can be pretty eye-watering.

It's really important, if you are looking to buy a puppy, that you find yourself a breeder who not only knows what they're doing, but is prepared to takes the steps to do as many health tests as possible BEFORE breeding. That said, new tests are becoming available all the time, so just because a test wasn't done in the past, doesn't mean it should not be performed on subsequent matings in the future. A good breeder will keep abreast of such topics and ensure that they do the absolute best they can to breed a healthy litter for the welfare of the puppy, and their owners, who will have to live with the breeder's choices for many years to come.

Often, different breeds will have specific genetic problems to test for – not all breeds suffer the same hereditary conditions, so you need to ensure that YOUR breeder has tested for all the problems which can be associated with your chosen breed.

There are MANY tests (and I do mean pages full!). These can range from everything including hip and elbow scoring to ensure sound and healthy joints which will less likely result in arthritis and mobility problems in later life, autoimmune diseases, early onset deafness, blindness, epilepsy, spinal problems, coat colour, coat length etc etc (the list truly is immense).

Just now in Ridgebacks, for example, a new test has become available to test for something called JME (Juvenile Myoclonic Epilepsy). I've just had my boys tested by submitting samples from them at Crufts (there are genetic labs in various countries who you can send samples of blood or cheek swabs away too and they will have the results back to you usually within a couple of weeks) – the laboratory we used was Laboklin UK – http://www.laboklin.co.uk/laboklin/

I'm very relieved that Axl and Chi's results have come back and been reported as clear (as have those of Chi's mother) which means they do not carry the gene and so any resulting puppies from either of them will not be affected either. When we used Axl at stud and he produced his family of 12 puppies, the need for this particular test wasn't known and wasn't available, but testing now not only means we know that Chi is clear should he sire a litter in the future, but it also means we can report back to Axl's puppy owners that another test has been done retrospectively and that their babies are clear too. When you breed a litter, a good breeder makes sure they are responsible for each and every pup FOR LIFE.

JME is something very new to most of us in the Ridgeback world, so to ensure it is not passed on in future litters, testing to see if it is in the lines of any dog which may be used in a breeding programme is a must.

Simply then, my advice would be that you research your chosen breed and find out which health tests are advisable specifically for them (some tests MUST be carried out in line with individual breed club requirements and also Kennel Club guidelines, but others are simply ADVISORY. However, just because a test is listed only as "advisory", doesn't mean that breeders should scrimp on the testing.). Find a breeder who is as particular about making sure the resulting pups will be sound as you are. After all, you will hopefully have a good 12 years or more with this bundle of joy and its 12 years you want to spend enjoying rather than going backwards and forwards to a vet for conditions that could have been avoided.

PUPPIES - VACCINATIONS

When you get your beautiful new puppy he has some immunity already, passed on through the milk from his mother. However, it is vitally important to protect him before he goes out into the big wide world.

The normal sequence of events is as follows though the timings for vaccinations is always being tweaked:-

@ 8-10 weeks, he will receive his first vaccination
@ 10-12 weeks, he will receive his second vaccination (NOT before 10 weeks)
@ 10-12 weeks, you may choose to have the kennel cough protection given

Two weeks following the kennel cough and second injection, he will be ready to face the world outside.

Before the full sequence above has been completed, your puppy is **NOT** protected enough to go out into the general surroundings. He may go out in your garden where you know only your dogs (who presumably were also vaccinated as puppies) will visit.

He may NOT go outside the front door where you have no idea what dogs may have been visiting and therefore may also NOT visit parks, or pavements where other dogs go.

When your puppy is one year old, he will be recalled by the vet for his booster vaccination. This booster should ensure good immunity for the rest of his life, although Distemper is frequently included in booster vaccinations for other diseases when combined vaccines are used.

There is a lot of discussion as to whether vaccinations should be repeated annually (as per usual veterinary practice), three-yearly (as per recent Kennel Club directives), or not at all. This is a very debatable subject and one which I cannot in unbiased conscience advise on, but I would suggest that you do your own research on the matter and do whichever you believe in your heart is the best option for the safety of your pet. Puppy vaccinations, however, are **NOT UNDER DEBATE**. Everybody is agreed that these are a must.

So why vaccinate a puppy before taking him outside? Well, even the most hardened anti-vaccination supporters would generally agree with **puppy vaccination,** as the diseases we vaccinate against include some very nasty infections indeed including Parvovirus and Distemper.

Parvo Virus: See alternate blog.

Distemper: Distemper is a virus which is spread through quite close contact allowing the virus to be directly inhaled into the respiratory system. The incubation period is around 2 weeks.

In some milder forms of the disease, it is possible that it may go unnoticed, however, the symptoms of more serious cases of Distemper include:

- high temperature
- nasal and eye discharge

- troublesome cough (caused by respiratory infection or pneumonia)
- diarrhoea and occasional vomiting
- lack of energy & poor appetite are common in the early stages

As the dog starts to recover, it may begin to exhibit signs of permanent damage to the central nervous system in the form of fits and convulsions or perhaps spasmodic twitches.

Diagnosis
The characteristic symptoms above, particularly the respiratory infection, and then a selection of the other symptoms together, would direct us to a diagnosis but confirmation is very difficult as laboratory tests are not 100% reliable.

Treatment
As with Parvo Virus, there is no cure and merely supporting the dog with nursing until his own immunity kicks in and sees off the infection is the only recourse. Antibiotics may be given to prevent complications arising from bacterial infections and intravenous fluids might be beneficial in easing the effects of vomiting and diarrhoea. It is important that all discharges (nasal and from the eyelids) be cleaned away carefully and the areas kept moist and clean at all times.

Recovery:
Recovery may take from weeks to months and with severe bouts of the disease some of the symptoms may be permanent. For dogs that have experienced severe damage to their nervous system, humane euthanasia may be the only course of action.

SKELETON - ARTHRITIS

We use the term a lot, but what exactly is arthritis? Well the Latin translation is:

Arth = joints
Itis = inflammation

The first thing to say is that it is not a single disease – it is a term that covers over 100 medical conditions. If you have trouble moving around or feel pain and stiffness in your body, you could have arthritis and the same is true of our furry friends. In the majority of cases arthritis causes pain and swelling in the joints. Eventually, a swollen joint can suffer severe damage.

Risk Factors contributing to Arthritis:

* Old age

* Overweight dogs

* Large breed dogs

* Previous joint injury

* Dogs with predisposing conditions e.g. hip dysplasia, osteochondritis dissecans (OCD)

Checklist for arthritic dogs:

* Keep daily exercise levels constant

* Swimming can be beneficial

* Give medication as prescribed but DO NOT increase the dose without advice

* Ensure the dog's bedding is well padded

* Reduce weight if necessary (with veterinary advice). Note that weight loss must be achieved by modifying the diet and not by increasing the amount of exercise.

* Be prepared for symptoms to vary a little in intensity from day to day, week to week and season to season – even when on medication

The following article was by www.dogsnaturallymagazine.com and is all about holistic treatments for arthritis, just in case you wanted to try a less pharmacological direction in looking after your dog.

http://www.dogsnaturallymagazine.com/holistic-treatment-of-arthritis/

SKELETON - LAMENESS

Lameness is usually caused by pain but non-painful lameness may also occur. Two examples of non-painful lameness are "mechanical lameness" where limb movement is restricted but pain-free, and neurological lameness which usually means paralysis of a limb or part of a limb.

Apart from non-painful lameness, anything which hurts the dog will cause it to... *limp*.

Usual causes are:-
Cuts or injury to the pad
Sprains and strains
Arthritis
Nail problems/over grown
Fractures
Dislocations
Bone inflammation or infection
Developmental problems in young dogs
Spinal or neck injuries
Bone tumour

A simple common cause of lameness in dogs is foreign bodies, e.g. glass or a grass seed lodged in the foot pad, between the toes or perhaps even a split in a toe nail.

Another very easy cause to consider is that of corns. If you can feel a build-up of hard skin on the foot pad, this may be a corn of which simple removal will make all the difference.

SKELETON - HIND LEG LAMENESS IN MORE THAN ONE LIMB

To try to ascertain if there is hind leg lameness, the dog should be trotted *slowly* away from the observer. The dog favours the *sore* leg by taking less weight on it.

The impression given is that the hindquarter on the GOOD side moves down more – the dog seems to fall onto it. The sore leg is the other leg.

Lameness in more than one leg

Lameness in more than just one leg at a time can be much harder to detect. The dog may seem to be generally sore and adopt a "paddling" or "pussy-footing" gait. More weight may seem to be taken on the front or hind legs, or on one or other side of the body. Two-limb lameness may only be able to be detected by the vet.

"Shifting" lameness is when all the legs are sore, either at once or at different times. This can be characteristic of bone inflammation in younger dogs or certain other rare conditions.

N.B. It's a good idea to have somebody film you as you trot your dog away from them so that you can view the gait a few times without needing to re-run the dog excessively. Sometimes the limp may be quite difficult to detect on the first viewing.

SKELETON - FRONT LEG LAMENESS

To ascertain if there is lameness in either of the front legs, the dog needs to be *trotted* towards the observer as lameness is harder to detect while walking unless it is very severe.

Trot the dog slowly in a straight line on a relaxed lead. If your dog scrabbles, pulls or leans to the side it can be impossible to see the lameness clearly.

The dog favours the sore leg by taking less weight on it. The impression given is that the dog "nods" downwards with its head **ON THE GOOD LEG**. The sore leg is the opposite one to the one which is nodded on.

Top Tip: It's a good idea to have the dog filmed as you trot him as the limp might be very discreet and require 3 or 4 viewings to be absolutely sure. It also means that you can video him again a couple of days later and see if there has been any improvement/deterioration in his motion rather than relying on your memory.

SKELETON - STRAINS, SPRAINS & FRACTURES

As with humans, a strain or sprain (for example as the result of a twisted ankle after a trip or fall, or shoulder muscle strain due to landing badly when jumping and playing) needs rest.

The little memory technique for treating a strain or sprain is **RICE**

R= REST
Crate rest is best as it prevents too much running about or jumping on and off the furniture. As the dog begins to feel better, he often does too much and goes back to square one, so crate rest really helps speed up the healing process.

I=ICE
Applying an ice pack or cold compresses may be helpful immediately after the injury & for a few days after. The simplest technique is to apply a bag of frozen food (eg peas) to the area for 10-20 minutes at a time, 4-6 times daily.

C=COMPRESSION
If you are competent in applying a bandage, you can use vet wrap to give support to the limb and keep any swelling to a minimum. Ensure that the dressing is not too tight as this will inhibit circulation. Remember that if the limb begins to swell within the dressing, it might get tighter as the swelling increases so check the dressing frequently making sure that the limb beyond the point of the dressing is a nice temperature – too cold tells you it's TOO TIGHT.

E=ELEVATION

As with any injury, a sprain or strain will cause the limb to swell. If we can elevate the injured part, this will help minimise the swelling a little. Therefore, if you can place the dog's limb on a cushion, this will elevate it enough to help. Obviously, keeping a dog in any one position is tricky, so don't beat yourself up if the little fella won't oblige!

FRACTURES (danger signs AFTER treatment for fractures)
If your dog has had a broken limb, it is important to follow your vet's advice to the letter, keeping your dog calm and his activity restricted. However, there are some danger signs we can look out for after treatment which may indicate things are not going well:-

* the dog seems depressed, off colour and is reluctant to eat
* the limb or paw swells up
* pain seems to be increasing rather than decreasing
* surgical wounds are swollen, discharging or not healing
* there is no attempted use of the leg several weeks after surgery
* a discharge is noted from underneath any dressing or around the pins of an external fixator

Should any of these signs occur, please contact your vet ASAP

SKELETON – MOVING A SPINAL TRAUMA PATIENT

A spinal injury can occur in all sorts of ways from a very unfortunate accident during normal play, to an awkward fall or perhaps a road traffic accident. Although he may have a loss of sensation, it is to be expected that most dogs who have experienced spinal trauma will be frightened and in pain so **ALWAYS** muzzle them as they may bite as you try to move them.

Signs that your dog may have experienced a spinal injury include:
Crying/Yelping
Swelling of the area
Wound/Deformity/Bulging of the area
Heat at the site of the injury
Paralysis (partial or complete)
Incontinence (bladder and/or bowel)

As well as the physical clues that would indicate a spinal injury, we must also consider what is known as the "mechanism of the injury" (sometimes you don't need to be a vet to know that the accident you've just seen will have caused a serious injury to the animal's spine due to the way the dog was hit or the way he landed).

Should we move the dog?

We must consider where the accident happened. If it is safe to leave the dog where you find him, then keep him calm, warm and still exactly where he is and call the vet **IMMEDIATELY**.

If it is NOT safe to keep him lying where he is (i.e. if he has been knocked down by a car and is currently lying in the middle of a road) then it is essential to get him to safety as quickly as possible. It might actually be safer to try to alert any on-coming traffic BEFORE you try to move him so that the procedure can be performed without rushing and without fear of being hit by a car yourself.

If you do have to move him, limit movement as much as possible, ideally by using a board strong enough to take his weight to keep him as still and straight as you can.

(Perhaps if there was a car involved, you may be able to use the parcel shelf from their car as a stretcher).

Because he will feel very cold due to the shock of the accident and the fact that he may "roll" during the lift, wrap a blanket or towel around him, AND the board, to secure him to it and stop the rolling effect. If you have no board, in an emergency, 2 people can hold the 4 corners of a blanket or jacket to make an impromptu stretcher. Try to keep the dog as flat/straight as possible as you put him onto the board or blanket. Calm and reassure the dog as much as possible throughout the lift – minimizing movement and any possible further trauma to the spine is essential.

If he becomes unconscious, gently extend his neck to make sure his airway remains open and pull his tongue forward. Ensure he is kept warm throughout and monitor his breathing/heart rate just in case you need to step in and perform artificial respiration or CPR. Transport the vet ASAP.

SKELETON - HARNESSES

Walking your dog on a harness has many benefits and maybe now is the time to consider getting one.

In the "old days" we used to use check or choke chains to control our dogs and in some cases people even used prong or electric collars to get their furry friend to walk nicely on the lead. We've come a long way since then I'm glad to say and with more and more people understanding the benefits of force-free training styles, those kinds of tools have pretty much gone by the wayside. So, what can you use to walk your dog? Well, obviously there is no substitute for good training. Methods like the "300 peck" technique will help your dog to understand what is required of him rather than having his neck yanked if he pulls – YouTube https://youtu.be/Bu5Kx7WrlBw

While you're getting to grips with their training, you can use tools such as a good head collar, which will guide the dog's head to one side if he pulls and makes walking even a large, boisterous dog very easy indeed. However, as with all new things, a head collar should be introduced slowly and gently with lots of treats and positive reinforcement so that wearing it is seen as a pleasure rather than a chore. The one I'd recommend is the "Dogmatic". This one fits nicely on the muzzle a little like a bridle. It won't ride up into the eyes, allows the dog to pant easily and even lets him carry his ball while wearing it. www.dogmatic.org.uk

The other and perhaps best choice of all is to get your dog used to walking on a harness. Harnesses were originally used to help dogs to pull things so many people think that walking a dog on a harness will undoubtedly encourage him to pull. With the right harness, that just isn't so. There are many available in all kinds of price ranges. Some are designed for sporting activities and others specifically to stop the dog pulling, but the key thing to look for is a ring not only on the top of the harness on the dog's back, but also on the front of the dog on his chest. This allows you to attach the lead at both points, giving you a nice level of control without any pressure being forced on to the neck.

When we use an ordinary collar to walk a dog who is strong or pulls, this pressure is directed to the sensitive structures such as his neck, spine, throat and even his thyroid gland, all of which can be seriously damaged if the dog pulls hard and strong repeatedly. That said, just one strong pull in the wrong way can damage your dog for life so considering a harness to walk them on is not just easier for you, but more comfortable them too.

Another safety aspect you get with a harness that you don't with a collar is that it is much more difficult for a dog to "reverse" out of a well-fitted harness and slip it. I know of several occasions where, whether because he was spooked by something or just had his naughty trousers on, that dogs have managed to slip their collar and run off (and two of these occasions saw the dog in question chasing along a very busy road)

Good makes that have been recommended to me include the PerfectFit harness which comes in segments so you can buy exactly the right parts to fit your dog's measurements perfectly. Another good one is that made by RuffWear. Both are very good quality harnesses and worth the money. The Perfect Fit harness is available at: www.dog-games-shop.co.uk/

SKELETON - HIP DYSPLASIA

Symptoms vary depending on severity – usually in young dogs in which bones are still growing (up to about a year old) or in older dogs which have developed signs of arthritis in the hip joints. The older dogs have always had HD but the condition has remained "silent" until arthritis eventually begins to cause problems. Often muscles of the hip area are noticed to be poorly developed or wasted in young and older dogs. Young dogs typically show a sudden onset of signs, although this can be the case in older dogs too (eg after strenuous exercise) or there can be a more gradual onset of stiffness and lameness.

Lameness & hind leg stiffness are the most common signs but other clues include:-

Juddering of a leg when standing still
Difficulty in getting up after rest
Difficulty in negotiating stairs (particularly up)
Difficulty in jumping in/out of cars
"Bunny hopping" gait when running
Characteristic sitting posture with legs pushed out to one side.

Irrespective of what painkillers are prescribed in young dogs, adequate rest and restriction of exercise, sometimes for several months, is vital. It is worth remembering that active young dogs made pain-free by strong painkillers may inadvertently do more damage to their joints, storing up problems for later on.

In the x-ray below taken from a large breed dog at 13 months of age, we can clearly see a case of HD with the round end of the bones on either side appearing to have a flat edge and even a slight "corner", rather than a completely curved surface. The flat appearance of the head of the femur in the socket will give rise to wear within the joint rather than a smooth, fluid movement and may cause possible problems in later life. The head of the femur should be smooth and round, with a tight fitting snug appearance inside the socket. There should be a clearly defined outline to the bone.

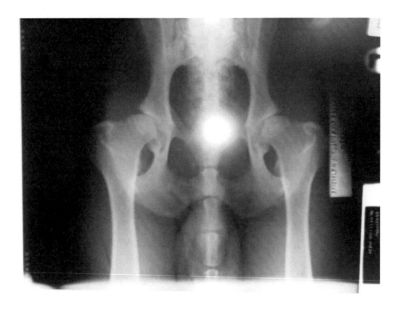

X-rays for "hip scoring" purposes can be done under General Anaesthetic or sedation depending on your veterinary practice's policy. Some people prefer to have this procedure done under sedation rather than using a full GA and knocking the dog out entirely, while others would argue that for the dog to be placed in the optimal position it would need to be completely unconscious.

It is now preferred to have your dog's elbows x-rayed and scored at the same time as having his hips done. Each breed has a specific list of health issues that should be screened for and for breeds who list hip problems as a possibility, only dogs with = or below the average score for their breed should be used in breeding programmes. If you are looking to buy a puppy and the breed you are considering is known to have a possible weakness of the hips, please ensure that the parents have been scored as average or below average and, if possible, look back at the scores of previous generations too to give your puppy the best chance of inheriting naturally healthy hips.

Not all HD problems are genetic. Some may arise due to the lifestyle of the puppy in his early months and years. It is important to minimise activities such as running up and down stairs, jumping in and out of the car or off furniture, long distance running by the side of a bicycle, agility training etc until the dog is at least a year or more of age (and with larger breeds, perhaps not until they are 18 months or so to be on the safe side.)

SKELETON - DISLOCATIONS

Dislocations occur at a joint when the angle of the connection is displaced causing the usual function of the joint to be disrupted. You may see a lump or bump where the bones are incorrectly aligned, notice that the dog is unable to use the limb or maybe it just looks plane wrong!

As in humans, it is important not to just plough in and try to relocate the joint yourself. This is something that does need an experienced hand and it is often preferable to x-ray the joint after the relocation to ensure no vessels or nerves have been trapped within the joint.

Dislocations are incredibly painful. It may be necessary to muzzle your dog before you try to help him.

First, check the paw beyond the dislocation to see that it is still nice and warm. If the paw begins to feel cool or cold, blood flow to the limb is being compromised. If the limb does not receive enough oxygenated blood, this can be very serious so please do treat it as an emergency. You need to phone your vet immediately and have the dog seen straight away. This is NOT something that can be left until the following day.

If the limb feels warm, your immediate panic can relax a little but you still need to ring your vet immediately for advice as to whether the dog needs to be seen now, or if it can wait until the next clinic time. Allow the dog to adopt whichever is the most comfortable position for himself and certainly do not try to manipulate the dislocation. Simply support it in the position it is in – it might be that putting pillows either side of the limb will keep it still or keep it pressed towards the body to stop it moving.

If at all possible, you can use R.I.C.E. to help soothe it:
R= Rest. Keep the dog from walking on the injured limb
I= Ice. Use an ice pack or cold compresses if the dog will tolerate it.
C= Compression. As above, stabilise the joint so it's not moving about.
E= Elevation. Raise the injured limb IF this does not alter its position.

If your dog has been given pain medication in the past (such as Metacam anti-inflammatory medication for example) then you can give an appropriate dose as previously prescribed by your vet if you still have some at home. N.B. Metacam should not be given on an empty stomach, so if the dog has not eaten you may wish to give a small snack at the same time to line the stomach. However, before giving ANY pain medication to your dog in this situation, please check with your vet as he may decide to sedate him straight away to relocate the dislocation and any food/medication he has been given prior to sedation could have an implication on the treatment your vet is able to give.

When an animal is in pain, he usually breathes more quickly. When you breathe more quickly, you take in less oxygen. When you have less oxygen, this can trigger shock.

Therefore, please keep an eye on 3 things:
How many breaths is he taking in 10 seconds?

How fast is his heart rate?

What colour are his gums?

If you feel that these things are increasing, he could be starting to go in to shock which is even more dangerous than the dislocation. If this is the case, please tell your vet immediately.

SKELETON – DISLOCATED KNEE

<u>Luxating (dislocating) Patella</u>

This condition is fairly common as far as dislocations go and owners of dogs affected with a dislocating patella can often learn to replace the kneecap themselves with veterinary instruction.

The limb is straightened at the stifle (knee) joint, and the patella slid or pushed back from its position on the inside of the joint.

Sometimes, if the patella is particularly loose, simply rubbing the extended joint is all that is needed. In affected dogs the condition is, of course, liable to recur.

SKELETON - SPONDYLOSIS

Spondylosis or "Spondylosis Deformans" in dogs sounds like a very serious diagnosis and there is no doubt that its effect on a dog's quality of life can be marked BUT what if I were to tell you that pretty much any dog that lives long enough, will eventually develop spondylosis to some degree? Didn't know that? Read on.

Although it is usually something that, as I say, effects older dogs, it is thought that it can also be triggered by traumatic injuries, excessive wear and tear, poor dietary management/nutrition, or even a genetic predisposition. It is most frequently seen in larger breed dogs, but please don't think that they have the monopoly on this disease – ANY breed can suffer with spondylosis.

So firstly, what is SPONDYLOSIS? Well, the spinal column is made up of 30 vertebrae (bones) and some tail bones too. Between each of these vertebrae is a spongy disc which acts as a shock absorber and allows the spinal column to flex and bend. As dogs get older, these vertebrae can develop bony spurs which, over time, can actually join together and form a kind of bridge along the bottom edge of the spinal column. As the vertebrae fuse together, bending and flexibility becomes less. It can also happen if the spinal column has been damaged and weakened through injury, in which case the body will form a bridge of bone along the gap of the injury to strengthen that area and shore it up.

As you'd imagine, this can be an extremely painful condition to experience although, that said, in many cases dogs live with it and show little or no signs of pain and still enjoy a good quality of life, perhaps with nothing more significant than a stiffness which reduces his flexibility. Clues that your dog may be experiencing this condition are many and really you, as his guardian, are probably the best person to spot the early onset of this condition. You may notice:

Change in their general mood, perhaps being more grumpy with people or other dogs.
A reluctance to trot up the stairs if they don't have to or to jump in/out of the car.
A difficulty in bending down to get to their bowl due to stiffness in the neck.
An arched back/low head appearance.
Stiffness.
Lameness.
Sensitivity to touch of the affected area.
Difficulty getting up or lying down.
Reluctance to walk a full distance daily walk.

So, how will your vet diagnose Spondylosis? Well firstly she will want to examine your dog and see what range of movement he has and detect any sensitive parts. As you'd imagine if it were you, this can be very painful so your vet may ask to muzzle your dog to do this, even if he is the sweetest dog in all the world. (If you have not taught your dog Muzzle Acceptance, this can add to the stress burden so please do try to acclimatise your dog to the use of muzzle for just such an occasion – see our blog on Muzzle Acceptance.

After a general examination, she may opt to perform more technical investigations such as X-Rays, CT Sans, MRI or something called Myelography which is where a contrast dye is used so that it shows up on X-Ray or CT scan and highlights any defect or problem area.

Once your dog has been diagnosed, there is unfortunately no cure or way of reversing the condition, although in severe cases surgery to remove the spurs could be considered. Alternatively, you may be offered Non-Steroidal Anti-Inflammatory medication as pain management with drugs such as Metacam, Loxicam or Previcox.

At this stage, I would probably recommend switching to a harness to walk your dog, if you do not already do so. A collar can put added strain on the neck which should be avoided. Perhaps also consider switching to a raised bowl to feed your dog if you are not already doing so. That extra effort to bend down to get to their food could probably be alleviated by this very easy modification ... and I'm sure they'd appreciate a pain-free dining experience.

To manage their comfort and aid with flexibility in the joints, there are some really good supplements you can also try (some work better for some dogs so do have a try with various ones to see which suits your dog best) Glucosamine and Chondroitin are popular supplements to try, as is YuMove which has very good reviews. Another joint supplement you could try is Canine Cortaflex HA which I have used on my boys with very good results. You simply add a measured sprinkle to their breakfast and that's you done. You may find that the best solution is to couple a pain medication with one of these joint supplements rather than relying solely on one or the other.

Many people who like to do things "naturally" also extol the virtues of turmeric paste as a natural anti-inflammatory (there are many groups of Facebook for example where you can speak to people who use this daily and are a wealth of knowledge on the subject). As with any natural or herbal approach, please do your research to ensure that this line of support is right for your dog, his history and any other medication he me also be on. Coconut oil is another natural approach which has proven to be very good with many aspects of health, including joint mobility, but please be aware that it is extremely calorific and if you are adding this into your dog's diet, you need to cut back on his calories somewhere else to accommodate its introduction. If you don't, your dog is likely to start piling on the pounds which, with this condition, he can ill afford.

Other things you can do to help the comfort and mobility of your dog include, firstly, ensuring that they continue with daily exercise and keep their weight under control. A dog who weighs more will be exerting more stresses on every joint in his body, including his vertebral column, so keeping him trim will definitely keep him more comfortable. Exercises such as swimming and walking are by far the better choices than high impact sessions such as running as they put less stress on the joints and in the case of swimming, the water actually supports the body while still allowing a vigorous workout. You may well find that therapeutic massage can really help as well. Massage is a complementary therapy which treats the whole body of the dog, reduces swelling, increases flexibility and also helps drain metabolic waste from muscles and tissues. Please ensure that your vet is happy with your chosen practitioner and that he or she has the necessary qualifications to carry out such treatments on your dog safely.

As with anything, as the condition deteriorates, they may need more and more support with pain relief to ensure a good quality of life. At this point, when everything else has been tried, your vet may suggest using steroids to help him cope. This is something that should be approached with caution and only after everything else has been exhausted as, sadly, there are side effects when used over the long term. I would certainly advocate discussing this with your vet and getting his professional opinion to balance your decision.

SKIN - DIAGNOSING SKIN PROBLEMS

Sometimes, helping the vet with diagnosing skin problems can be quite a challenge. Because there are lots of possible causes of skin infection, from trauma, to topical allergies, to food allergies, to bites, to bacterial infections and autoimmune problems etc, it is a good idea to go through some questions yourself before your vet appointment so that if your vet asks, you already know the answers i.e. such questions as:-

* Is this the first time this condition has occurred?
* Are the ears or feet affected?
* Do any other animals in the house have similar symptoms?
* Do any people in the house have symptoms of skin disease?
* Have carpets been changed/treated with chemicals recently?
* Has different bedding/washing powder been used?
* Has his diet been changed?

* What does the problem look like – scabs, redness, dandruff, weepy?
* Is he bathed frequently & if so what are you using?
* Have you recently moved/walk in a new area?
* Does your pet suffer with an autoimmune problem such as hypothyroidism?
* Are there any other symptoms apart from the skin ones?

The answer to these or a combination of answers could lead the way to a diagnosis. Do not neglect skin conditions in the belief that they are not serious. If left, a lengthy course of treatment may be required to put the problem right and the dog will suffer in the meantime. Sometimes, an itch is just an itch, but sometimes

SKIN - TUMOURS, LUMPS & BUMPS

When you notice a lump on your dog, it's very scary. You instantly start thinking the worst as to what it could be, how long has it been there and whether you should have noticed it sooner. The important thing is that now you <u>HAVE</u> noticed it, you need to keep an eye on it to determine whether it is changing at all (be that in colour, shape, size or texture).

Axl, our fabulous demonstration dog had a tumour scare at the very beginning of 2013. I had no idea what the lump was, and was obviously just as worried as you would be, but I decided to document his investigations and outcome in a timeline in the hopes that our Rhodes 2 Safety followers might be able to gain something positive from his experience – regardless how it turned out in the end.

In this blog, I've also added some tips on keeping a record of the progress of the lump and the kind of things that separates benign (non-cancerous) tumours from the nasty malignant (cancerous) ones. As always, if you are worried that the lump your dog has is a "nasty", then your vet is the best person to check with as soon as possible.

I will say here and now that all is well with Axl and my big fella is now back to all his usual work, breed shows and agility competitions again.

So, here's how it all went down .....

<u>1st January, 2013</u> – "Axl has developed a new, warty, lumpy, moly "thing". Why do these things always turn up out of hours, on weekends on or bank holidays? Anyway, I'll be off to the vet with Axl tomorrow morning and will report back with the vet's opinion – wish us luck" - Possibly a histiocytoma

Monitoring a skin lump:-

Use a ruler or tape measure to put an actual figure to the dimensions of the lump. You can also take a photograph (with something you instantly recognise the size of alongside the lump to give scale – something like a coin or even your finger will be a constant size to refer to so it's easy to tell if it's getting bigger or shrinking) or sketch out the shape, noting any features on the surface of the lump such as colour, bobbly bits or indentations.

Be sure only to check it every few days, or every week, as if you check it too frequently you can miss slow growing changes or the anxiety can make you imagine lumps are growing when they are not.

When checking, refer back to your notes, sketch or photograph so you have a firm target to compare to.

Most cases of lumps like these turn out to be benign. If monitored lumps appear to be growing, most vets will opt to remove them unless anaesthesia poses special risks for the individual patient (perhaps if they are old, overweight or have breathing difficulties).

Some features of **BENIGN** (not dangerous) tumours:-
* Appear and grow slowly
* Loose & moveable
* Appearance stays the same
* Well demarcated edges (clearly defined)
* Do not spread other than locally
* Do not re-grow after surgical removal

Some features of **MALIGNANT** (dangerous) tumours:-
* May appear and grow more quickly
* Fixed to underlying or surrounding tissues
* Change in appearance
* Poorly demarcated edges
* Can spread and cause disease in other areas of the body
* May re-grow after surgical removal

20th January, 2013 – am I kept a close eye on Axl's lump and it turned from what looked exactly like a small, cream coloured tick on New Year's Day, into a speckled charcoal-coloured lump within 18 days – I noted the change in size and colour.

20th January, 2013 – pm, Axl was shaved from crown to crown across his ridge and had his lump removed, some 18 days after it first appeared. The scar was pretty neat.

The histological findings of the lump took 5 days to come through and diagnosed it as a benign trichoepithelioma (i.e. a non-cancerous tumour within his hair follicle) – and three weeks later, his stitches were removed.

<u>20th April, 2013</u> – After 3 months, apart from a slight change in the direction of his hair growth, all evidence of the worry he put us through has now disappeared. He has been back in the show ring since and, as the change in hair growth is down to surgery rather than a natural genetic fault, it has made no difference to his show career at all.

Scary as lumps are, they aren't necessarily a death sentence and the sooner you have them checked out by a qualified professional, the better your dog's chances of getting over them. Here is a brilliant article written by a vet for the website theveterinaryexpert.com. It explains exactly what happens when biopsies are taken, the reasons they are necessary and what information can be gained from them. It's well worth a read if you find yourself in this position as sometimes the not knowing is more scary that the information itself.

Here's the article:
http://www.theveterinaryexpert.com/surgery/biopsy-explained/?inf_contact_key=a167b618c6cd306410899e15169700 2d634fca3fd5c859068f8a6bc33ce58940

SKIN - CANINE ACNE

Really?? Yes, dogs do get "zits"!!!!!

This condition causes abnormalities in the hair follicles especially around the chin and muzzle. Larger, short coated breeds are affected most often eg Great Dane, Rhodesian Ridgeback, Boxer, Doberman, Rottweiler etc. Acne is seen first in young adult animals (both my first two Ridgebacks have suffered mildly with this and I've just noticed today, at age 10 months, my puppy is starting with it too), but can flare up from time to time – at 6 years old my older Ridgeback had another episode of acne that lasted about a month or so.

The signs and symptoms are multiple blackheads on the chin, lips, and muzzle. A blackhead or "comedone" is where the hair follicle has been plugged by natural secretions like oily sebum and skin debris. When the hair follicle is blocked like this, it swells causing spots and raised reddened plaques which eventually "pop" and cause scabs. They may weep fluid and develop ulcerated patches. They are not particularly itchy and most dogs don't seem to notice it, however if the dog does find it itchy, you may notice him rubbing his face and muzzle along the carpet in an effort to ease the irritation.

If skin problems are present elsewhere on the dog, then acne may not be the cause and one should consider something else e.g. skin mites, mange or staphylococcal infections.

In most cases, treatment for canine acne is unnecessary although you can treat with medicated shampoos, Aloe Vera or something such as Sudocrem. If the spots have ruptured and possibly developed a secondary infection as a result, or for cases of really severe irritation, antibiotics may be prescribed. In most cases, however, perhaps after several bouts, the dog just "grows out of it" as he matures.

SKIN - HOT SPOTS & WET ECZEMA

Hot Spots & Wet Eczema are the same thing. Dermatitis is "doctor-speak". If you break down the parts of the word you get <u>derm</u> which means skin and <u>itis</u> which means inflammation; therefore, if you or your dog are suffering from <u>dermatitis</u>, it simply means inflammation of the skin. In dogs, it can be caused by anything that irritates the skin but the most common causes are:-

Topical skin allergies,
Food related skin allergies,
Skin infections,
Skin fold problems,
Skin parasites such as the flea, mite, lice or fly strike.

Patches of wet eczema, also known as a "hot spots," or "moist eczema", are usually a recurring condition in dogs. They occur where a dog licks and scratches too much. When the skin itches, the dog scratches or licks it. This in turn makes the skin sore and inflamed, which is uncomfortable and itchy so the itch/scratch cycle is perpetuated. This causes the formation of a wet scab on the skin under the fur. The dermatitis can be confined to a very small area or alternatively you may find that it affects the entire surface of the skin. Because of the sparse hair covering on the underside of the abdomen, this is often the easiest place to notice wet eczema, but hair that appears moist and lifted up is likely to be lying over the top of a hot spot.

Wet eczema can often be treated successfully at home without the need to see a vet. However, if the condition is a very serious case, the treatment you are giving is not working well or perhaps the condition keeps recurring, it is best to have your vet give his opinion as to the best treatment as soon as possible.

Treatment
Sometimes anti-inflammatory treatments in the form of creams, tablets or injections may be given to ease the intense discomfort and a common remedy for this condition is cortisone because it minimises the itching.

1. Firstly, expose the affected region to the air by trimming the fur away from the area around the wet eczema. If the area is large, you will need to gently shave off the fur and expose the wet eczema patch. Exposing to the air should help enable the wet eczema to dry (as its name implies, "wet" eczema may be weeping or oozing).

2. Use an antiseptic spray or gentle shampoo on the infected area. **Make sure whatever product you use is gentle on the skin.** When using the shampoo, be very gentle when you work it into a lather and thoroughly clean the area. Pat the surface dry carefully and avoid any abrasive rubbing of the area. Once the affected surface is clean and dry, apply hydrocortisone cream, which will help the wound to heal and minimise the itching.

3. In order to allow the area a realistic chance of healing, you must break the itch/scratch cycle so it is important to prevent further licking or scratching of the hot spot. It may be necessary to fit your dog with an Elizabethan or Buster type collar for any times when you are unable to supervise their activities and ensure they leave it alone. It is also a good idea to ensure your

dog's nails are trimmed neatly to minimise the amount of damage they may do in scratching – perhaps even popping on a pair of socks to the paws to protect the wound.

4. If you feel that the affected area is not healing or is maybe getting worse or even spreading, it is important to visit your vet for professional advice and treatment, possibly including tablets, a topical lotion to be applied directly to the skin surface or even an injection of cortisone. It is important to follow your vet's instructions to the letter when treating cases of dermatitis to ensure that this very uncomfortable condition clears up as quickly as possible.

SKIN - ALOE VERA

Aloe Vera is well known for its soothing, healing properties and while there are lots of pharmaceutical treatments on the market, there are several of the Aloe products that I truly wouldn't be without. The two that I most go back to again and again both come from the Forever Living range, although Aloe Vera in whatever form you can get your paws on is always going to be a great addition to your first aid kit.

Aloe Vera Veterinary Formula

The Aloe Veterinary Formula is a smashing "go to" product. Because it is a fluid, it's great for spraying on sore patches within the hair without shaving them down, or to clean a wound, or to soothe itchy paws from allergies and nibbling.

During the summer when grass seeds can be a huge problem, particularly for dogs with longer coats, the Aloe Veterinary Formula can be sprayed on to paws and between the toes to help tease out those pesky seeds and to soothe any pollen irritation under the paw, between the toes or at the nail bed.

As my guys have a short coat, we don't struggle quite so much with this. For us, our main use comes in the winter time after we've been out on muddy walks, walks through woodland where there is a suggestion of Alabama Rot risk, or walks on pavements that may have been salt treated because of ice. When we return home, a quick wash of the feet, towel dry and a squirt of Aloe Vera spray to the paws and up the legs not only soothes any irritation but also helps reduce any fungal build up which I'm sure we all recognise as "Popcorn Paws" or "Frito Feet" when they emanate that savoury odour!

Aloe Vera Lips

Another Aloe product I always have to hand (for the dogs and for me too – although I do have a separate one for me) is the Forever Aloe Lips lip balm. Yes, you can of course use it as a lip balm but because it is self-contained in its own little tube, it's great for popping in to your first aid kit.

When skin dries, it dies. This means that if you allow the skin around a graze or wound to dry out, or to scab over, it will take much longer to heal and will possibly leave a scar as a result. If you can keep the skin hydrated and moist (not WET) the healing time speeds up and the skin is less itchy and tight. Whenever a wound starts to heal and the skin tightens, this can be irritating for your dog and often is the main cause of them nibbling and licking the area. This great little product can simply be twisted out, as you would a lip stick, and a clean finger rubbed over the tip to transfer the Aloe Vera to the graze or sore patch to moisturise the area, keep it clean and help to soothe it all at the same time.

LIMP OR LIMBER TAIL

If your dog suddenly appears to have a hanging, droopy tail, all types of causes for the way he is holding his tail should be considered such as has he injured his back or his spine in any way? Could he have injured his tail with rough and tumble when playing? Did he trap it in a door or perhaps he was stepped upon by accident? Is there any chance that his anal glands could be impacted or infected, as this too could make your dog carry his tail differently? If none of these things seem likely, it could be something called Limber Syndrome.

In Limber Tail Syndrome, the tail becomes limp, lifeless and flaccid. My first dog, Paddy, a huge Golden Labrador had this once in his life and one of our Rhodes 2 Safety followers asked me about it last year so I thought we'd cover it today.

Symptoms include:

- A limp tail that "hangs" with no or very little wagging
- Tail may extend horizontally for a few inches, then drops flaccidly
- Hair standing up at base of tail which looks like the hackles are up

- Pain when you touch it
- Local swelling and warmth to the touch

Things your faithful friend could have been doing to bring on his limp tail include:

Swimming
Frantic wagging (particularly working dogs engaging in the thrill of the hunt)

A hot bath following an outdoor adventure followed by sleeping it off in his crate

Any breed of dog with a tail can develop Limber Tail Syndrome, but some are more prone to it than others – particularly working and sporting breeds:

Labradors and Golden Retrievers
Flat Coat Retrievers
English Setters
English Pointers
Beagles
Foxhounds
Cocker Spaniels

Although a definite trigger is yet to be ascertained, the most common causes include:

Overexertion/Use of the tail
Swimming
Climate changes/exposure to cold weather

Being crated for a long time or in an inappropriate sized crate
Warm or cold bath
Excessive exercise beyond the dog's normal capabilities

Therefore, it is important to build up your dog's exercise routine gradually, avoiding sudden and prolonged periods of exercise after long periods of inactivity.

Ensure you allow him to use a crate big enough to turn around and stretch in and that he is dried off fully following his activity.

Treatment for Limber Tail

If you are at all unsure, a veterinary opinion should always be sought and, if Limber Tail Syndrome is diagnosed, it is easy enough to treat:-

Try applying warm packs at the base of the tail
Anti-inflammatory drugs ONLY as prescribed by your vet.
Rest, calming atmosphere and MINIMAL WAGGING!!!

For a full recovery it may take as much as a couple of weeks but in most instances we would expect the pain to subside within 24 to 48 hours. Complete recovery is mostly seen within a couple of weeks. On occasion, during the recovery period, the tail may appear to hang to one side or the other. If this happens please don't panic. It should get itself back to normal fairly quickly.

CHAPTER 23: TEMPERATURE ISSUES

TEMPERATURE – WHAT'S NORMAL?

Temperature can be indicative of an animal's general health. The average temperature of a dog is 101 degrees F or 38 degrees C. That said, the "normal" temperature for an adult dog can vary from anywhere between 100 and 102.5 degrees F, or 37.8 and 39.2 degrees C.

Sometimes, you look at your dog and something just doesn't seem right. Maybe he's acting a little oddly, looks sad or doesn't want to interact with his surrounding in his normal way but you just can quite put your finger on whether there is REALLY something wrong. One of the things that can help you decide if your dog is actually ill could be as simple as taking his temperature.

There are lots of thermometers on the market but really you just need something quite simple. So long as it's accurate, it doesn't need to be too high tech.

Each thermometer will come with its own user-instruction guide but essentially all you need to do is lubricate the end you are going to insert into the dog (something like Vaseline or Petroleum Jelly is fine for this). Reassure the dog and lift the tail to expose his anus. Gently and slowly insert the tip of the thermometer into the anus and apply a little pressure. The thermometer will begin to enter the dog and the sphincter will react by becoming tighter. Wait just a second or so until the dog relaxes and you will be able to put it in a little further. Insert the thermometer just a couple of centimetres or so and wait until it beeps or alerts you that the reading is ready to be taken. It may be helpful to have somebody with you to distract and placate the dog at one end with treats, while you are doing the unpleasant job at the other.

Write down the time and reading so you can refer to it either later in the day if you are concerned about him, or the following day if you are checking to see if he is recovering.

Finally, remember to mark clearly on the thermometer that it is for the dog! You don't want to pick up the wrong one when you are poorly.

TEMPERATURE ISSUES - ANTIFREEZE

Antifreeze is different from De-Icer which is different from screen wash. There are many DIY recipes for making screen wash, but the following is the one my elderly uncle uses and recommends (I would suggest doing a bit of research and seeing which version suits you best):

1) 1 Tablespoon of dishwashing liquid
(Fairy by preference which apparently DOES make a difference)
2) 250 ml of Rubbing Alcohol
3) Make the solution up to 1 gallon in volume by adding water
4) Works out at about £2.60 per gallon and should work to about -30 degrees

De-icer is something that is used on your car windscreen to break down the ice rather than having to scrape the window. His recipe for this would be:

50% water -v- 50% rubbing alcohol in a small spray bottle – works brilliantly
(better than the stuff you can by commercially apparently)

Now back to the point of the blog. **Antifreeze** – Antifreeze is something that is added to the cooling system of your car so that the radiator does not freeze when temperatures plummet. Antifreeze may be listed on containers as either ethylene glycol or ethan-1,2-diol (the newer more correct name for ethylene glycol). It's the same substance and highly toxic to dogs and cats.

Antifreeze can be dangerous in three ways either by absorption through the skin should the dog walk through it, say from a dripping car radiator, from secondary ingestion should the animal try to lick his coat clean, and by primary ingestion if the dog should come across the actual puddle of antifreeze itself and lap it up (apparently, they just love the taste of it!)

Antifreeze can cause convulsions, collapse, coma and may even be fatal so swift action is required.

IMPORTANT – Administer an emetic ASAP
(an emetic is a substance that will make the dog vomit – for full information on treating poisons and inducing vomiting, please check out our Poisoning blog)

A good thing to try is either an appropriately sized lump of washing soda crystals, hydrogen peroxide 3%, mustard powder made into a paste or rock salt/salt water)

– Ensure the dog discontinues licking   ASAP

– Wear gloves when cleansing the contaminant away

– Clean in/around the mouth with water (use a flannel if necessary)

– Ensure the dog does not swallow the cleaning water

– Clean the fur thoroughly with soap/water

– Contact the vet and transport **immediately to the vet**

– Make a note of the time it occurred

– Monitor A,B,C's (Airway, Breathing, Circulation) and be ready to step in and perform CPR or artificial respiration as required.

Consideration should also be given to the use of VODKA as a possible aid to treatment (the brand is irrelevant). Ideally this should be administered intravenously (IV) by your vet but a measure of vodka to drink (preferably after the dog has vomited) as a non-prescription treatment to get things underway certainly won't do any harm.

Please make sure you know how much vodka you have given the dog so you can tell the vet when you arrive as it may alter his dosage and treatment of your pet. Also, please take a bottle of vodka with you if you have it, just in case the vet does not have any on site when you arrive and would like to use this method to help your dog.

TEMPERATURE ISSUES - GRITTED AND SALTED ROADS

When it's icy and snowy the ground becomes very dangerous and to combat that our local councils tend to make the surfaces of roads and pavements either gritted or salted to help us with our footing. While this is very helpful to us as bipeds with poor balancing skills, it can pose a couple of problems to our four-legged friends – including CATS!

1) The salt, if left on the pads of the paws, can burn and cause irritation.

2) When the animal licks his paws to remove the salt he will ingest it and this can be extremely toxic and may poison the animal. As the salt levels within the body increase, the kidneys will be put under extreme pressure to try to remove the salt from the body and can, in severe circumstances, prove fatal.

PLEASE WASH THEIR PAWS on return from your walk or if the cat has been out. While I am sure they may well not like having their paws washed, it is most certainly preferable to the alternative.

If the irritation is severe enough, it should be classed as a chemical burn. Anytime that you become aware of a chemical burn, the faster you are able to deal with the problem, the less damage will be inflicted on the animal. Many people who know their dogs are sensitive to salt/gritted surfaces advocate the use of lavender in the cleaning water to help soothe the skin.

Once the paws are clean, they should be dried off as normal and inspected to ensure that the surface of the pad is not damaged in any way. If the skin is not broken but you sense there may be any kind of irritation, it's a good idea to wash the foot further to ensure you prevent absorption of the salt any further into the layers of the skin.

Aveeno Oatmeal Moisturising Cream or Aloe Vera are both excellent preparations to apply to the skin to soothe and help repair any damage – but please try if possible to stop your dog licking it off (a pair of children's socks will probably come in very handy here!)

If you are **ever** in doubt as to the severity of a burn, please '**phone your vet**

If you are looking at an easy way of washing the paws "on the go" check out our Mud Daddy review on
YouTube: http://www.rhodes2safety.co.uk/mud-daddy/

TEMPERATURE ISSUES - HYPOTHERMIA (EXTREME COLD)

"Winter is coming!" No, that's not a nod just for the Game of Thrones fans (of which I count myself), it's a serious fact. Hypothermia can be lethal ... and prevention is definitely better than the cure.

During the winter time, our pets that live outside grow a heavier coat to protect them through the harsher months but even so, they should be brought inside when it's very cold be that from ice and snow or the wind chill factor, which can make temperatures FEEL much lower than they are actually reported.

If your dog is in a kennel, crate or cage, please ensure that you have enough insulation between the crate floor and the dog. Lying on a cold surface will chill the animal very quickly indeed and simply placing a few layers of newspaper or a thin towel beneath the crate is not enough. Several layers of thick insulation are required and perhaps consider lifting the crate itself off the floor AND THEN using insulation on top of the crate floor to protect the dog.

The hair of an animal's coat is designed to trap air next to their skin and keep them warm. This works excellently provided that they are healthy and well-groomed with no matts. Matting, poor condition or being wet will drastically reduce their ability to keep warm as the integrity and insulating properties of the coat are diminished.

Some dogs are more susceptible to the cold than others including new-born puppies, toy breeds, short coat varieties and geriatric dogs. Dogs with autoimmune problems such as hypothyroidism also feel the cold more so if you know your dog falls into one of these categories, prevention is definitely better than cure.

Possible causes of hypothermia:

Exposure to a cold environment for a long time
Exposure to cold water (or water + wind-chill factor)
Exposure to water for a long period of time
Wet fur and skin
Anaesthetic over a long period of time
Shock

Symptoms:

The less surface area that is exposed to the cold, the better. For this reason a dog's first response will be to curl up in a little ball to reduce the area.

If he still feels cold, it's likely that you'll see his hackles go up (the hairs on the shoulders, along the back and the tail). Adrenaline causes the muscles to contract and the hair stand on end to trap as much warm air close to the skin as possible.

His gum colour will grow paler, and no longer be such a lovely salmon pink. His breathing is likely to become slower, and more shallow than normal.

The next stage is a strong shivering, with the muscles in spasm in an effort to generate more heat as his metabolic rate begins to fall.

Below the temperature of around 94°F shivering will stop and he will become quite lethargic, possibly with a kind of vacant, staring expression.

The heart rate will slow down, possibly with some irregularities in the pattern of the beats, and become more difficult to detect.

If the hypothermia is not treated quickly, he may slip into a coma, heart failure and possibly die.

Treatment:

The normal temperature range for a dog is 100.5 to 102.5. With any suspicion of hypothermia, a thermometer is your best friend. Any deviation above or below this range should be of concern.

Always use plenty of lubrication & CAUTION! With temperatures of greater than 98°F it is often (but not always) enough to simply increase the ambient temperature of the room you are in, snuggle up to them with your own body heat and cover them with a blanket. It's a good tip to pop the blankets or towels quickly on the radiator or in the tumble dryer to warm them before use.

If the dog's rectal temperature is below 96°F then you must contact your vet urgently. Simply covering him with a blanket will likely not be enough so start warming him rapidly. For this you will need water bottles filled with warm water. Please remember that although this water may only feel "warm" to you, to a hypothermic dog, it will feel much hotter so care must be taken to wrap the water bottles in a towel to protect the dog's skin from burning. Be especially careful that you do not lay him directly in contact with a radiator or too close to a fire and never be tempted to use a hairdryer as the heat from all these sources will be too dramatic.

Once you have wrapped the bottles in towels, apply them to the armpits, abdomen and chest and recover the dog in his blanket.

Offer warm drinks for your dog to lap and repeat taking his temperature around every 10 minutes or so to enable you to monitor his progress (remember to mark down the readings as it is very easy to become confused when you are frightened for the welfare of your dog).

Once the temperature has risen to 100°F or above, keep the dog warm but remove the hot water bottles to avoid him overheating.

You know your dog and you know how he acts when things are "normal", but as a rule a wag of the tail is a good indicator that he is feeling a little better.

TEMPERATURE ISSUES - DEHYDRATION.

Just as with humans, dehydration is very dangerous for your dog. It could be due to a number of things including kidney failure, vomiting/diarrhoea, extremely high temperatures, or even just the fact that you haven't left him enough to drink. It is good practice to ensure that there is always a clean, cool, water supply available to your dog – 24/7.

Some signs could direct you other illnesses including kidney failure, liver disease, adrenal or pituitary gland malfunctions or diabetes, but there are several pointers that could indicate your dog is dehydrated. For example, when dehydrated he will naturally try to conserve as much fluid as he possibly can and in order for this to be successful, the amount of urine he passes will decrease markedly and the colour and viscosity of the urine itself will change.

Signs To Look Out For:
Excessive drinking
Eyes appear sunken and lack moisture
Excessive panting
Reduction in urination & dark, deep, golden colour
Sticky or dry gums rather than usual wet/slimy
Sticky viscosity to the texture of the urine
Listless/lethargic demeanour
Change in attitude – hesitant behaviour
Delayed action and elasticity of skin on the neck/back

So, if you think that your dog may be dehydrated, there are a couple of really easy things you can do to test your theory.

How To Check:

Simply touch your dog's nose. How does it feel? A dog's nose should generally be cold and wet. If the nose feels dry or warm to you, then he could be mildly dehydrated.

Next, we need to see what the gums themselves feel like. If your dog is anything like mine, you'll know they produce a fair amount of saliva and EVERYTHING in that mouth is usually pretty soggy. If the gums feel dry and/or sticky when you touch them with your finger, then your dog needs a drink to replenish his fluids.

Still thinking about the gums, we need to check to see how long it takes for the colour to return after you press your finger firmly on the gum line. When you remove your finger there will be a pale mark where your finger was but this should quickly (instantly) return to the natural pink colour. The longer it takes to return to pink, the more poorly your dog is.

To test if the skin isn't as elastic as it should be, try pinching a small amount of skin at the scruff between your thumb and forefinger. When you let go, the skin should nicely return to its normal position. If the skin takes longer to return than you would normally expect, or even does not return at all, then this is a clear sign.

If you have a rectal thermometer you can take his temperature. A temperature of above 105° F is very serious.

Sometimes if they are really quite dehydrated, a drink alone is not enough for your dog. If this is the case, then giving them a few spoonful's of electrolyte replacement medication will help no end. Products such as Dioralyte that you may use on holiday if you've had a touch of tummy upset will do the trick for us humans, but as with so many things these days, it contains Xylitol as its sweetening agent. Many vets are still recommending its use, unaware that there is Xylitol in the ingredients (as I was myself until this was pointed out to me only VERY recently). Xylitol is extremely toxic to dogs and as such, over the counter medications like Dioralyte should not be given to your dog.

There are specific animal versions that are safe to use such as Lectade. Another good one, recommended to me by friends who run sled dogs up in Scotland with great results is Culpeppers Hydrolyte

Please remember that if your dog has not drunk for a long period, then re-hydration must start slowly with a few sips every minute or so. Should he drink too much too quickly, it will likely lead to vomiting. When you vomit, you lose fluids, which is the absolute opposite of what we are trying to achieve.

If he has gone a long time without drinking, then it can be a kinder process to re-hydrate him by allowing him to lick ice cubes. Hold them individually in your hand and allow him to gently lick at the surface, controlling how vigorously and for how long he licks.

If you cannot get your dog to drink, then please seek immediate advice from your vet.

TEMPERATURE ISSUES – WINTER FALLS & TRIPS

The UK is experiencing some pretty icy winter weather at the moment so it has been suggested that I pop a blog up regarding falls and slips:-

If either YOU or YOUR DOG has a slip or fall on the ice, your word of the day to remember is RICE:

R = rest – rest the limb and take the weight off ASAP
I = ice – use ice or a cold compress to minimise swelling
C = compression – apply a firm (but not too tight) bandage to minimise swelling
E = elevate – raise the limb on a cushion

If you use a pack of frozen peas etc on either a dog or a human, make sure to avoid a freezer burn to the skin by wrapping it in a tea towel or something to protect it from coming into direct contact with the skin surface.

Don't forget to check the limb higher up from the sore bit – as it might be that the limb is damaged in another place too but the pain is being masked by the more pressing injury ie if the dog's ankle is hurt, check the knee/hip with a hind leg or the shoulder/elbow of a foreleg too.

If there are ANY signs or possibility AT ALL that the limb could be fractured (severe swelling, excessive heat, lack of pulse beyond the injury, bone sticking out, abnormal shape to the limb, shortening of the limb) take the dog to the VET for urgent attention – and if YOU are the casualty, go straight to A&E for an x-ray pronto.

Remember to look out for signs of shock including pale gums, rapid heart -beat and excessive panting/shallow breathing. Should you see any of these things, keep the dog warm, raise his whole back end up on a cushion and call the vet immediately.

TEMPERATURE ISSUES - CHRISTMAS CONSIDERATIONS

There's lots of great advice, suggestions and reminders floating about on the net and on FB so I thought I'd try to group them all together into a bit of a Canine Christmas 101.

Routine:
Please remember that dogs do not celebrate Christmas. They have no idea why the normal day-to-day running of the house is all upside down. They have no idea why the kids are giddy, over excited and bouncing off the walls. They have no idea why 6 million people are visiting their usually quiet home and no idea why they aren't receiving the same level of attention that they usually do.

As much as possible, please try to keep some kind of normal routine for your dog, including going for his usual length of walk (no scrimping just because you have a packed schedule!) He will settle and cope with the chaos a whole lot easier after a nice bit of exercise.

If he is crate trained, make sure he has ready access to his crate or "safe place" where he can retreat from the madness of the day if he needs too – if you have visitors with children, it's a good idea to make sure they all know that this is Rover's safe place and if he is in there, he should be left alone.

Please feed him his normal food. As those eyes bore into your head while you indulge in wonderful food all day, stay strong and resist the urge to "treat" him with bits of what you are eating. While you may think "hey, it's Christmas, why not", remember that he is not used to eating such rich foods and in fact it may well upset his digestive system and I can guarantee you won't feel nearly so festive when you are scrubbing the carpet if he has an unexpected "food escape" accident! If they do have an upset tummy, check out our blog on an UPSET TUMMY

Not everything we consume over the festive period is good for our dogs and some things are down-right dangerous. It's easy to become distracted, so take care where you leave left overs, unsupervised bins and any unguarded "foody" presents.

Foods to avoid include:

Christmas Pudding (the raisins are extremely toxic)
Macadamia Nuts (cause paralysis)
Grapes (toxic)
Garlic (toxic in larger quantities)
Onions (toxic)

Mushrooms (some are positively evil to dogs and cats)
Alcohol (no, it's not funny to get your dog drunk!)
Turkey carcass (NEVER allow your dog to eat ANY cooked bones)
Scented candles/soaps (watch out for scented products which smell like food)
Chocolate (I'm sure by now we all know this one so watch where the kids leave their selection boxes and make sure any foil covered chocolate decorations are on the higher branches of the tree).

Please make sure you know what to do if your dog does manage to get hold of something undesirable off this list or if he swallows something he shouldn't. Tips on poisoning and getting your dog to vomit if necessary can be found in our blogs on "Eating Stuff They Shouldn't" and also "Poisoning"

Christmas Tree Safety:
Securely anchor your tree so pets cannot knock it over
Sweep up pine needles to avoid them being eaten
Keep breakable or edible ornaments up high
Keep pets from drinking the tree water as it may have toxic preservatives in it
Keep puppies away from tree lights – no chewing!
Place only safe presents under the tree just in case Rover takes an interest and if the present is from somebody else, please remember to ask them if it is safe to be under your tree – you don't have to spoil the surprise and ask what's in the gift, but knowing if it should be stored elsewhere until the big day could save a whole lot of heart ache.

Professional Safety

Remember to check out the arrangements for your veterinary surgery over the festive holidays. Clinic times will vary considerably and what may usually be a perfectly normal clinic time may become an emergency call out over Christmas time. It's a good idea to make sure you have your emergency vet number to hand or the number of the veterinary practice who is covering your usual service.

TEMPERATURE ISSUES - PREVENTION OF ICE BURNS & PAD DAMAGE

If you know that your dog will be walking on icy or heavily salted surfaces, please consider protecting their pads before you start.

The easiest form of protection to consider is a wax that you can apply to the pads to provide a protective layer on the tissue. This wax has been used effectively for many years by mushers and sled dogs who find the ice an occupational hazard. There are several varieties of wax available but something such as Musher's Secret Paw Wax is ideal for this kind of job (and no, I'm not on commission!) This product is also perfect for protecting the pads when running on rough terrain or giving the dog grip when he is walking on slippery flooring such as ceramic tiles.

Please do not try to use any techniques to harden the skin on the pad. A hard pad will lose its elasticity and will not cope with uneven surfaces and is, in fact, likely to crack and cause the dog much pain and discomfort. It is far better to keep the pad fit, healthy, moisturised and elastic to allow it to adapt to differing surfaces.

Another way of protecting your dog's paws, particularly if you already know that they are sensitive to the cold or have perhaps had a recent injury to the pad, is to use canine boots. There are many versions available and the price range for the different products varies considerably.

When ordering your dog's boots, have him stand on a piece of paper so that his weight is distributed properly on his paw as it will be when he is walking normally. Then, draw around the outline of the paw. Measure across the width of the foot print and generally this should enable you to purchase the correct size for your dog. Remember that their front feet will be bigger than their back feet so you will need to order two different sizes per dog. A boot that goes higher up the leg and is securely fastened with Velcro will usually save you a lot of fuss and hassle and prevent them falling off, particularly in deep snow or when running.

A few years ago now, the ice seemed to last for ever and on one occasion I noticed tiny spots of blood on the ice. On closer inspection I was horrified to find that Axl had freezer burns to one of his pads and every step he took was shredding a layer of tissue from his paw, but as I always carry vet wrap with me, I was able to fashion a temporary bootie to cover his foot and allow him to finish the last mile of our walk comfortably. Once home, I was straight on the internet to order him some boots of his own to save him from future discomfort. I would suggest spending a reasonable amount on them if you want them to last as I found to my cost that you really do get what you pay for. I spent £50 on Axl's first set and they didn't even last a full season before they fell apart.

TEMPERATURE ISSUES - HEATSTROKE

In a nutshell, **heatstroke** occurs when a dog is subjected to atmospherically high temperatures so that might be where a dog cannot get out of the heat, for example if they are left in a car in warm weather – or perhaps if you have a "sun-worshiper" who just loves to be out baking his brain in the sunshine all day and doesn't know when enough sun is enough. In your capacity as responsible dog-owner, it's up to you to try to make sure your dog doesn't stay too long in the sun.

A great tip (courtesy of Lothlorien Dog Services: http://www.lothloriendogservices.co.uk/) is to provide a towel, soaked in cold water, spread out on the garden for them to lie on. The cold towelling on their underside is very refreshing.

So, how long is too long? Well, that depends very much on the individual dog and the strength of the sun, but things that can exacerbate this condition include:

* Old or very young animals
* Poor fitness levels / being over-weight
* Over-excitement
* Dehydration (perhaps due to vomiting or diarrhoea)
* Wearing a muzzle preventing panting
* Brachycephalic dogs – (short-faced breeds such as Pugs/Bulldogs) may have trouble cooling due to their compressed upper respiratory system.

Signs of heat exhaustion include:

- heavy panting
- hyperventilation (deep breathing)
- increased salivation early then dry gums as the heat prostration progresses
- weakness
- confusion or inattention
- vomiting or diarrhoea
- lack of appetite
- glazed/confused expression

As the condition progresses towards heat stroke there may be:

- shallowing of the breathing efforts
- slowed or absent breath efforts
- obvious paleness or greying to the gums
- vomiting and diarrhoea that may be bloody
- seizures or coma

So, what should you do if you suspect your dog has heat exhaustion?

Protect from further heat and provide shade – generally speaking bringing them indoors is the best start.

Cool him down immediately with cool (not COLD) running water particularly on the chest, and paws, or provide a paddling pool.

Cover in a purpose made cool coat, towelling robe or towels soaked in cold water, if possible so that the underside of the dog is cooled too.

N.B: If you are using this method, please remember to re-soak the towel regularly as the heat from the dog will make the water on the towel heat up. This heat layer will be trapped between the dog and the towel causing what is known as the sauna effect.

Towelling robes soaked in water provide excellent cooling
The feet/face/chest are the most effective areas to cool quickly
Try wet flannels in the groin/armpit area
Offer lots of cool water to rehydrate though if he is already in full crisis with true heat exhaustion/stroke, then avoid ice cubes or iced water as this extreme cold can cause the blood vessels to constrict, preventing the body's core from cooling and actually causing the internal temperature to further rise.

DO NOT plunge your dog into freezing cold water as this could easily send him into shock or even cause a heart attack.

DO NOT bring his temperature down too far. Hypothermia is EQUALLY dangerous and once a dog's temperature falls dangerously low, it will then continue to fall and be very difficult to bring back up.

It is vital that you seek emergency veterinary attention should your dog develop heatstroke as this can prove fatal.

Average Canine Temp:
The average temperature of a healthy dog is 101 °F (38 °C), however, the normal temperature of a healthy dog may range from around 99 °F to 102.5 °F (37.2 °C–39.2 °C).

TEMPERATURE ISSUES - GAMES TO PLAY WHEN IT'S HOT OR YOU CAN'T GET OUT TO WALK

Personally, I walk my dogs every day hail, rain or shine. But there are occasions when you'd normally be out with your dog, that doing so is either just not possible, or maybe even NOT SAFE.

NOT IN THE HEAT

In hot weather, walking your dog can actually be life-threatening (even more so for dogs with shorter muzzles and breathing difficulties). The heat itself can cause heatstroke, collapse and in severe cases dogs do not recover. The pavements/sidewalks may be so hot that walking on them can cause blistering and burns to your dog's paws. In these cases, please walk your dog either very early in the morning or at dusk/after dark, when the ambient temperature and that of the pavements have cooled to a sensible level.

NOT IN THE COLD

In very cold weather, for some dogs a walk is just not a "cool" idea. Older dogs with arthritis and joint problems will find walking in the cold and on cold surfaces very uncomfortable indeed. Dogs with hypothyroid problems often have a very low tolerance to the cold and should only be exposed to cold temperatures for short periods of time. Some dogs find walking on icy surfaces very difficult indeed, not just from a balance/mobility angle, but also if they have very delicate paws (again as in dogs with hypothyroidism) you can find the ice actually burns the flesh necessitating protective booties for your furry friend. If you cannot protect your dog adequately with layers (particularly if they are old, have sparse hair coverage or a very short coat) then very cold temperatures are not the time to walk him either.

NOT IF HE IS ON REDUCED EXERCISE
If your dog has recently been ill, had a physical injury or undergone surgery, your vet may advise that exercise should be reduced and walking held off until they have recovered sufficiently to resume normal exercise. Obviously, if your vet says no walks, that's no walks ... even if Rover is begging to go out! If you have bitches who have not been spayed, then you'll know how important it is to keep them safe during their seasons as off-lead exercise can be fraught with problems. It's times like these that mental stimulation can be a real God-send.

HOW CAN WE ENTERTAIN THEM?
Well, if Mohammed can't go to the mountain ..... you have to turn things around and bring the entertainment to the dog! If your dog is a "foodie" then games are always much easier to plan and devise. From the most basic things like popping your dog in another room while you simply hide a treat or two and then let him in to "Find it" or maybe getting three cups, popping a treat under one of them, swizzling them around to change places and asking the dog which cup has the treat in. This kind of thing they adore as it not only fills their tummy (which is always their number 1 goal) but also works their brain and allows them to use their sense of smell too. And when they find it, remember to give LOADS OF PRAISE and tell them how fab they are. I guarantee there will be little in life to compare to spending quality time with you while being fed and praised – it's as good as it gets!

I asked a good friend of mine what she does with hers on days like these and this is what Kate told me "Snuffle boxes, brainwave of another friend of mine I think. Fill a box with paper (I make crumpled balls of paper and sometimes use shredded paper). I then wrap up some treats in toilet rolls (you can fold the ends in to keep the treats in place) or stuff more paper in to keep treats secure."

"I have dogs that love destroying things (God bless a terrierist) so I bought some Holey Moley balls and I stuff them with strips of fleece, sometimes with treats or squeakers hidden inside. They get to de-stuff something without really killing it".

If you have a DIGGER, then something as simple as a large planter with something tasty hidden inside a tearable cover and popped in for them to dig up is great fun.

If you are pretty good with training your dog, perhaps you could include teaching little behaviours like crossing their paws, taking a bow, weaving through your legs and even closing the door. Small sessions with lots of clear direction and plenty of praise are great fun for both of you and if you teach something like clearing away their toys and putting them in a box, for example, they can even prove helpful to you in the future!

If you're looking for something a bit more purpose built, you can of course get brain-games and puzzles specifically for dogs where levers need to be pushed, lids opened, covers slid etc etc. The list is endless and basically comes down to how much you want to pay for them. If you are going to purchase one of these, please make sure it is suitable for the breed you have – ie a large, powerful breed like my Ridgebacks needs a very well made, heavy duty game to stand up to their massive paws and jaws!

So, you don't want to spend money on the games? No problem. There are lots of things you can make yourself that will test Rover's ability just as much as anything you buy – a simple search on Google or YouTube will bring up lots of things you can construct easily yourself, and a phrase such as "Mental Enrichment for dogs" will present you with lots of interesting games and ideas.

And don't forget, being trapped in the house is a good opportunity to carry out those regular grooming duties that can sometimes get put off when you are busy; give him a good brush (or even a bath if he needs one), clip or Dremel those claw, brush those teeth and give him a general "once over" to check for any lumps or bumps and while you're checking, perhaps a little bit of gentle massage will go down an absolute storm.

So, just because you can't get out, don't just switch off .... have fun with your dog and stay safe.

TEMPERATURE ISSUES - BLUE GREEN ALGAE

As we move into and through the warmer summer months, we often see something in our lakes, ponds and rivers called Blue-Green Algae (though sometimes, rather confusingly, it can appear red, black or even a murky brown colour!) I know lots of you will have heard of it, but what exactly is it and what dangers does it pose for our dogs?

With very warm weather, many of us opt not to walk our dogs until the late evening, when the sun's strength is reduced. It's tempting to visit bodies of water for our dogs to cool off in too, but please steer well clear of stagnant ponds or any bodies of water that show a film, scum or algae. The water may be a breeding ground for a disease called Leptospirosis or may be playing host to blue-green algae. As the temperature of the water increases, so too does the likelihood of a highly toxic blue-green algae bloom.

Algae is usually more concentrated towards the edges of the water but even small amounts can contain lethal doses. What makes this even more tricky for dog owners is that it can live on the surface or the bottom of the water, so the pond won't always have a scum on the surface.

Some types of algae produce extremely poisonous toxins and should a dog drink this contaminated water, death is sadly all too common and rapid with symptoms occurring within 15 minutes to an hour of ingestion of it. Death can result within as little as 10-30 minutes (in some instances, dogs have been found dead at the edge of the water), and certainly within 24 hours of swallowing the toxins.

When I posted this blog, I received this great extra comment from Rachel Gaines so thought I'd share it with you:

"Just check the water with the local authorities first – then you'll know if it's safe or not. I have working Newfies who are constantly in and out of water, some of which has had blue green algae spores in it and other than one incident last year, all has been well. BUT my dogs are used to different waters and algae and I am used to spotting it. So whilst I would say not all ponds, lakes, puddles etc can be a problem, I would also say just be sensible. As an additional note, blue green algae can also occur in non-stagnant water, whether there has been no rain or lots of rain. So it's not just stagnant water people need to be cautious about. The best thing to do is not walk your dog when it is too hot, take plenty of water with you, then they don't need to go in water."

Please remember that even if the dog doesn't actually drink the contaminated water, if he swims in it and then grooms himself, he will take in the toxins that way too.

Signs to look out for:
* severe vomiting which may contain blood
* breathing difficulties
* collapse and death

Action

So, it is important that if you have any concerns that your dog may have come into contact with blue-green algae, PLEASE SEEK IMMEDIATE VETERINARY ATTENTION. Although affected dogs can survive if treated quickly, clinical effects may show over a longer period of time and they may develop kidney or liver failure.

N.B. THIS ADVICE APPLIES TO YOUR CHILDREN TOO. PLEASE DO STAY SAFE!

TEMPERATURE ISSUES –

HEATSTROKE / HYPERTHERMIC COLLAPSE

Hyper is Latin and means high, above or over. It is not to be confused with conditions with names starting with **Hypo** (Hypo means exactly the opposite, ie low, below or under)

Today's tip is about **Hyperthermic Collapse** (collapse due to the dog having a very high temperature or being subjected atmospherically to high temperatures)

We would expect situations where a dog cannot get out of the heat to cause their body temperatures to rise, for example if they are left in a car in warm weather, even with the window down – or perhaps if you have a "sun-worshiper" who just loves to be out baking his brain in the sunshine all day and doesn't know when enough sun is enough. However, when dogs are ill, having an epileptic seizure or even being worked very hard, particularly in warmer weather, they run the risk of developing hyperthermic collapse.

If you are unsure whether it is too hot to walk your dog, consider how you would feel if you were wearing a fur coat, fur hat and no shoes. Would you still wish to go outside and walk in the searing heat and on the hot road surface? Try placing the back of your hand on the asphalt, tarmac or pavement for 10 seconds and consider how it must feel for a dog to walk his paws directly on such scorching areas. If it's too hot for you, then it's too hot for them.

Please never engage in vigorous exercise in hot weather – even a gentle walk can raise your dog's temperature dangerously high so restructuring your day to walk your furry friend in the early morning or late evening when things have cooled somewhat is definitely the safest option. Also, perhaps try to seek out areas with more shade – woodlands make excellent summer walking venues. Some dogs are in more danger than others and things that can exacerbate the situation include:

Infections
Seizures
Poor fitness levels / being over-weight
Normal/high level of exertion or exercise but performed on hot days
Over-excitement
Wearing a muzzle for too long preventing panting
Brachycephalic dogs – (short-faced breeds such as Pugs/Bulldogs) These breeds may have trouble cooling themselves due to their compressed upper respiratory system.

Signs of heat exhaustion include:

- heavy panting
- hyperventilation (fast deep breathing)
- increased salivation early then dry gums as deterioration progresses
- weakness
- confusion or inattention
- shivering
- vomiting or diarrhoea
- sometimes bleeding

As the condition progresses towards heat stroke there may be:

- obvious paleness or greying to the gums
- sticky or dry gums/tongue rather than the usual wet/slimy texture
- shallowing of the breathing efforts
- slowed or absent breathing efforts
- vomiting and diarrhoea that may be bloody
- seizures or coma

So, what should you do?
Protect from further heat and provide shade
Cool him down immediately with running cool (not cold) water or
Provide a paddling pool to stand in, allowing him to drink freely as he stands
Cover in a purpose bought cooling coat, towelling robe or towels soaked in cold water.

N.B: If you intend to use this technique, remember to keep replenishing the cold water on the towel. If you do not, the water on the inside of the towel will actually heat up and cause what is known as the "sauna effect" and obviously, this is counter-productive to what you are trying to achieve.

Towelling robes soaked in water provide excellent cooling
The feet/face/chest/top of the head/base of the skull are the most effective areas to cool quickly
(Following a seizure, back of the neck/top of head/spine are good places to cool)
Try wet flannels in the groin/armpit area

Offer lots of cool water to rehydrate quickly – if the dog is merely showing signs that he is hot, then frozen Kongs, ice chips or ice cubes in the water will help bring his temperature down. However, if the dog is actually in crisis and you suspect full blown heatstroke, then iced water or ice cubes should be avoided as these can cause a serious reaction in your dog equally as dangerous, or even more so, than the temperature problem itself.

DO NOT plunge your dog into freezing cold water as this could easily send him into shock or even cause a heart attack.

DO NOT bring his temperature down too far. Hypothermia is EQUALLY dangerous and once a dog's temperature falls dangerously low, it will then continue to fall and be very difficult to bring back up.

It is vital that you seek emergency veterinary attention should your dog develop heatstroke as this can prove fatal. Ring your vet immediately and have him meet you at the veterinary clinic for urgent rehydration and cooling treatment. Please ALWAYS ring ahead of your arrival to ensure the vet is ready for you so he is able to treat your dog without delay.

Average Canine Temp:
The average temperature of a healthy dog is 101 °F (38 °C), however, the normal temperature of a healthy dog may range from around 99 °F to 102.5 °F (37.2 °C–39.2 °C).

TEMPERATURE ISSUES - WATER INTOXICATION

I confess that until 2014, I'd only ever heard rumours about Water Intoxication but of late, and especially due to the hot weather, this is something that has come to my attention a couple of times (once in a really good, straight forward blog by JoAnna Lou of TheBark.com) so I thought it worth chatting about, just to make sure we all know what it is, how to recognise it and what to do should it occur.

We tend to assume that the safest place for our dogs to be in such hot and sunny weather would be playing safely in a river or pond (obviously, provided that your furry friend is a confident swimmer) or perhaps cavorting about on the lawn with the sprinkler on. Its great fun, cooling and very enjoyable but since looking into Water Intoxication in a little more depth, I would always advocate that they take regular breaks from the water.

The most recent story that came from JoAnna's blog involved a lady who was out with her pack. They were diving in, swimming, having fun and retrieving a ball from a local river when one of her dogs emerged staggering and vomiting liquid. She wasted no time at all in taking her dog to the vet but the symptoms quickly worsened on the way. The poor dog spent a few harrowing days as an In-Patient at the vet's office but, fortunately, he made a full recovery.

When diving in to the water again and again with his mouth open to try to catch and retrieve the ball, it seems that the dog had inadvertently drunk too much water. This massive amount of fluid caused his electrolyte levels to drop (electrolytes such as Potassium, Sodium, Chloride and Bicarbonate are substances that become ions in solution and acquire the capacity to conduct electricity. Electrolytes are present in the human body, and the balance of the electrolytes in our bodies is essential for normal function of our cells and organs). When the electrolyte levels drop, the blood plasma is thinned and this leads to swelling of the brain and other organs. So please remember, water intoxication progresses quickly.

The symptoms to look out for are:-
Lack of co-ordination
Lethargy
Nausea
Bloating
Vomiting
Dilated Pupils
Glazed Eyes
Light Gum Colour
Excessive salivation

Advanced symptoms include:-
Difficulty Breathing
Collapse
Loss of Consciousness
Seizures.

Don't forget – Playing in and out of a sprinkler and drinking copious amounts of water from it can also cause a problem if they go at it a bit too strongly. Water intoxication can affect humans as well as our furry companions, so please make sure your kids stay safe too.

TEMPERATURE ISSUES - ICED WATER – IS IT BAD?

Is it bad to give your dog Iced Water or Ice Cubes to cool them?

Straight answer = NO

It seems that there has been a post floating around the net and on Facebook over and over telling of a very tragic incident which was put down to the use of iced water.

Having spoken at length with various veterinary professionals, the opinion from those who "know their onions" is that there is no specific published data on ice cubes or iced water causing gastric dilation whatsoever. However, it is a multifactorial issue with many factors being involved such as eating habits, diet, exercise, heatstroke, stress & panting, and mostly problematic in large dog breeds due to the deeper nature of the thoracic cavity.

Therefore, people should not be worried and alarmed by this mythical thread on iced water and should feel perfectly fine in continuing with its use as a general aid in warmer seasons to help cool our dogs **BUT NOT IF THE DOG IS IN CRISIS.**

If after saying all of this, you are still concerned, then simply using cool water should be enough to quench the thirst and reduce the temperature.

General cooling maintenance of a dog in this fashion is, as I say fine, but it is worthy of note that a **dog who is suffering with heatstroke should NOT be cooled dramatically with either iced water/ice cubes while in crisis or by plunging them into**

very cold water. It is not safe to give to dogs showing signs of heat stress or even worse heat exhaustion/stroke and this is a point which needs to be clarified.

Extreme cold can cause the blood vessels to constrict, preventing the body's core from cooling and actually causing the internal temperature to further rise. In addition, over-cooling can cause hypothermia, introducing a host of new problems. When the body temperature reaches 103.9°F, stop cooling. At this point, your dog's body should continue cooling on its own.

I hope this clears up any worries that anybody has and I thank the follower who asked me the question initially very much for bringing it to my attention.

Keep those furries cool!

URINARY TRACT- URINARY OBSERVATIONS

Important urine observations to help the vet

What pointers might you see to indicate a bladder or urinary tract infection? Well, there are several questions you might ask yourself when considering bladder problems – the same ones your vet is likely to ask of you if you do decide you need a professional opinion:-

* Is the urine being passed more or less frequently than normal?
* Is the amount normal, increased or reduced?
* Does the dog strain to pass urine?
* Does the dog cry/whimper when passing urine?

* Is a steady stream of urine produced?
* Is there any blood present? (collect sample if possible)
* Is the dog's bedding damp?
* Has the dog been urinating in the house overnight?
* Is this the first occurrence of symptoms?
* If not first occurrence, when did symptoms last occur?
* Are there any other symptoms present e.g. increased thirst, weight loss, poor appetite or vomiting?

Does he have any discharge from the tip of the penis or from her vaginal area? A milky/greenish discharge from the tip of the penis is normal in unneutered males but if this seems more than normal or if your dog has been neutered and you are seeing this discharge for the first time, then a bladder or urinary tract infection may be possible.

A urinary tract infection is incredibly uncomfortable and an appointment with your vet should be made as soon as possible if you have any concerns. Your vet will examine the dog physically, check his temperature and will very likely require a urine sample to aid with the diagnosis and to enable him to prescribe the correct antibiotics for the particular bacterial infection he has.

URINARY TRACT –

MEASURING WATER INTAKE/URINE OUTPUT

Obviously, the first thing to do is collect a urine sample. Measurement of both of these provides very useful information for the vet when urinary symptom problems are suspected. To measure water intake, you must ensure that no other animal has access to the water you are measuring and that there is only one source of water available, to which your dog has CONSTANT access. It is best to measure the amount taken over several 24 hour periods and then work out an average of, say, 4 occasions. This eliminates day-to-day variations. A useful routine is:

1. Fill a large container/basin with water up to a specific mark. This should contain MORE water than your dog is likely to drink in 24 hours.

2. Note the time

3. 24 hours later measure the amount of water needed to return the water level exactly to the mark. Measure in millilitres/litres.

4. Obviously, other animals drinking from the same source could lead to confusion and account would need to be taken of this.

A healthy dog should NOT drink more than 100 ml of water per kilogram of body weight per day.

URINARY TRACT - COLLECTING A URINE SAMPLE:

The sample should be as fresh as possible as changes can occur if it is allowed to stand.

In an ideal world, it is preferable for you to obtain a sample pot from your vet into which you can transfer the urine sample. However, any container can be used to collect a sample so long as it is absolutely clean and dry. Confusion could easily result if, for example, traces of sugar were present in a bottle or jar. This may lead to the mistaken finding of glucose in the urine (a symptom of diabetes). The bottle should be washed in hot detergent, rinsed repeatedly and then allowed to dry before it is used for urine.

Do not collect the very first urination of the day as this will be a very strong sample and if possible try to obtain a "mid-stream" sample from your dog, i.e. not the very beginning or end of the urine flow. I appreciate, however, that sometimes getting any sample at all can be a chore.

As a rule, male dogs are easier to collect from than females.

You can purchase specific tools to help you collect a sample but any wide necked vessel will do the job.

If you do not wish to purchase a special tool for the job, you may be able to slide a margarine tub or shallow cake tin under your dog during urination. You might also try taping a wide-neck container or a plastic bag (without holes in it) to something like a badminton racket or a child's fishing net. The extra length of the handle can help you pass the container under the bitch while she squats or into the dog's urine stream without getting too close and disturbing them – obviously, this container must also be sterile so as not to contaminate the sample. Another top tip is to secure a plastic lid to a selfie stick so you can hold the lid AND slot it under the dog – thanks to Margot Delaney for that one!

On many occasions, it's the fact that you are doing something strange or out of the ordinary under him when he is trying to pee that is putting him off. If this seems to be the case, then a few sessions of getting him acclimatised to the act of having a jug put under him will help.

Start with the dog on the lead in the house and have lots of high value treats ready.

Stand the dog up and put the jug under him.
Click (if you are used to using a clicker) or say "Yes" or "Good Boy" as soon as the jug goes under.
Take it straight out and give him a yummy treat.

Repeat this step over and over with the time you have him standing over the jug getting longer and longer – each time being rewarded handsomely for standing over the jug without freaking out. If he freaks out, try again and reduce the amount of time you have the jug under him – if you go through the steps too quickly you will need to go back again.

After a few sessions of this, you should find that when you take him into the garden for his toilet break, he will happily allow you to pop the jug under him without freaking and collecting a sample will be much easier for you.

If you MUST store the sample, enclose it completely in 2 plastic bags which are tied and sealed, and keep in the fridge, preferably in an air tight container.

EXTRA TIT-BIT OF INFO

I found this interesting "home treatment" via E-How which I did think was worth a quick mention too: "You can try treating the infection at home, but if your dog doesn't respond to the treatment or begins straining to urinate, you'll want to get her to a vet immediately. The infection can travel to her kidneys and cause a serious illness if it is not treated. Your vet will likely prescribe an antibiotic to treat the infection.

Just like cranberry juice can help a person with a urinary tract infection, it can help a dog with the same illness. Cranberry keeps bacteria from sticking to the bladder, and some reports suggest that it also acidifies the urine to create an inhospitable environment for bacteria. It will likely be difficult to convince your dog to drink cranberry juice, but you can add an extract capsule to his food, about 20mg per pound of body weight.

Cantharis - Cantharis is a homeopathic remedy made from the Spanish fly and is used for treating urinary tract disorders. It is said to provide comfort from the pain and burning that accompanies such conditions. The cantharis pellets can be given to the dog inside peanut butter or another treat to encourage him to swallow them."

URINARY TRACT - UNDESCENDED TESTICLES

The condition of Undescended Testicles is also known as Cryptorchidism.

When a male puppy is born, his testicles will still be within his abdomen. As he develops and grows, they will slowly start to descend down the tubes until they arrive at their permanent place in his scrotum. It is important for mammals to be able to keep their sperm cool and this is why the testicles sit in the scrotum outside of the body rather than remaining inside the abdomen where the temperature would be much higher. You will probably notice, on a hot day, that the testicles seem to hang lower between the legs in an effort to keep them cooler and away from the body heat as much as possible.

Sometimes, owners may notice that their new puppy has just the one, or possibly no testicles at all in the scrotum. Each dog is different and the testicles of different dogs do descend at different rates although as a rule, both testicles are usually to be found within the scrotum by the time the animal is six weeks of age – and certainly we would be expecting them to be there by eight to ten weeks). If one or both testicles are not present in the scrotum by twelve weeks of age, the likelihood is that they probably never will be. This is what is referred to as cryptorchidism or 'retained testicles'. This disorder can be hereditary and may well be passed from generation to generation.

Unless you specifically go looking to see if both testicles have arrived, it is unlikely you would notice. The dog will show no signs or abnormalities because of his condition. Things like their energy levels, behaviour and growth pattern are unlikely to be affected and while it is possible that their fertility levels may be reduced, if the dog has one testicle in the scrotum it may still be possible for him to be a father. (Because this condition is often genetic, it is advisable that such dogs should not be bred from, especially as dogs with retained testicles may have a higher risk of testicular diseases such as cancer and torsion).

<u>If your dog has undescended testicles, what should you do?</u>

It is strongly recommended that you neuter your dog if one or both of his testicles have not come down into the scrotum. Neutering is not only to prevent passing on this genetic problem to future offspring, but also to protect the dog from possible testicular diseases in the future, as mentioned above.

While the dog is having his neuter operation, the vet will search within the abdomen for the retained testicle – which might be quite a tricky thing to find! The retained testicle could be hiding anywhere from the muscle area in the groin or elsewhere in the abdomen around the kidney.

However, I do know of cases where the testicle has appeared much later than usual – another good reason for discussing things with your vet before deciding what action to take.

URINARY TRACT - DISCHARGE FROM THE PENIS

Having girl dogs means that unless the bitch is spayed, you will have to contend with hormones, seasons, phantom pregnancies and the like. My house is only big enough for one set of girlie hormones and I'm afraid they're mine! For this reason, I opt to have boy dogs in my life but the boys do come with their own sex-specific problems too. One of those "problems" is the production of a discharge from the penis, and often excessive licking (and slurping).

The discharge is usually of a milky appearance and may have a yellow or green kind of tinge to it. This discharge is totally normal in male dogs that have not been neutered and is called smegma. Some dogs produce more than others and the amount can be affected when the dog becomes aroused or is aware of a bitch in heat (as he ejaculates). Another thing that could result in "gunk" at the tip of the sheath could merely be dried urine if it is more "crusty" in appearance.

This smegma is generally made up of semen (hence why we say it is entirely normal in intact males) and sebum which the body produces to clean the area. If this discharge is becoming a problem as he leaves what my friend colourfully describes as "willy custard" marks (sorry, I know that's gross) on your carpets or furniture, then the only real solution is to have him neutered either permanently with surgery or as a chemical castration.

A temporary fix for this problem is something called a belly band. This length of fabric can be worn around the dog's middle to cover the opening of the sheath and prevent drips and splodges on your soft furnishings. It is also used for incontinent dogs and those dogs that can't resist scent marking when you are visiting friends and new places.

I have to say I'm not mad keen on these for any real length of time as it is possible that they cause a warm, moist environment where bacteria would flourish. If you decide that something of this type might be beneficial for your dog, please ensure you get a washable version and keep it fresh, hygienic and regularly laundered.

If, however, your dog has been neutered and you are seeing this discharge, it could well indicate that there is infection present, particularly if he is licking the penis excessively. If you notice him peeing more often than usual, in small amounts, it could also well be that he has a bladder infection. A trip to the vet just to be sure is strongly advised. If possible, please take a fresh urine sample with you so that your vet can test for the presence of bacteria which obviously would require antibiotics as this is a very uncomfortable problem.

(See our blog on taking a urine sample to help you with this – or wear a rain coat!)

URINARY TRACT - ENLARGED PROSTATE

An **enlarged prostate** is something that usually occurs in middle to older aged male dogs. An enlarged prostate is the result of altered hormone levels and has many of the same symptoms as urinary obstruction due to blockages such as stones etc.

An internal examination by your vet will usually diagnose an enlarged prostate and further testing with x-ray or ultrasound will confirm the diagnosis and can give a good, but not 100% assurance that it is benign.

Treatment for this condition is monitored by the use of urine samples to detect blood or protein in the urine, together with repeat examinations.

The most effective treatment is castration, although in very old or sick animals where anaesthetic risk is high, hormone injections may be tried first.

Symptoms which may indicate prostate disease:

* Middle age or older male dogs
* Straining to pass urine
* Blood in the urine or blood droplets at the penis
* Lethargy
* Abdominal Pain
* Constipation

If you note any of these symptoms, please visit your vet for a thorough check up, just in case.

URINARY TRACT - URINARY OBSTRUCTION

Symptoms of urinary obstruction – this is an emergency situation and should you feel that your dog is experiencing any/some of the following symptoms, please do not hesitate to ring your emergency vet and tell him you are on your way. The symptoms we would associate with POSSIBLE urinary obstruction are:-

* Abdominal pain, agitation
* Shivering
* High Temperature
* Crying/Whimpering while trying to pee
* Depression
* Vomiting
* Disorientation and collapse
* Frequent straining to pass urine but only a few drops produced.
* Urine usually containing blood (may look rusty coloured).

Urinary obstruction is a condition most often seen in male dogs when a small urinary stone obstructs the urethra (the narrow tube which carries urine from the bladder to the outside). It can, however, be associated with an enlarged prostate which is pressing on the urethra and making urination difficult.

As we have said, it is imperative that you seek your vet as soon as you can for further examination and treatment. If possible, take a fresh sample of pee with you to the vet which will allow them to test for the presence of blood and also any possible infection or bacteria. Take what is known as a "mid-stream" sample i.e. you don't want the first part of the pee stream. Also, if possible do not take a sample of the very first pee of the morning as this will be very strong, more acidic and concentrated and will not give an accurate picture of the "normal" urinary composition.

The vet will take his temperature and give him a general physical examination including palpating his tummy to see if there is any swelling showing that the bladder is very full, or any pain. He will likely check his prostate too which can be quite painful for the dog if it is enlarged. If the prostate is the underlying problem, then the suggestion may be made to neuter the dog to prevent further episodes in the future.

About the Author

Kerry Rhodes grew up in the tiny East Yorkshire village of Leven.

Obsessed with all things canine from the word go, it took 13 years of incessant nagging before being allowed her first dog, Paddy – a MASSIVE Golden Labrador/Labrador Retriever. The pair were inseparable, and the love affair began – and she's never been without a dog to share her life since.

Kerry spent 20 years working for the NHS, specialising in Obstetrics, Gynaecology and Colorectal Surgery, but in 2001 she gave it all up, retrained as a teacher and opened her First Aid Training business – and Rhodes 2 Safety was born.

In 2008, Kerry decided to return to college and study Advanced Canine First Aid. After passing her qualification with honours, Canine First Aid was added to the Rhodes 2 Safety product list and in 2012 the Facebook page was launched with regular tips and advice blogs appearing on both the website and Facebook. It is this collection of blogs over from over the past 6 years that feature in this book – a comprehensive guide that should be on every dog-owner's book shelf.

In 2017, Rhodes 2 Safety won the Business Excellence Award for First Aid Training and also the Global Excellence Award as the UKs number 1 Training provider. In 2018, Rhodes 2 Safety won the award for UK First Aid Training Company of the year and, at the time of going to print, we await the results of the Global Excellence Awards for 2018.

If you have any queries, please check out Rhodes 2 Safety on Facebook or on the website at: www.Rhodes2Safety.co.uk

Notes: